INTRODUCTORY
CALCULUS
with Analytic Geometry

INTRODUCTORY
CALCULUS

WITH ANALYTIC GEOMETRY

EDWARD G. BEGLE

YALE UNIVERSITY

HENRY HOLT AND COMPANY, NEW YORK

Preface

This text covers the topics usually treated in a first course in calculus, i.e., differentiation and integration of algebraic, exponential and logarithmic, and trigonometric functions. In addition, analytic geometry through the conics is included. However, this text differs from most others in this field in that it treats calculus as a branch of mathematics rather than a mere adjunct of the physical and engineering sciences.

This is not to say that the relationships between mathematics and the sciences are neglected. On the contrary, we use the sciences to provide a motive for studying the basic concepts of calculus and we study many of the applications of calculus to the sciences, enough, we believe, to show how useful and powerful a tool calculus is.

Nevertheless, we treat calculus as a body of knowledge which is formally independent of the sciences and which is organized in a mathematical fashion. We start with a list of axioms, and we show how the theorems of calculus are derived from these axioms.

Our aim in presenting calculus in this fashion is to give the student more of an understanding of the basic concepts of the subject than is usually done in an introductory course. It is our belief that such an understanding is becoming more and more necessary for the student of science or engineering. In these fields, the mathematical techniques employed have become so numerous and varied that no student can be expected to master more than a few of them without a framework of theory around which they can be organized.

We also feel that for the student for whom this is a terminal course in mathematics it is desirable to show the logical structure of calculus rather than to concentrate entirely on the problem-solving techniques which are the end products of calculus.

This text is based on many years of experience by the staff at Yale in teaching the theory as well as the practice of calculus to beginning students. This experience has shown that such students can be given a good understanding of the concepts of derivative, integral, etc., and at the same time can develop a reasonably satisfactory technique in using these concepts. We do not claim to be able to turn out expert theorem-provers. The degree of understanding that we mean here is best illustrated by describing one of the techniques we use for measuring it. This is to present the student with a theorem together with an incomplete proof of it. The student is then asked to fill in the missing reasons or steps in the proof. Examples of this type of question are introduced in Chapter 1.

We are convinced that in order to understand a definition of a mathematical concept it is important to see how the definition is used in the proofs of some of the theorems about this concept. By providing a proof for each of our theorems, we make it possible for the instructor to delve as deeply into the theory as his inclination and the caliber of his class may indicate. We have placed in the body of the text only those theorems which are necessary. Finer points of the theory are relegated to the problems where they will not obstruct the students' view of the development of the logical structure of the subject.

On the other hand, we have provided a large number of problems, at all levels of difficulty, so that the instructor using this book may place the emphasis at any point between the extremes of pure theory and pure technique that he may choose.

Our experience has dictated some changes in the list of concepts studied and in the order in which they are taken up. For example, we have found it essential to lay the emphasis on functions rather than on variables. We therefore consider the notion of function at some length before taking up the study of limits. We have also found it extremely helpful to discuss absolute values and inequalities before limits, since much of the difficulty which a student ordinarily has when he first meets this concept is in reality due to his inability to handle absolute values and inequalities, rather than to the limit concept itself. Similarly, a facility with inequalities is an immense help in studying the Least Upper Bound Axiom and its use and also in studying the definite integral.

The definite integral is defined in terms of lower and upper integrals. This approach makes it much easier to motivate the concept of integral and in addition makes it possible to present the complete theory of definite integrals in a short space.

The logarithmic function is defined by means of a definite integral. By exploiting what the student has already learned about definite integrals, the derivatives of this function and its inverse, the exponential function, are easily found. A similar procedure is used with the trigonometric functions. Here we start with arc sin, which is easily expressed as a definite integral, and then use properties of definite integrals and inverse functions to find quickly the derivatives of the trigonometric functions.

We mention also certain matters of notation. We find it helpful to denote the sum of the functions f and g by $\{f + g\}$, since this notation emphasizes that the sum of two functions is a single new function, and similarly for the difference, product, quotient, and composition of two functions.

We denote the definite integral of the function f over the interval from a to b by the symbol $\int_a^b f$, but we later introduce and use the customary notation $\int_a^b f(x)\ dx$.

The author would like to acknowledge the assistance which he has received from many of his colleagues. First and foremost, he owes a great debt to the late Professor Wallace A. Wilson, who first demonstrated to this author, by actual practice, the possibility of introducing theory into the beginning calculus course. Professor Charles E. Rickart, who read each draft of the manuscript, furnished very many helpful suggestions. Thanks are due to Professor M. J. Norris, of the College of St. Thomas, who first pointed out to the author the advantages of the development of the definite integral found in Chapter 7. Finally, the author expresses his thanks to all his other colleagues, too many to mention by name, who used this text in a preliminary form and furnished many useful suggestions.

E. G. B.

January, 1954
Yale University

Contents

INTRODUCTORY
CALCULUS
with Analytic Geometry

Foundations

1. INTRODUCTION

Mathematics is a language. It has its own vocabulary, its own grammar, and its own literature. The vocabulary of mathematics contains such words as "circle," "triangle," "2," "number," "+," "$\sqrt{}$," and "function." The grammar of mathematics tells us, for example, that the sentence $a + b = \sqrt{a - b}$ is grammatically correct, while the sentence $a^+ - b = \sqrt{}$ is not. The literature of mathematics consists of all its theorems together with their proofs. This literature is important and interesting for its own sake, just as English literature is important and interesting. But the literature of mathematics is also important because mathematics is the language best suited for the discussion of exact quantitative concepts. Consequently scientists, engineers, etc., find this language indispensable in their daily work.

In this book we shall study one chapter in the literature of mathematics, the chapter entitled "Calculus," and we shall also observe how this part of mathematics is useful to those working in other fields of knowledge, the sciences in particular.

2. AXIOMS

Compared with other languages, mathematics is unique in one respect. The fundamental statements of its literature are few in number and can be written down explicitly, and all the theorems which form the rest of the literature can be derived from them by logical arguments. These fundamental statements are called *axioms*.

The reader is already familiar with axioms and theorems from his first course in geometry. However, little mention of them is made in introductory algebra courses. Nevertheless, all the procedures of algebra can be stated as theorems which can be derived from a small list of axioms. To emphasize this point we list these axioms below.

The objects with which algebra deals are the real * numbers. We usually

---

* The adjective "real" is used in mathematics merely to distinguish the ordinary numbers from another class of quantities called "complex" numbers. It has only a historical connection with the philosophical concept of reality. Similarly, the word "rational" when used in mathematics does not mean "intelligent" or "reasonable." Instead, it always refers to a ratio, i.e., a quotient.

denote these by small Latin letters, e.g., a, b, c, $\cdots$, m, n, $\cdots$, x, y, z. If two numbers, a and b, are equal, we write "$a = b$" or "$b = a$." There are two operations on real numbers, addition and multiplication. The first is symbolized by "$+$," so that "$a + b$" means the number obtained by applying to a and b the operation of addition. The second operation is symbolized by the sign "$\cdot$" so that "$a \cdot b$" means the number obtained by applying to a and b the operation of multiplication. However, it has become customary to omit this symbol whenever it causes no confusion and to write merely "ab."

The axioms which these operations satisfy are:

E1   If a, b, and c are numbers, and if $a = b$ and $b = c$, then $a = c$.

A1   For every pair of numbers, a and b, $a + b = b + a$.

A2   For any three numbers, a, b, and c, $(a + b) + c = a + (b + c)$.

A3   There is one and only one number, which we denote by "0," such that for each number a, $a + 0 = a$.

A4   For each number a there is one number, which we denote by "$-a$," such that $a + (-a) = 0$.

E2   If a, b, and c are numbers, and if $a = b$, then $a + c = b + c$.

M1   For every pair of numbers, a and b, $ab = ba$.

M2   For any three numbers, a, b, and c, $a(bc) = (ab)c$.

M3   There is one and only one number, which we denote by "1", and which is different from 0, such that for each number a, $a \cdot 1 = a$.

M4   For each number a, except 0, there is one number, which we denote by $(1/a)$, such that $a(1/a) = 1$.

E3   If a, b, and c are numbers, and if $a = b$, then $ac = bc$.

D   For any three numbers, a, b, and c, $a(b + c) = ab + ac$.

Note that axioms $A1$ through $A4$ refer to the operation of addition and $M1$ through $M4$ to that of multiplication. Axiom D, which is called the distributive law, connects these two operations. The E axioms, which Euclid would have called "postulates" rather than axioms, connect the relation of equality with the operations of addition and multiplication.

Using axioms $A4$ and $M4$ we can bring in the operations of subtraction and division. We define $a - b$ to be the number $a + (-b)$, and, if $b \neq 0$, we define a/b to be the number $a(1/b)$.

In addition to the operations discussed above, there is also a relation between real numbers, the order relation. This relation is denoted by "$<$," and we read "$a < b$" as "a is less than b." The axioms which this relation satisfies are:

O1   For any two numbers, a and b, one and only one of the following relations holds: $a = b$, $a < b$, $b < a$.

O2   For any three numbers, a, b, and c, if $a < b$ and $b < c$, then $a < c$.

O3   For any three numbers, a, b, and c, if $a < b$, then $a + c < b + c$.

O4   For any three numbers, a, b, and c, if $a < b$ and $0 < c$, then $ac < bc$.

E4 If a, b, and c are numbers, and if $a = b$ and $c = d$, and if $a < c$, then $b < d$.

If $a < b$, we also write $b > a$. The notation $a \leq b$ means that either $a < b$ or $a = b$, and similarly for $a \geq b$. If $a < b$ and $b < c$, we write $a < b < c$, and say that b is between a and c.

From these axioms, together with one final axiom which we discuss later in Section 5, all the usual rules and procedures of algebra can be derived, just as all the theorems of geometry can be derived from its axioms. We do not wish to go through all these derivations in detail since the way is long and after a while it becomes very tedious. In any case, the reader is already familiar with most of the results. The problems below, however, illustrate the procedures which would be involved.

PROBLEMS

1. Prove the following theorem:

Theorem 1.1: *If a is a number, and if b is a number such that $a + b = 0$, then $b = -a$.*

Proof:

1) $a + b = 0$	Hypothesis
2) $a + b = b + a$	A1
3) $b + a = 0$	Steps 1 and 2, and E1
4) $(b + a) + (-a) = 0 + (-a)$	Step 3, and E2
5) $(b + a) + (-a) = b + (a + (-a))$	A2
6) $b + (a + (-a)) = 0 + (-a)$	Steps 4 and 5, and E1
7) $a + (-a) = 0$	A4
8) $b + 0 = 0 + (-a)$	Steps 6 and 7, and E1
9) $b + 0 = b$	A3
10) $b = 0 + (-a)$	Steps 8 and 9, and E1
11) $0 + (-a) = (-a) + 0$	A1
12) $(-a) + 0 = -a$	A3
13) $b = -a$	Steps 10, 11, and 12, and E1

Remark: Another way of stating this theorem is: For each number a there is only one number b such that $a + b = 0$.

2. Prove the following theorem:

Theorem 1.2: *If a is a number, if $a \neq 0$, and if b is a number such that $ab = 1$, then $b = 1/a$.*

3. Fill in the missing reasons in the proofs of the following theorems:

Theorem 1.3: *For any number a, $-(-a) = a$.*

Proof:

1) $a + (-a) = 0$
2) $a + (-a) = (-a) + a$
3) $(-a) + a = 0$
4) $a = -(-a)$ Theorem 1.1

Theorem 1.4: *For any number a, $a \cdot 0 = 0$.*

Proof:

1) $1 + 0 = 1$
2) $a(1 + 0) = a \cdot 1$
3) $a(1 + 0) = a \cdot 1 + a \cdot 0$
4) $a \cdot 1 = a$
5) $a + a \cdot 0 = a \cdot 1$
6) $a + a \cdot 0 = a$
7) $a \cdot 0 = 0$ Step 6, and A3

4. Fill in the gaps in the proof of the following theorem:

Theorem 1.5: *For any number a, $(-1)a = -a$.*

Proof:

1) $1 + (-1) = 0$ A4
2) $a(1 + (-1)) = a \cdot 0$ Step 1, and E3
3)   Step 2, Theorem 1.4, and E1
4) $a(1 + (-1)) = a \cdot 1 + a(-1)$
5) $a \cdot 1 + a(-1) = 0$
6)   M3
7) $a + a(-1) = 0$
8) $a(-1) = (-1)a$
9) $a + (-1)a = 0$
10) $(-1)a = -a$ Step 9 and Theorem 1.1

5. Prove the following theorem:

Theorem 1.6: *For any numbers a and b, $-(a + b) = (-a) + (-b)$.*

6. Prove the following theorem:

Theorem 1.7: *If $a < b$, then $-a > -b$.*

Proof:

1) $a < b$ Hypothesis
2) $a + (-b) < b + (-b)$ Step 1 and O3
3) $b + (-b) = 0$ A4
4) $a + (-b) < 0$ Steps 2 and 3, and E4
5) $(a + (-b)) + (-a) < 0 + (-a)$ Step 4 and O3
6) $(-a) + (a + (-b)) < (-a) + 0$ Step 5, A1, and E4

7) $((-a) + a) + (-b) < (-a) + 0$ Step 6, A2, and E4

8) $(a + (-a)) + (-b) < (-a) + 0$ Step 7, A1, and E4

9) $0 + (-b) < (-a) + 0$ Step 8, A4, and E4

10) $(-b) + 0 < (-a) + 0$ Step 9, A1, and E4

11) $(-b) < (-a)$ Step 10, A3, and E4

7. Prove each of the following theorems:

Theorem 1.8: *If* $-a < -b$, *then* $a > b$.

Theorem 1.9: *If* $a > b$ *and* $c < 0$, *then* $ac < bc$.

3. PROOFS OF THEOREMS

The most common type of proof of a theorem consists of a sequence of steps, starting with the hypothesis of the theorem and ending with the conclusion. Each step must follow from the preceding steps by virtue of one or more axioms or definitions or previously proved theorems. All the proofs in the preceding section are of this type.

One method for displaying the details of a proof is to list the steps of the proof in a column at the left of the page and to indicate in a second column, on the right, the axioms or theorems which justify each step. This is the method which we used above. However, for reasons of economy of time and printer's ink, we usually write these proofs in a more condensed fashion, omitting some of the easier steps and reasons. When a proof is presented in this form it is the task of the reader to supply the missing parts of the proof.

As an example, we present the proof of Theorem 1.7 in condensed form:

Proof: By O3, $a + (-b) < b + (-b)$. But $b + (-b) = 0$, so $a + (-b) < 0$. Then $(-a) + (a + (-b)) < (-a) + 0$, (Why?) and so $((-a) + a) + (-b) < (-a) + 0$. Hence $0 + (-b) < (-a) + 0$, or $(-b) < (-a)$.

As in the above, we shall often insert the question "Why?" at crucial points in a proof to indicate to the reader that he should take special care to fill in missing steps and reasons.

In addition to the straightforward type of proof just illustrated, there is another type which is most important and much used. This is the so-called *indirect* proof. The idea of such a proof is to assume tentatively that what we want to prove is not true. Then from this assumption we derive a contradiction, i.e., something which is impossible. From this we conclude that our tentative assumption was wrong and hence that what we want to prove is true. Out next theorem illustrates this kind of proof.

Theorem 1.10: $1 > 0$.

Proof: Let us assume that it is not true that $1 > 0$. Then, by O1, we have $1 = 0$ or $1 < 0$. The first is impossible because of M3, so we have $1 < 0$.

Now, in Theorem 1.9, let us set $a = 0$, $b = 1$, and $c = 1$. Then $a = 0 > b$ $= 1$, and $c = 1 < 0$, so the hypotheses of this theorem are satisfied. Then $ac < bc$, or $0 \cdot 1 < 1 \cdot 1$, or $0 < 1$. Thus we have $1 < 0$ and $0 < 1$ at the same time, which is impossible by O1. Our assumption that $1 > 0$ is false thus leads to an impossibility, and so it is true that $1 > 0$.

Note: As in the case of the straightforward proofs, indirect proofs can be written out either in condensed form, as above, or in an expanded form, with steps in one column and reasons in another.

The reader has already discovered in his geometry course that it is one thing to read and understand a proof which has been written out for him but a much different and more difficult thing to have to construct the proof himself. In the first case it is merely necessary to check each step and see that it is correct. But in the second case it is necessary to find a sequence of steps which starts from the hypothesis and ends with the conclusion. Unfortunately, there are no rules which tell us how to go about finding such a sequence. The usual procedure is that of trial and error together with a liberal use of the imagination, guided by the experience gained in the study of the proofs of other similar theorems.

There will be some proofs in this book which will cause the reader some difficulty. However, a little reflection in such cases will usually show that the difficulty lies not in understanding the proof itself but in understanding how anyone was ever able to discover it in the first place. This should never alarm the reader. To be able to construct such proofs requires much more experience in mathematics than the reader has had. In any case, it is not the object of this book to make the reader an expert theorem-prover. Instead, the object is to show the reader the logical structure of a particular part of mathematics, calculus, to show how the theorems of calculus are, on the one hand, consequences of a few simple axioms and, on the other hand, powerful tools which can be applied to many important and practical problems.

PROBLEMS

1. Write out the proof of the following theorem in expanded form:

   Theorem 1.11: *For any two numbers, a and b,* $(-a)(-b) = ab$.

   Proof: $(-a) = (-1)a$ and $(-b) = (-1)b$ by Theorem 1.5. Hence $(-a)(-b) = (-1)a(-1)b = (-1)(-1)ab$. Now $(-1)(-1) = -(-1)$ by Theorem 1.5 and $-(-1) = 1$ by Theorem 1.3. Hence $(-a)(-b)$ $= 1 \cdot ab = ab$.

2. Write out the proof of the following theorem in expanded form:

   Theorem 1.12: *For any two numbers a and b, if* $ab > 0$ *then* $a > 0$ *and* $b > 0$ *or* $a < 0$ *and* $b < 0$.

Proof: Assume the conclusion is false. We cannot have $a = 0$ or $b = 0$ (Why?). So we have $a > 0$ and $b < 0$ or $a < 0$ and $b > 0$. In either case, by O4 we have $ab < 0$, which is impossible.

3. Prove the following theorem:

Theorem 1.13: *For any number a, if $a > 0$ then $1/a > 0$.*

Hint: Use an indirect proof and apply Theorem 1.9.

4. DEFINITIONS

Whenever a new concept is introduced in this book, a formal definition of the concept is given. The reader must study these definitions with great care, since they form the vocabulary of the language of mathematics.

A possible source of confusion lies in the custom of using ordinary English words for the names of these concepts. Such a word has then, in addition to its dictionary meaning or meanings, the mathematical meaning given it by the definition in which it appears. In this book, only the meaning given by the definition is to be used. For example, in Webster's Collegiate Dictionary, there are five meanings listed for the word "limit." No one of these, not even the one listed there as the mathematical meaning, is to be used when this word appears in this book. Instead, the word "limit" in this book has always the meaning given in its definition in Chapter 3.

As an example of the kind of definition to be found in this book, we present here the definition of the absolute value of a number.

Definition 1.1: *The **absolute value** of a number a, which we denote by $|a|$, is the number a itself if $a \geq 0$ and is the number $-a$ if $a < 0$.*

Thus, for example, $|3| = 3$, since $3 > 0$. But $|-7| = 7$, for $-7 < 0$ so $|-7| = -(-7) = 7$.

The concept of the absolute value of a number will turn out to be very useful. The theorems below indicate most of the important properties of absolute value.

PROBLEMS

1. Write out the proof of the following theorem in expanded form:

Theorem 1.14: *For any number a, if $a \neq 0$ then $|a| > 0$.*

Proof: By O1, $a < 0$ or $a > 0$. In the first case, $|a| = -a$ and $-a > 0$ by Theorem 1.7. In the second case $|a| = a > 0$.

2. Find a proof for the following theorem:

Theorem 1.15: *For any number a, $|a| = |-a|$.*

Hint: Consider separately each of the three possible cases specified by O1 for the pair of numbers a and 0.

3. Complete the proof of the following theorem:

Theorem 1.16: *For any two numbers a and b, $|a| \cdot |b| = |ab|$.*

Proof: If $a > 0$ and $b > 0$, then, by the definition of absolute value, $|a| = a$ and $|b| = b$, so $|a| \cdot |b| = ab$. On the other hand, by O4, $ab > 0$, so $|ab| = ab$. Hence, in this case, $|a| \cdot |b| = |ab|$ by E1.

The other three cases, $a > 0, b < 0$; $a < 0, b > 0$; and $a < 0, b < 0$ can be worked in similar fashion.

4. Answer the question "Why?" wherever it appears in the proofs of the following theorems:

Theorem 1.17: *For any two numbers a and b, $|a + b| \leq |a| + |b|$.*

Proof: Consider first the case where $a + b \geq 0$. Notice that $a \leq |a|$ and $b \leq |b|$. (Why?) Hence $a + b \leq |a| + |b|$. (Why?) But since $a + b \geq 0, |a + b| = a + b$, so $|a + b| \leq |a| + |b|$.

Next consider the case where $a + b < 0$. Notice that $-|a| \leq a$ and $-|b| \leq b$. (Why?) Hence $-|a| - |b| \leq a + b$, and so $-(a + b) \leq |a| + |b|$. (Why?) Since $a + b < 0, |a + b| = -(a + b)$, so $|a + b| \leq |a| + |b|$ in this case also.

Theorem 1.18: *For any two numbers a and b, $||a| - |b|| \leq |a - b|$.*

Proof: Consider first the case where $|a| - |b| \geq 0$. Then $||a| - |b|| = |a| - |b|$. Now $a = a - b + b$, so $|a| = |a - b + b| \leq |a - b| + |b|$ (Why?). Hence $|a| - |b| \leq |a - b|$. Next consider the case where $|a| - |b| < 0$. Then $||a| - |b|| = -(|a| - |b|) = |b| - |a|$. Now $b = b - a + a$, so $|b| = |b - a + a| \leq |b - a| + |a|$. Hence $|b| - |a| \leq |b - a|$. But $|b - a| = |a - b|$ (Why?). Therefore in this case $|b| - |a| \leq |a - b|$. Hence we have shown in each case that $||a| - |b|| \leq |a - b|$.

5. Solve the equation $|x + 1| = 3$.

Solution: From the definition of the absolute value of a number, either $|x + 1| = x + 1$ or $|x + 1| = -(x + 1)$. Thus the only two possibilities are $x + 1 = 3$ and $-(x + 1) = 3$. The first gives $x = 2$ and the second $x = -4$, which are solutions as can be seen by substitution in the original equation.

6. Solve the equations

   a) $|2 - x| = 1$. Ans. $x = 1$ and $x = 3$.
   b) $|2 - x| = 4$.
   c) $|4x + 1| = 7$.
   d) $|x + 1| = x$. Ans. No solution.

e) $|x - 1| = 2x + 4.$ f) $|x + 1| = |x - 2|.$ Ans. $x = \frac{1}{2}.$

g) $|2x + 3| = |4 - x|.$ h) $|3x + 2| + |2x + 3| = 0.$

7. Solve the equations

a) $|x + 1|^2 - 3|x + 1| + 2 = 0.$

Hint: This is a quadratic equation in $|x + 1|$. Solving, we have $|x + 1| = 1$ or $|x + 1| = 2$. The first gives $x = 0$ or -2 and the second $x = 1$ or -3.

b) $|x - 1|^2 - 5|x - 1| + 6 = 0.$

c) $|2x + 1|^2 + |2x + 1| - 2 = 0.$ Ans. $x = 0$ and $x = -1.$

d) $|1 - x|^2 - 2|1 - x| = 0.$

e) $|x + 3|^2 + 4|x + 3| + 3 = 0.$

f) $|x + 2|^3 = 8.$

8. Solve the following pairs of simultaneous equations:

a) $|x| = 1$ and $|x - 2| = 1.$

b) $|x - 3| = 2$ and $|x - 7| = 2.$

c) $|x - 3| = 2$ and $|x + 3| = 1.$

d) $|4 - x|^2 + |4 - x| - 6 = 0$ and $|3 - x| - 3 = 0.$

5. THE LEAST UPPER BOUND AXIOM

Among the real numbers there are certain special kinds of numbers which are important. First of these are the integers, namely 0, 1, 2, 3, $\cdots$ and $-1, -2, -3, \cdots$. Next are the rational numbers, i.e., those which can be written in the form p/q, where both p and q are integers.

One of the most important properties of the rational numbers is that they are spread out very densely throughout the real numbers, in the sense that between any two numbers whatsoever there is a rational number, in fact infinitely many rational numbers. On the other hand, there are numbers which are not rational, for example $\sqrt{2}$ (see Problem 1, p. 10). Such numbers are called irrational. The irrational numbers are spread out just as thickly as the rationals. Thus if we were to throw away all the irrational numbers, the collection of numbers remaining, the rationals, would be full of "holes," i.e., the places formerly occupied by the irrationals. The same would be true if we were to throw away the rationals and keep the irrationals.

But in the collection of all real numbers, rational and irrational together, there are no such holes. For the precise statement of this fact, however, we must first make some more definitions.

Definition 1.2: *A number* a *is an* **upper bound** *of a collection* M *of numbers if* $m \le a$ *whenever* m *is a number in* M.

For example, if M is the collection of all real numbers between 0 and 1, inclusive, then 2 is an upper bound of M. So also are 3, 5, $\frac{19}{2}$, 1,000,000, and 1, while -3, 0, and $\frac{1}{2}$ are not upper bounds of M. The collection of all positive integers, on the other hand, has no upper bound. The definition of a lower bound of a collection M is obtained from that of an upper bound by reversing the inequality sign.

Definition 1.3: *The number a is a **least upper bound** of a collection M if a is an upper bound of M and if $a < b$ whenever b is any other upper bound of M.*

In the example above, 1 is a least upper bound of the collection of numbers between 0 and 1.

Our final axiom for the real numbers is the following:

Least Upper Bound Axiom. If a collection M of numbers has an upper bound then it has a least upper bound.

The significance of this axiom can be glimpsed from the fact that the system of rational numbers, which satisfies all our other axioms, does not satisfy this one. The collection of all positive rational numbers whose squares are less than 2 has an upper bound, 3 for example, but no rational number is a least upper bound for this collection. The only number which could be a least upper bound is $\sqrt{2}$, and this is not a rational number.

However, the full significance of this axiom will only appear later, as we use it in deriving the important theorems of calculus.

PROBLEMS

1. Show that $\sqrt{2}$ is not a rational number.

   Solution: If $\sqrt{2}$ were a rational number, we would have $\sqrt{2} = p/q$, where p and q are integers. We may assume that this fraction is written in lowest form, i.e., that all common factors of the numerator and denominator have been cancelled out. Then, squaring, $2 = p^2/q^2$ or $2q^2 = p^2$. Hence p^2 is an even integer. But this means that p itself is even, so $p = 2r$, where r is some integer. Then $2q^2 = (2r)^2 = 4r^2$, and so $q^2 = 2r^2$. Thus q^2 is even and so is q and $q = 2s$, where s is an integer. But this means that p and q have the common factor 2, which is impossible.

   Remark: This is another *indirect* proof.

2. Show that $\sqrt{3}$, $\sqrt[3]{3}$, and $\sqrt{10}$ are not rational numbers.
3. Write a definition of a greatest lower bound. Find a greatest lower bound for the set of numbers between 0 and 1 and also for the set of negative rationals whose squares are less than 3.
4. Prove that if a collection of numbers has one upper bound, then it has infinitely many of them.

5. Prove that any collection of numbers can have at most one least upper bound.

6. Give examples of collections which have

   a) an upper bound and a lower bound,
   b) an upper bound but no lower bound,
   c) a lower bound but no upper bound,
   d) no upper bound and no lower bound.

7. Prove that if a collection M of numbers has a lower bound, then it has a greatest lower bound.

   Proof: If M is the collection, and a is a lower bound for M, denote by N the collection of all numbers of the form $-x$, where x is in M. Since a is a lower bound for M, $a \leq x$ for any x in M. Hence, by Theorem 1.7, $-x \leq -a$. Thus $-a$ is an upper bound for N. Hence, by the Least Upper Bound Axiom, there is a least upper bound for N, say b. Thus $-x \leq b$ for any element $-x$ of N, and $b < c$ for any other upper bound c of N. Now we assert that $-b$ is a greatest lower bound for M. By Theorem 1.7, $-b \leq x$ for any x in M. If d is any other lower bound for M, then $-d$ is an upper bound for N, so $b < -d$. Then $d < -b$, which proves our assertion.

8. Let M be a collection of numbers and t a fixed positive number. Let N be the collection of numbers obtained by multiplying each number in M by the number t. Show that if b is the least upper bound of M, then tb is the least upper bound of N.

9. Let M be a collection of numbers and let b be the least upper bound of M. Show that if e is any positive number, no matter how small, there is a number m in M such that

$$b - e < m \leq b.$$

   Hint: Since b is the *least* upper bound of M, no number less than b, in particular $b - e$, is an upper bound of M.

6. CONCLUSION

In this short chapter we have tried to indicate that, like geometry, algebra is a logical system: all the theorems, rules, procedures, and techniques of algebra can be deduced from its axioms. One of the aims of this book is to show that the same is true for the last of the three great subdivisions of mathematics, analysis. The axioms for calculus, which is the beginning part of analysis, are those of algebra together with the Least Upper Bound Axiom. The basic concepts used in calculus, however, are much different from those of algebra. They will be taken up in Chapter 3.

We have stated that all of algebra can be derived from the axioms in Section 2 above. Lack of time prevents us from carrying through this derivation. That our statement is correct, however, can be verified by any student who is industrious enough to read the appropriate books. In all that follows, we shall assume that this has been done, and we shall use freely whatever algebraic techniques we need. This should cause the reader no difficulty, since he is already familiar with these techniques, though not with their derivations.

REVIEW PROBLEMS

1. Prove that if $ab > 0$ and $a < b$, then $1/a > 1/b$.
2. Prove that if $a > 0$ and $b > 0$, then $a + b \geq 2\sqrt{ab}$.
3. If $a < b$ and $c < d$, what can you say about $a - c$ and $b - d$? What can you say about $a - d$ and $b - c$?
4. Prove that $|a/b| = |a|/|b|$.
5. When is $|a - b| \leq |a| - |b|$?
6. Prove that for any number a, $-|a| \leq a \leq |a|$.
7. When is $|a + b| < |a| + |b|$?
8. Prove that $\frac{1}{2}(|a| + a) = a$ if $a \geq 0$. What is the value when $a < 0$?
9. Prove that if a and b are any two rational numbers, then there is a rational number between them.
10. Show that the following numbers are irrational: $\sqrt[3]{5}$, $\sqrt[12]{2}$, $\sqrt[3]{2}$.
11. Is $\sqrt{2} + \sqrt{3}$ rational or irrational? Ans. Irrational.
12. Show that if $2^a = 3$, then a is irrational.
13. Show that if $a > 0$ and $b > 0$, then there is an integer n such that $na > b$.

    (*Hint:* Use an indirect proof and consider the LUB of all numbers of the form na, where n is an integer.)

14. Show that if $a > 0$ there is an integer n such that $1/n < a$.
15. Let M and N be two collections of numbers. Let a be the least upper bound of M and b the least upper bound of N. Let P be the collection of all numbers which can be obtained by adding a number in M and a number in N. Show that $a + b$ is the least upper bound of P.

Analytic Geometry

1. INTRODUCTION

Analytic geometry is the result of linking together algebra and geometry. It will enable us to solve many difficult geometric problems by relatively easy algebraic methods. Conversely, geometry will often throw light on algebraic problems. Finally, the language of analytic geometry is very useful in calculus.

To build a connection between algebra and geometry, we start by assigning to each point of a given straight line a number. Choose any point of this line, call it O, and assign to it the number 0. We call this point the origin. Choose any other point and assign to it the number 1. We call this point the unit point, and the distance between these two points the unit distance. To any point P on the same side of the origin as the unit point, we assign that real number which is the number of unit distances from the origin to P. To any point on the other side of the origin we assign that real number which is the negative of the number of unit distances from the origin to the point. In either case, the number assigned to the point is called the coordinate of the point.

In this fashion we assign to each point, which is a geometric entity, a real number, which is an algebraic entity. This is the basic idea of analytic geometry.

In the above process of assigning numbers to points, each point receives a coordinate and different points receive different coordinates (Why?). Furthermore, this process uses up all the real numbers so that each real number is the coordinate of one and only one point. The proof of this fact, however, involves difficult and deep theorems of geometry.

If P_1 and P_2 are two points of our line, the distance between them is $|x_1 - x_2|$, where x_1 is the coordinate of P_1 and x_2 that of P_2. (See Problem 7, p. 15.) The history of analytic geometry has shown that it is useful to combine the idea of distance with that of direction.

Definition 2.1: *If P_1 and P_2 are points, the **directed distance** from P_1 to P_2 is the distance between P_1 and P_2 if the direction from P_1 to P_2 is the same as the direction from the origin to the unit point, and otherwise it is the negative of the distance between them.*

13

Theorem 2.1: *If P_1 and P_2 are points with coordinates x_1 and x_2, the directed distance from P_1 to P_2 is $x_2 - x_1$, and the distance between P_1 and P_2 is $|x_2 - x_1|$.*

The proof of this theorem is contained in Problems 7 and 8 below.

PROBLEMS

1. Draw a line, set up a coordinate system on it, and locate on this line the points whose coordinates are

   a) 1, 2, 3, −1, −4.
   b) 1, 2, 4, 8, 16.
   c) 1, $\frac{1}{2}$, $\frac{1}{3}$, $\frac{1}{4}$, $\frac{1}{5}$.

2. Find the coordinate of each of the points P described below. (Take the unit point to the right of the origin.)

   a) P is 2 units to the right of the point whose coordinate is 3.   Ans.   5.
   b) P is 2 units to the left of the point whose coordinate is 6.
   c) P is 1 unit to the left of the point whose coordinate is −4.
   d) P is on the opposite side of the origin from the point whose coordinate is 3 and twice as far from the origin.
   e) The point which is 3 units to the right of P has coordinate 7.
   f) The origin is halfway between the point whose coordinate is 2 and the point which is 4 units to the left of P.   Ans.   2.
   g) The origin is halfway between the point 6 units to the left of P and the point 2 units to the right of P.

3. Find the distances between the pairs of points

   a) The origin and the point whose coordinate is 4.
   b) The origin and the point whose coordinate is −4.
   c) The point with coordinate 2 and the point with coordinate −2. Ans. 4.
   d) The point with coordinate 3 and the point with coordinate −1.
   e) The point with coordinate −2 and the point with coordinate −3.
   f) The point with coordinate 1 and the point with coordinate $\sqrt{2}$. Ans. $\sqrt{2} - 1$.
   g) The point with coordinate $\sqrt{2}$ and the point with coordinate $-\sqrt{3}$.
   h) The point with coordinate $\frac{1}{2}$ and the point with coordinate $1/\sqrt{2}$.

4. In each part of Problem 3, find the directed distance from the first point to the second.   Ans.   a) 4; e) −1.

5. If the coordinate of the point P is 2, find the coordinate of a point Q such that the distance between P and Q is

   a) 1.   Ans.   1 or 3.   b) 3.   c) $\frac{1}{2}$.
   d) 0.   e) −1.   f) $\sqrt{2}$.

6. If the coordinate of the point P is 3, find the coordinate of the point Q such that the directed distance from P to Q is

  a) 1.   Ans.   4.   b) -2.   c) 5.
  d) x.   Ans. $x + 3$.   e) $4x - 3$.   f) $a^2 + \sqrt{a}$.

7. Show that the distance between the points P_1 and P_2, with coordinates x_1 and x_2, is $|x_1 - x_2|$.

  Hint: Break this up into cases. Consider first the case where $0 \leq x_2 \leq x_1$.

8. Show that the directed distance from P_1 to P_2 is $x_2 - x_1$.
9. Find the coordinate of the point halfway between the pair of points whose coordinates are

  a) 2,4.   Ans.   3.   b) 1,2.   c) $-1,3$.
  d) $-1,-4$.   e) 1,x.   f) x_1,x_2.   Ans. $\frac{1}{2}(x_1 + x_2)$.

10. If P_1, P_2, and P_3 are any three points on a line, show that the sum of the directed distances from P_1 to P_2, from P_2 to P_3 and from P_3 to P_1 is always zero.

2. INTERVALS

Definition 2.2: *The **open interval** determined by two given numbers, a and b, with a < b, is the collection of all numbers which lie between a and b.*

We denote this open interval by (a,b). If we wish to add to this open interval either or both of the end points, we indicate this by replacing the appropriate round bracket by a square bracket. Thus, $[a,b)$ is the collection of all numbers x such that $a \leq x < b$. Such collections also are called intervals, and in particular, $[a,b]$ is called the closed interval determined by a and b. We also agree to call the collection of all numbers x such that $a < x$ an interval and denote it by * (a,∞), and similarly for $(-\infty,a)$, $[a,\infty)$, $(-\infty,a]$, and $(-\infty,\infty)$.

In the previous section we set up a correspondence between points on a line and numbers. This allows us to carry over the concept of interval from numbers to points: the collection of all points whose coordinates form an interval of numbers is an interval of points.

We shall find this concept of interval useful in many places. One place where it arises naturally is in problems involving inequalities.

PROBLEMS

1. Solve the inequality

$$-1 < 3 - 2x < 0.$$

(To solve an inequality means to find all numbers which satisfy it.)

* It must not be assumed that ∞ is a number. It is not.

Solution: Adding -3 to each term we have $-4 < -2x < -3$. Multiplying each term by $-\frac{1}{2}$, we have $2 > x > \frac{3}{2}$. (Remember that multiplying by a negative number reverses the inequality. (Why?)) Thus we see that any number which satisfies the original inequality lies in the interval $(\frac{3}{2},2)$.

On the other hand, we can start with any number x in the interval $(\frac{3}{2},2)$, i.e., $\frac{3}{2} < x < 2$, and reverse our steps to show that $-1 < 3 - 2x < 0$. Therefore any number in $(\frac{3}{2},2)$ is a solution of the original inequality. Consequently the numbers in $(\frac{3}{2},2)$, and no others, are the solutions.

2. Solve the inequalities

a) $2 \le x - 2 < 4$.   Ans. $4 \le x < 6$, or $[4,6)$.
b) $8 \le 4x - 2 \le 9$.
c) $-3 \le 3x + 3 \le 0$.
d) $2 \le 1 - x \le 5$.   Ans. $-4 \le x \le -1$.
e) $1 \ge 2 - 3x > -4$.

f) $\dfrac{1}{2} \le \dfrac{10 - x}{3} \le 2$.

g) $2x + 3 \ge 1$.   Ans. $[-1,\infty)$.
h) $3 - 2x \le 4$.

i) $\dfrac{1}{x + 1} < 2$.   Ans. $-\frac{1}{2} < x$ and $x < -1$.

j) $\dfrac{1}{2x + 3} < 4$.

k) $\dfrac{x + 1}{2x + 3} < 4$.

l) $1 < \dfrac{1}{x + 1} < 3$.   Ans. $-\frac{2}{3} < x < 0$.

m) $0 \le \dfrac{1}{1 - x} < 1$.

n) $\dfrac{x + 1}{4x - 3} < 1$.   Ans. $(-\infty,\frac{3}{4})$ and $(\frac{4}{3},\infty)$.

o) $\dfrac{x - 1}{2x + 1} < 2$.

p) $\dfrac{x - 1}{2x + 1} < 0$.   Ans. $-\frac{1}{2} < x < 1$.

q) $\dfrac{2 - 3x}{3 + 2x} < 0$.

r) $(2 - 3x)(3 + 2x) < 0.$

s) $(x - 2)(3 + x) > 0.$

3. Solve the inequality

$$|x - 1| < 4.$$

Solution: If $x - 1 \geq 0$, then $|x - 1| = x - 1$, so we have $x - 1 < 4$ or $x < 5$. This is for the case $x - 1 \geq 0$, or $x \geq 1$. Hence $1 \leq x < 5$. On the other hand, if $x - 1 < 0$, we have $|x - 1| = -(x - 1)$, so we have $-(x - 1) < 4$ or $x - 1 > -4$. Hence $x > -3$. But this is for the case $x - 1 < 0$ or $x < 1$. Hence $-3 < x < 1$. Combining these, we have $-3 < x < 5$. Thus any number satisfying the inequality $|x - 1| < 4$ is in the interval $(-3, 5)$. Conversely, starting with any number in this interval, we can retrace our steps to show that it satisfies the original inequality. Thus the numbers in $(-3, 5)$, and no others, are the solutions.

4. Solve the inequalities

a) $|x + 2| < 3.$ Ans. $-5 < x < 1.$

b) $|2x - 1| < 1.$

c) $|2 - x| < 4.$

d) $|2 - x| > \frac{1}{2}.$ Ans. $x < \frac{3}{2}$ or $\frac{5}{2} < x.$

e) $|2x + 4| > 3.$

f) $|x - 1| < a.$ Ans. $1 - a < x < 1 + a.$

g) $|x + 1| < a.$

h) $|x - 3| < b.$

i) $|x - c| < a.$ Ans. $c - a < x < c + a.$

j) $|x + c| < a.$

3. COORDINATES IN THE PLANE

In Section 1 we set up a coordinate system on a line. Such a coordinate system assigns to each point a number. We now define a similar correspondence for the plane.

Choose two perpendicular lines in the plane, and label one of them the x-axis and the other the y-axis. Set up a coordinate system on each of these lines, choosing for the origin of each system the point O of intersection of the two lines, and also choosing the unit distance to be the same on the two lines. By convention, the x-axis is taken to be horizontal, with its unit point to the right of the origin, and the y-axis vertical with its unit point above the origin.

Now let P be any point in the plane. Construct a line through P perpendicular to the x-axis and let this line meet the x-axis at the point P_x.

Similarly, let the perpendicular to the y-axis through P meet the y-axis at P_y.

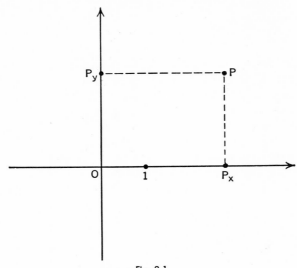

Fig. 2.1

Definition 2.3: *The x-coordinate or **abscissa** of P is the directed distance from O to P_x. The y-coordinate or **ordinate** of P is the directed distance from O to P_y.*

We always write this pair of coordinates in the order (x,y), with the x-coordinate first.

By this procedure we assign to each point P a pair of real numbers, (x,y). Conversely, to each pair of real numbers there corresponds one and only one point in the plane.

Note that this definition of coordinates uses directed distances, so that one or both of the coordinates of a point may be negative. In fact, if a point P lies to the left of the y-axis, its x-coordinate is negative, and if it lies below the x-axis, its y-coordinate is negative.

PROBLEMS

1. Locate, using the same coordinate system for each collection, the collection of points whose coordinates are

   a) $(1,3)$, $(-4,1)$, $(6,4)$, $(1.5,3.5)$.
   b) $(2,0)$, $(0,2)$, $(-2,0)$, $(0,-2)$, $(2,-2)$, $(-2,2)$.
   c) $(1,1)$, $(2,2)$, $(-3,-3)$, $(10,10)$.
   d) $(0,0)$, $(4,0)$, $(1,3)$, $(5,3)$.
   e) $(0,0)$, $(4,0)$, $(-1,2)$, $(3,2)$.
   f) $(0,0)$, $(2,-2)$, $(-2,2)$, $(5,-5)$.

2. Draw the triangle with the given vertices and find its area:

    a) $(1,0)$, $(4,0)$, $(1,6)$.   Ans.   Area $= 9$.   b) $(2,3)$, $(-4,3)$, $(2,-1)$.
    c) $(4,3)$, $(6,5)$, $(4,-1)$.   d) $(2,-2)$, $(-2,2)$, $(2,5)$.
    e) $(2,a)$, $(2,b)$, $(3,a)$.   Ans. $\frac{1}{2}|a - b|$.   f) (p,q), (p,r), (s,t).

3. If (p,q) is in the second quadrant, where are $(-p,q)$, $(p,-q)$, $(-p,-q)$, (q,p), and $(-q,-p)$? (The x- and y-axes together divide the plane into four regions, called quadrants. These are numbered in counterclockwise order, the first quadrant being the one above the x-axis and to the right of the y-axis.)

4. The same as 3, for (p,q) in the fourth quadrant.

5. Which points (x,y) have

    a) $x \geq 0$.   b) $x > 2$.
    c) $y < 1$.   d) $0 \leq x \leq 1$.
    e) $0 < x < 1$ and $0 < y$.   f) $1 \leq x - 2 < 4$.

    g) $3 \leq 2 - x < 7$ and $0 < y - 3 \leq 1$.
    h) $|x| = 3$.   i) $|x| \leq 3$.
    j) $|x| \geq 3$.   k) $|x| < 1$ and $|y| > 1$.
    l) $|x - 3| < 2$.   m) $|y + 3| < 1$.
    n) $|1 - x| < 1$ and $|2 + y| < 2$.   o) $x = y$.
    p) $x = |y|$.   q) $|x| = |y|$.

6. Find the coordinates of the third vertex of an equilateral triangle if the first two vertices are

    a) $(0,0)$ and $10,0)$.   Ans. $(5,\sqrt{75})$ or $(5,-\sqrt{75})$.
    b) $(1,1)$ and $(3,1)$.
    c) $(-1,1)$ and $(-1,-1)$.

7. Find the coordinates of the fourth vertex of a parallelogram if the coordinates of the first three vertices are

    a) $(0,0)$, $(2,0)$, $(1,1)$.   Ans. $(3,1)$ or $(1,-1)$ or $(-1,1)$.
    b) $(1,-1)$, $(-1,-1)$, $(-2,-2)$.
    c) $(3, -2)$, $(5,0)$, $(3,5)$.
    d) $(0,0)$, $(a,0)$, (b,c).

4. DIRECTED LINES AND ANGLES

We have already decided which of the two possible directions is to be the positive one on two particular lines, the x- and y-axes. On the x-axis it is from left to right and on the y-axis it is upwards. We now extend this convention to all lines in the plane: By convention, on any horizontal line, the direction from left to right is taken to be the positive direction, and on any other line, the upwards direction is taken to be the positive one.

Having chosen positive directions for each line, we can now talk about directed distances along any line.

Definition 2.4: *The **directed distance** from a point P to a point $\overline{P}$ is the distance between P and $\overline{P}$ if the direction from P to $\overline{P}$ along the line determined by these two points is the already chosen positive direction, otherwise it is the negative of the distance between them.*

Just as there are two possible directions on a line, there are two possible directions of rotation in the plane, clockwise and counterclockwise. We shall agree to consider the counterclockwise direction as the positive direction of rotation, so an angle measured in the clockwise direction will be negative.

Two intersecting lines in the plane determine two angles, one of which is the supplement of the other. In order to avoid confusion between these two angles we introduce the following definition.

Definition 2.5: *Given two lines in the plane, L_1 and L_2, intersecting at a point P, the **angle from** L_1 to L_2 is that angle through which L_1 must be rotated around P in the counterclockwise direction to reach L_2.*

Note that the angle from any one line to any other is always less than 180°.

5. SOME THEOREMS

In this section we present some definitions, formulas, and theorems which will be our chief working tools in analytic geometry.

Definition 2.6: *Let P and $\overline{P}$ be two points in the plane. Let Q be the point of intersection of the vertical through $\overline{P}$ and the horizontal through P. The **horizontal distance** from P to $\overline{P}$ is the directed distance from P to Q, and the **vertical distance** from P to $\overline{P}$ is the directed distance from Q to $\overline{P}$.*

Theorem 2.2: *If $P(x,y)$ and $\overline{P}(\bar{x},\bar{y})$ are any two points, then the horizontal distance from P to $\overline{P}$ is $(\bar{x} - x)$ and the vertical distance from P to $\overline{P}$ is $(\bar{y} - y)$.*

Proof: Let P_x and $\overline{P}_x$ be the points where the verticals through P and $\overline{P}$ meet the x-axis. On the x-axis, the coordinate of P_x is x and $\overline{P}_x$ is $\bar{x}$. The directed distance from P_x to $\overline{P}_x$ is $\bar{x} - x$. But, by geometry, the directed distance from P_x to $\overline{P}_x$ is the directed distance from P to Q, which, by definition, is the horizontal distance from P to $\overline{P}$. Thus the latter is $\bar{x} - x$.

The proof that the vertical distance from P to $\overline{P}$ is $\bar{y} - y$ is carried out in a similar fashion, using the points P_y and $\overline{P}_y$.

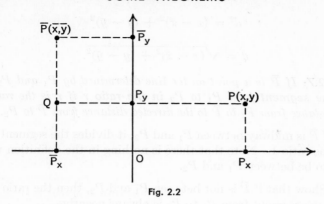

Fig. 2.2

Exercise: Write out the complete proof that the vertical distance from P to $\bar{P}$ is $\bar{y} - y$.

Theorem 2.3: *If $P(x,y)$ and $\bar{P}(\bar{x},\bar{y})$ are any two points in the plane, then the distance between P and $\bar{P}$ is*

$$d = \sqrt{(x - \bar{x})^2 + (y - \bar{y})^2}.$$

Proof: Draw a vertical line through P and a horizontal line through $\bar{P}$, and let Q be the point of intersection of these lines. By construction $PQ\bar{P}$ is a right triangle whose hypotenuse is $P\bar{P}$. By the Pythagorean theorem, the square of the length of $P\bar{P}$ is the sum of the squares of the lengths of $\bar{P}Q$ and QP. But, the length of $\bar{P}Q$ is either the horizontal distance from P to $\bar{P}$ or else the horizontal distance from $\bar{P}$ to P, depending on the location of P and $\bar{P}$, and hence is $|x - \bar{x}|$, and we have $|x - \bar{x}|^2 = (x - \bar{x})^2$.

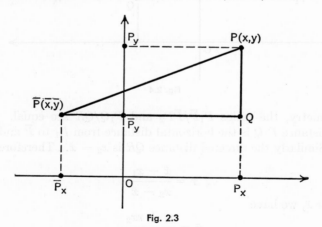

Fig. 2.3

Similarly, the square of the length of QP is $(y - \bar{y})^2$. So, by substitution in the Pythagorean theorem,

$$d^2 = (x - \bar{x})^2 + (y - \bar{y})^2$$

or

$$d = \sqrt{(x - \bar{x})^2 + (y - \bar{y})^2}.$$

Definition 2.7: *If $\bar{P}$ is a point on the line determined by P_1 and P_2, then $\bar{P}$ **divides the segment** from P_1 to P_2 **in the ratio** r if r is the ratio of the directed distance from P_1 to $\bar{P}$ to the directed distance from $\bar{P}$ to P_2.*

Thus, if $\bar{P}$ is midway between P_1 and P_2, it divides the segment between them in the ratio 1. Note that there is nothing in the definition which requires $\bar{P}$ to be between P_1 and P_2.

Exercise: Show that if $\bar{P}$ is not between P_1 and P_2, then the ratio in which it divides the segment from P_1 to P_2 is always negative.

Theorem 2.4: *The coordinates of the point $\bar{P}(\bar{x}, \bar{y})$ which divides the segment from $P_1(x_1, y_1)$ to the point $P_2(x_2, y_2)$ in the ratio r are*

$$\bar{x} = \frac{x_1 + rx_2}{1 + r} \quad and \quad \bar{y} = \frac{y_1 + ry_2}{1 + r}.$$

Proof: Let the verticals through $\bar{P}$ and P_2 meet the horizontal through P_1 at Q and R respectively.

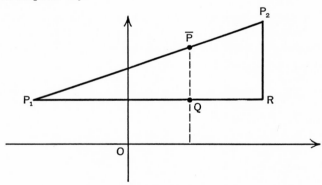

Fig. 2.4

By geometry, the ratios $P_1\bar{P}/\bar{P}P_2$ and P_1Q/QR are equal. But the directed distance P_1Q is the horizontal distance from P_1 to $\bar{P}$ and hence is $\bar{x} - x_1$. Similarly the directed distance QR is $x_2 - \bar{x}$. Therefore

$$r = \frac{\bar{x} - x_1}{x_2 - \bar{x}}.$$

Solving for $\bar{x}$, we have

$$\bar{x} = \frac{x_1 + rx_2}{1 + r}.$$

The formula for $\bar{y}$ is obtained similarly.

Note that if $\overline{P}$ is midway between P_1 and P_2, then $r = 1$ and these formulas become

$$\overline{x} = \frac{x_1 + x_2}{2}, \quad \overline{y} = \frac{y_1 + y_2}{2}.$$

PROBLEMS

1. Find the distances between the following pairs of points:

   a) $(2,3)$ and $(6,1)$.   Ans. $\sqrt{20}$.
   b) $(1,1)$ and $(2,-2)$.   Ans. $\sqrt{10}$.
   c) $(2,3)$ and $(-6,1)$.
   d) $(0,5)$ and $(5,0)$.
   e) $(a,3)$ and $(2,2)$.   Ans. $\sqrt{a^2 - 4a + 5}$.
   f) $(a,-2)$ and $(4,-a)$.
   g) $(a,1)$ and $(b,2a)$.

2. Find the perimeters of the triangles whose vertices are

   a) $(0,1)$, $(4,3)$, $(6,2)$.   Ans. $3\sqrt{5} + \sqrt{37}$.
   b) $(10,10)$, $(-1,-2)$, $(-4,6)$.
   c) (p,q), $(-p,-q)$, $(2p,-3q)$.

3. If P is on the line parallel to the x-axis and 4 units above, and if the distance between P and $(4,7)$ is 5, what are the coordinates of P?

4. Find the coordinates of the midpoint between

   a) $(2,6)$ and $(-4,0)$.

   Solution: The midpoint divides the segment from $(2,6)$ to $(-4,0)$ in the ratio 1.   By Theorem 2.4, $\overline{x} = \dfrac{2 + (-4)}{2} = -1$ and $\overline{y} = \dfrac{6 + 0}{2}$
   $= 3$, so the midpoint is $(-1,3)$.

   b) $(4,5)$ and $(10,8)$.   Ans. $(7,6\frac{1}{2})$.
   c) $(-8,2)$ and $(1,-6)$.
   d) $(a,3)$ and $(3,a)$.
   e) (a,b) and $(3b,4a)$.

5. Find the coordinates of the point which divides the segment from P_1 to P_2 in the given ratio if

   a) $P_1 = (1,1)$, $P_2 = (2,-4)$, $r = 2$.   Ans. $(\frac{5}{3},-\frac{7}{3})$.
   b) $P_1 = (1,1)$, $P_2 = (2,-4)$, $r = \frac{1}{3}$.
   c) $P_1 = (1,1)$, $P_2 = (2,-4)$, $r = -\frac{1}{2}$.
   d) $P_1 = (a,b)$, $P_2 = (b,a)$, $r = \frac{1}{2}$.

6. Find the distance between the point $(2,6)$ and the point which divides the segment from $(2,2)$ to $(4,6)$ in the ratio -3.   Ans. $\sqrt{13}$.

7. Find the coordinates of the point which is equidistant from the points (4,6), (−4,2), and (−3,−1). Ans. (1,2).
8. Find the distances between the midpoints of consecutive sides of the quadrangle whose vertices are (1,1), (4,2), (5,7), (2,6).
9. Show by means of the formulas of this section that the medians of the triangle (0,0), (a,b), (c,0) meet at a point which is two-thirds of the way from any vertex to the midpoint of the opposite side.
10. Show, by means of the formulas of this section, that the diagonals of the parallelogram (0,0), (10,0), (a,3), (10 + a,3) bisect each other.
11. Show, by means of the formulas of this section, that the points (1,−1), (2,2), and (4,8) are on a straight line.

6. STRAIGHT LINES

Next to a point, the simplest geometric object is a straight line. We are now in a position to obtain some algebraic information about straight lines.

Definition 2.8: *The inclination of a line is the angle from the x-axis to the line.*

Definition 2.9: *The slope of a line is the tangent of its inclination.*

We denote the inclination of a line by α and its slope by m, so we have the formula

$$m = \tan \alpha.$$

Note that the inclination of a line parallel to the y-axis is 90°. But the tangent of this angle does not exist, so the slope of a vertical line is not defined. A horizontal line, however, has slope 0.

Theorem 2.5: *If $P(x,y)$ and $\overline{P}(\bar{x},\bar{y})$ are any two points on a line of slope m, then*

$$m = \frac{\bar{y} - y}{\bar{x} - x}.$$

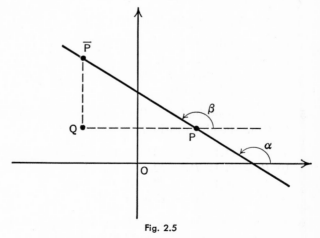

Fig. 2.5

Proof: Let the perpendicular from $\bar{P}$ meet the horizontal from P at the point Q. Let α be the inclination of our line. By geometry, α is equal to the angle β from the line through Q and P to our line, so $m = \tan \alpha = \tan \beta$. But by trigonometry, $\tan \beta$ is the ratio of the vertical distance from P to $\bar{P}$ to the horizontal distance from P to $\bar{P}$. By Theorem 2.2 then

$$\tan \alpha = \frac{\bar{y} - y}{\bar{x} - x}.$$

Theorem 2.6: *Two nonvertical lines L_1 and L_2 are parallel if and only if $m_1 = m_2$.*

Proof: If L_1 and L_2 are parallel, they have the same inclination and hence the same slope. Conversely, if their slopes are equal, then $\tan \alpha_1 = \tan \alpha_2$. Since the inclination of a line is never less than $0°$ and is always less than $180°$, it follows that $\alpha_1 = \alpha_2$ and the lines are parallel.

Theorem 2.7: *Two nonvertical lines L_1 and L_2 are perpendicular if and only if $m_1 m_2 = -1$.*

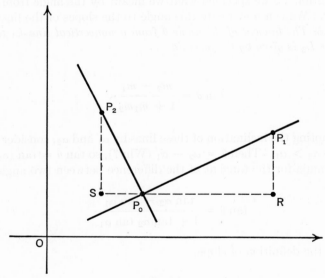

Fig. 2.6

Proof: Let two perpendicular lines meet at the point $P_0(x_0, y_0)$. Choose a point $P_1(x_1, y_1)$ on one line and $P_2(x_2, y_2)$ on the other. Let the verticals through P_1 and P_2 meet the horizontal through P_0 at R and S. Then the triangles P_0RP_1 and P_2SP_0 are similar, and corresponding sides are proportional.

$$\frac{SP_0}{SP_2} = \frac{RP_1}{P_0R},$$

or

$$\frac{x_0 - x_2}{y_2 - y_0} = \frac{y_1 - y_0}{x_1 - x_0}.$$

Hence

$$\frac{y_1 - y_0}{x_1 - x_0} \cdot \frac{y_2 - y_0}{x_2 - x_0} = -1.$$

By Theorem 2.5, $m_1 \cdot m_2 = -1$.

Conversely, suppose $m_1 \cdot m_2 = -1$. Then $m_1 \neq m_2$, so the lines are not parallel, and they intersect at a point P_0. Let L_3 be a line perpendicular to L_1 at P_0, with slope m_3. Then, by the above, $m_1 \cdot m_3 = -1$. But $m_1 \cdot m_2 = -1$, and so $m_2 = m_3$. Thus both L_2 and L_3 pass through P_0 with the same slope, and hence with the same inclination. Since there can be only one such line, L_2 is the same as L_3, and so is perpendicular to L_1.

In Definition 2.5 we specified what we meant by the angle from one line to another. We can now relate this angle to the slopes of the lines.

Theorem 2.8: *The tangent of the angle θ from a nonvertical line L_1 to a nonvertical line L_2 is given by the formula*

$$\tan \theta = \frac{m_2 - m_1}{1 + m_1 m_2}.$$

Proof: Denoting the inclination of these lines by α_1 and α_2, consider first the case where $\alpha_2 > \alpha_1$. Then $\theta = \alpha_2 - \alpha_1$ (Why?), so $\tan \theta = \tan (\alpha_2 - \alpha_1)$. By the formula for the tangent of the difference between two angles,

$$\tan \theta = \frac{\tan \alpha_2 - \tan \alpha_1}{1 + \tan \alpha_2 \tan \alpha_1}.$$

Hence, by the definition of slope,

$$\tan \theta = \frac{m_2 - m_1}{1 + m_2 m_1}.$$

If $\alpha_1 > \alpha_2$, then $\theta = 180f - (\alpha_1 - \alpha_2)$, so $\tan \theta = \tan (180f - (\alpha_1 - \alpha_2))$. By trigonometry, $\tan (180f - (\alpha_1 - \alpha_2)) = -\tan (\alpha_1 - \alpha_2) = \tan (\alpha_2 - \alpha_1)$, and we can proceed as above.

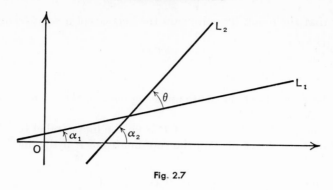

Fig. 2.7

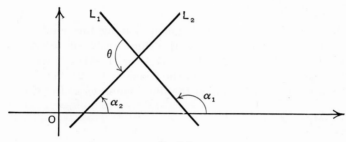

Fig. 2.8

PROBLEMS

1. Find the slopes of the lines joining the following pairs of points:

   a) $(1,7)$ and $(-4,2)$.   Ans.   1.
   b) $(0,4)$ and $(-2,-2)$.
   c) $(-3,5)$ and $(5,-5)$.
   d) $(2,7)$ and the midpoint between $(1,3)$ and $(-3,1)$.
   e) $(-3,4)$ and the point dividing the sequent from $(6,6)$ to $(-8,-1)$ in the ratio $-\frac{1}{2}$.

2. For each line in Problem 1, find a value for b such that the line is parallel to the line joining $(-1,0)$ to $(4,b)$.   Ans.   a) $b = 5$.
3. For each line in Problem 1, find a value for a such that the line is perpendicular to the line joining $(2,-2)$ to $(a,3)$.
4. Find the tangent of the angle from each line in Problem 1 to the line joining $(1,-2)$ to $(-2,4)$.   Ans.   a) 3.
5. Find the tangents of the angles of the triangle whose vertices are

   a) $(1,-1)$, $(-7,7)$, and $(5,9)$.   Ans. $\frac{7}{3}$, $\frac{7}{5}$, and $\frac{28}{17}$.
   b) $(3,6)$, $(-3,2)$, and $(0,-8)$.
   c) $(0,0)$, $(-4,0)$, and $(2,2)$.
   d) $(1,a)$, $(3,a)$, and $(2,-2)$.

6. Show that the following points are the vertices of a right triangle:

   a) $(5,0)$, $(8,4)$, $(-4,13)$.
   b) $(1,-6)$, $(8,8)$, $(-7,-2)$.
   c) $(-1,-1)$, $(2,2)$, $(5,-1)$.

7. Find the tangents of the acute angles of each of the triangles of Problem 6. Ans. a) 3, $\frac{1}{3}$.

8. If Q is the point $(-1,-2)$ and if P is on the line parallel to the y-axis and 3 units to the right, find the coordinates of P if the line joining P and Q is

   a) parallel to the line joining $(-2,3)$ and $(1,1)$,
   b) perpendicular to this line.

9. The base of a triangle is the segment joining the points $(-1,0)$ and $(9,0)$. Find the coordinates of the third vertex if the slopes of the other sides are $\frac{1}{2}$ and -2. Ans. $(7,4)$ or $(1,-4)$.

10. Find the slope of each median of the triangle $(1,-2)$, $(3,6)$, and $(-2,4)$.

11. Find the value of p for which the line joining $(p,2)$ to $(3,p)$ has slope

   a) 2. Ans. $\frac{8}{3}$.   b) 1.
   c) 0.   d) -1.

12. Show that the midpoints of the sides of the quadrilateral $(1,1)$, $(3,-4)$, $(5,2)$, $(2,7)$ are the vertices of a parallelogram.

13. Two opposite vertices of a square are $(4,2)$ and $(3,-1)$. What are the coordinates of the other two vertices?

7. APPLICATIONS TO GEOMETRY

In this section we illustrate how the preceding material can be used to obtain geometric results. The solution to the first problem below brings out the points which must be kept in mind when working such problems.

PROBLEMS

1. Show that the midpoints of the sides of any quadrilateral are the vertices of a parallelogram.

Solution: In order to apply the formulas which we now have at our command, we must assign coordinates to the vertices of our quadrilateral. However, it clearly makes no difference where the quadrilateral is located in the plane, so we can move it into a position which makes these coordinates as simple as possible. For example, we can move it into such a position that one vertex is at the origin. Then, by rotating around the origin, we can have one side of the quadrilateral fall on the x-axis. Then one vertex has the coordinates $(0,0)$, and another vertex has its y-coordinate zero. We now label the other co-ordinates. Since we are to work this problem for an arbitrary quadri-lateral, we cannot assign specific numbers for these coordinates, but must use symbols instead which can represent arbitrary numbers. Figure 2.9 shows one way of labeling the coordinates.

Now, using the midpoint formulas (Theorem 2.4) we find that

$$P_1 = \left(\frac{a}{2}, 0\right), \quad P_2 = \left(\frac{b+a}{2}, \frac{c}{2}\right), \quad P_3 = \left(\frac{d+b}{2}, \frac{e+c}{2}\right), \quad \text{and} \quad P_4 = \left(\frac{d}{2}, \frac{e}{2}\right).$$

Using the slope formula (Theorem 2.5), we find that the slope of the line joining P_1 and P_2 is

$$\frac{\dfrac{c}{2}}{\dfrac{b+a}{2} - \dfrac{a}{2}} = \frac{c}{b}.$$

Next, the slope of the line joining P_3 and P_4 is

$$\frac{\dfrac{e}{2} - \dfrac{e+c}{2}}{\dfrac{d}{2} - \dfrac{d+b}{2}} = \frac{c}{b}.$$

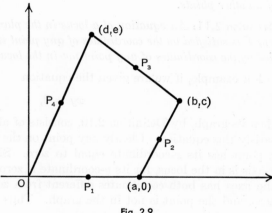

Fig. 2.9

Hence, by Theorem 2.6, these two lines are parallel.

A similar calculation shows that the lines joining P_2 to P_3 and P_1 to P_4 are also parallel.

2. Show that the diagonals of any parallelogram bisect each other.

3. Show that if the diagonals of a rectangle are perpendicular, then it is a square.

4. Show that the diagonals of any isosceles trapezoid are equal.

5. Show that in any triangle the sum of the squares of the medians is equal to three fourths the sum of the squares of the sides.

6. Show that the sum of squares of the sides of any parallelogram is equal to the sum of the squares of the diagonals.

7. Show that the midpoints of the sides of any rectangle are the vertices of a rhombus.
8. Show that the trisection points of a diagonal of any parallelogram together with the other two vertices are the vertices of another parallelogram.
9. Show that the midpoint of the hypotenuse of any right triangle is equidistant from the three vertices.
10. Show that the medians from the ends of the base of an isosceles triangle are equal in length.

8. THE BASIC DEFINITIONS OF ANALYTIC GEOMETRY

In setting up a coordinate system in the plane, we associate with each point, which is a geometric entity, a pair of numbers, which is an algebraic entity. The following definitions extend this correspondence to other geometric entities.

Definition 2.10: *The* **graph** *(or* **locus***) of an equation in x and y is the collection of all those points in the plane whose coordinates satisfy the equation, and of no other points.*

Definition 2.11: *An* **equation** *of a locus in the plane is an equation in x and y which is satisfied by the coordinates of any point in the locus, and is not satisfied by the coordinates of any point not in the locus.*

For example, if we are given the equation

$$xy = 0,$$

then its graph, by Definition 2.10, consists of all points whose coordinates satisfy this equation. Clearly any point on the y-axis is included, for such a point has its x-coordinate equal to zero. Similarly, any point on the x-axis is in the locus, for its y-coordinate is zero. A point not on either of the axes has both coordinates different from zero, so their product is not zero, and the point is not in the graph. Thus the graph of this equation consists of the x- and y-axes together.

Exercise: Show that the graph of the equation $x = 0$ is the y-axis, and of $y = 0$ is the x-axis.

Note that in the second definition we use the phrase "an equation" rather than "the equation." The reason for this is that two different equations may have the same graph.

Exercise: Show that $y = 0$, $2y = 0$, $y^2 = 0$, $x^2y + y^3 = 0$ are equations of the x-axis.

Consequently, if we start with a locus, the graph of any of its equations is the original locus. But if we start with an equation, then an equation of its graph may not be the same as the original equation.

Notice that if the coordinates of a point satisfy both of two different equations, then the point is on both graphs, and hence is a point where the two curves cross. Conversely, any point at which two loci intersect has coordinates which satisfy the equations of both loci simultaneously.

In the next two sections we shall apply these definitions to the special cases of the straight line and the circle.

PROBLEMS

1. Draw the graphs of the equations

   a) $x = 1$.
   b) $x = -1$.
   c) $x = 3$.
   d) $y = 2$.
   e) $y = -4$.
   f) $|x| = 1$.
   g) $|x| = 3$.
   h) $|x| = 0$.

2. Draw the graphs of the equations

   a) $|x - 3| = 2$.
   b) $|y + 2| = 1$.
   c) $x = y$.
   d) $x + y = 0$.
   e) $x = y + 1$.
   f) $|x| = y$.
   g) $x^2 + y^2 = 0$.
   h) $x(x^2 + y^2) = 0$.
   i) $|xy| = 0$.
   j) $(x - 1)(y + 2) = 0$.

3. Write an equation for

   a) the line parallel to the x-axis and 2 units below it.   Ans. $y = -2$.
   b) the line passing through the origin with slope 2.
   c) the line passing through the point (1,0) with slope 2.
   d) the circle with center at the origin and radius 5.

   (*Hint:* Remember the definition of a circle and use the distance formula.)

4. Definition 2.10 refers to the graph of an equation. There is no need however to restrict ourselves to equations:

   Definition: *The **graph** of a relation between x and y is the collection of all points in the plane whose coordinates fulfill this relation, and of no other points.*

   Show that the graph of $xy > 0$ consists of all points inside the first and third quadrants.

   Solution: If (p,q) is inside the first quadrant, then $p > 0$ and $q > 0$, so $pq > 0$, and the coordinates of the point (p,q) do satisfy the given relation. If (p,q) is in the third quadrant, then $p < 0$ and $q < 0$, so $pq > 0$ again. If (p,q) is in the second quadrant, then $p < 0$ and $q > 0$, so $pq < 0$ and the coordinates of the point (p,q) do not satisfy the given relation, and similarly for (p,q) in the fourth quadrant.

Finally, if (p,q) is on the boundary of any quadrant, then $p = 0$, or $q = 0$, so $pq = 0$, and (p,q) is not in the graph.

5. Discuss the graphs of the relations

a) $x > 0$.

b) $|x| \leq 1$.

c) $x < y$.

d) $|x| < |y|$.

e) $x^2 + y^2 < 1$.

f) $x^2 + y^2 > 1$.

9. EQUATIONS OF THE STRAIGHT LINE

One way of specifying a particular line is to give two points on it. Another is to give one point on it and its inclination or slope. By Theorem 2.5, two points determine the slope, so the following theorem covers both these cases.

Theorem 2.9: *The line through the point $P_0(x_0,y_0)$ with slope m has for an equation*

$$y - y_0 = m(x - x_0).$$

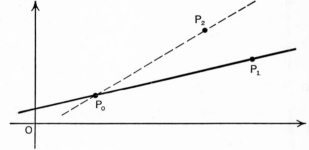

Fig. 2.10

Proof: According to Definition 2.11, we must show first that if $P_1(x_1,y_1)$ is any point on the line, then its coordinates satisfy this equation, i.e., that $y_1 - y_0 = m(x_1 - x_0)$. First we notice that the coordinates of P_0 satisfy the equation: $y_0 - y_0 = m(x_0 - x_0) = 0$. Next, consider $P_1 \neq P_0$. Since the line has a slope, it is not vertical, so $x_1 - x_0 \neq 0$. By Theorem 2.5, $m = \dfrac{y_1 - y_0}{x_1 - x_0}$, and so $y_1 - y_0 = m(x_1 - x_0)$.

Next we must show that if $P_2(x_2,y_2)$ is not on the line, then its coordinates do not satisfy the equation. Draw the line P_0P_2. This line is either vertical, in which case $0 \neq y_1 - y_0$ and $m(x_1 - x_0) = 0$, or else has a slope $\bar{m}$ which is different from m. By Theorem 2.5, $\bar{m} = \dfrac{y_2 - y_0}{x_2 - x_0}$. If $y_2 - y_0 = m(x_2 - x_0)$, then we would have $\dfrac{y_2 - y_0}{x_2 - x_0} = m$, which is impossible.

Note that this theorem does not tell us an equation for a line which has no slope, that is, for a vertical line.

Theorem 2.10: *The line through the point $P_0(x_0,y_0)$ parallel to the y-axis has for an equation*

$$x = x_0.$$

Exercise: Prove this theorem.

The equation of Theorem 2.9 is called the *point-slope* equation of a line. If a line is not vertical, it must meet the y-axis, at a point which we always denote by $(0,b)$. If we are given this point of a line and its slope, then the point slope equation is

$$y - b = m(x - 0)$$

or

$$y = mx + b.$$

This convenient equation is called the *slope-intercept* equation of the line.

Note that any line, vertical or not, has an equation which is of the first degree in both x and y. The converse is also true.

Theorem 2.11: *Any equation of the first degree in x and y is an equation of a line.*

Proof: Any first-degree equation in x and y can be written in the form

$$Ax + By + C = 0.$$

There are two cases: 1) $B = 0$, and 2) $B \neq 0$.

Case 1 $B = 0$.

Now A cannot be zero, or else the equation would not be of the first degree. Hence we can divide through by A and obtain

$$x = \frac{-C}{A}.$$

Now consider the line parallel to the y-axis and passing through the point $\left(\frac{-C}{A},0\right)$. By Theorem 2.10, an equation for this line is

$$x = \frac{-C}{A},$$

which is the same as the equation above. Hence we have found in this case a line for which $Ax + By + C = 0$ is an equation.

Case 2 $B \neq 0$.

Dividing through by B, we obtain

$$y = \frac{-A}{B} x + \frac{-C}{B}.$$

Now consider the line whose slope is $-A/B$ and which crosses the y-axis at the point $\left(0, \dfrac{-C}{B}\right)$. The slope-intercept equation of this line is

$$y = \frac{-A}{B}x + \frac{-C}{B}$$

which is the same equation as the one above. Hence in this case also we have found a line for which $Ax + By + C = 0$ is an equation.

PROBLEMS

1. Write an equation for the line passing through the points (4,2) and (−3,3).

   Solution: We can use the point-slope form of the equation of a line: $y - y_0 = m(x - x_0)$. The slope of this line is $\dfrac{-1}{7}$, by Theorem 2.5, so an equation of the line is $y - 2 = \dfrac{-1}{7}(x - 4)$ or $x + 7y = 18$. (If we use the point (−3,3) instead of (4,2) we get $y - 3 = \dfrac{-1}{7}(x + 3)$ or $x + 7y = 18$, i.e., the same equation.)

2. Write an equation for the line passing through the points

   a) (1,2) and (3,−1). Ans. $3x + 2y = 7$.   b) (2,1) and (5,0).
   c) (−1,3) and (1,3). Ans. $y = 3$.   d) (3,−1) and (3,1).
   e) (0,0) and (4,2).   f) (2,−3) and (−4,6).
   g) (2,q) and (3q, 6).   h) (a,b) and (c,d).
   i) (a,0) and (0,b).

3. Find the slope of the line whose equation is $5x - 2y = 4$, and find the points where the line crosses the axes.

   Solution: It is best to use the slope-intercept form of the equation of the line: $y = mx + b$. Solving our equation for y we obtain $y = \frac{5}{2}x - 2$. Comparing this with $y = mx + b$, we see that $m = \frac{5}{2}$ and $b = -2$. Therefore the slope of our line is $\frac{5}{2}$ and it crosses the y-axis at the point (0,−2).

   To find the point where the line crosses the x-axis, denote the coordinates of this point by (a,0). (Why is the second coordinate 0?) Since this point is on the line, its coordinates satisfy the equation of the line, so $5a = 4$, or $a = \frac{4}{5}$. Thus the line crosses the x-axis at the point $(\frac{4}{5},0)$.

4. For each of the following lines, find the slope and the points where it crosses the axes:

a) $x + y + 1 = 0$. Ans. $-1, (-1,0), (0,-1)$.
b) $x - y + 2 = 0$.
c) $2x + 3y - 4 = 0$.
d) $2x - 2y = 0$.
e) $6x - 4y + 3 = 0$. Ans. $\frac{3}{2}, (-\frac{1}{2},0), (0,\frac{3}{4})$.
f) $2x + 5 = 0$.
g) $2y + 5 = 0$.
h) $y/2 - x/3 + \frac{1}{4} = 0$.

5. Which pairs of the lines of Problem 4 are parallel and which perpendicular?

6. Write an equation for the line

a) containing $(1,-2)$ and with slope 2;
b) through the origin and parallel to the line joining $(4,4)$ and $(2,5)$;
c) through the point $(4,4)$ and perpendicular to the line with equation $x + 2y + 3 = 0$.

7. The sides of a triangle lie on the lines whose equations are $x + y + 1 = 0$, $x - 2y + 2 = 0$, and $2x + 3y - 4 = 0$. What are the coordinates of the vertices?

Solution: Let (a,b) be the vertex where the sides lying on the first two lines meet. Then this point is on each line and so its coordinates must satisfy both equations at the same time:

$$a + b + 1 = 0.$$

$$a - 2b + 2 = 0.$$

Solving these equations simultaneously, we find $a = -\frac{4}{3}$ and $b = \frac{1}{3}$. One vertex, therefore, is $(-\frac{4}{3},\frac{1}{3})$.

The other two vertices can now be found by the same method and are $(-7,6)$ and $(\frac{2}{7},\frac{8}{7})$.

8. Find the vertices of the triangle whose sides lie on the following lines:

a) $x = y$, $x + y = 1$, $x - 2y - 3 = 0$. Ans. $(\frac{1}{2},\frac{1}{2})$, $(-3,-3)$, $(\frac{5}{3},-\frac{2}{3})$.
b) $x = y$, $2x + y - 3 = 0$, $x + 2y = 0$.
c) $4x - y - 2 = 0$, $x - 3y + 5 = 0$, $3x + 2y + 4 = 0$.
d) $4x + 3y - 15 = 0$, $6x - 5y - 13 = 0$, $x - 4y - 18 = 0$.

9. Show that $3x + 4y + 5 = 0$, $x - 2y = 0$, $6x + 8y = 8$, and $4y = 2x + 2$ are the sides of a parallelogram, and find its vertices.

10. The vertices of a triangle are $(9,3)$, $(3,6)$, and $(-1,-2)$. Find

a) the equations of the sides;
b) the equations of the altitudes;
c) the equations of the medians;
d) the point of intersection of the medians.

10. THE CIRCLE

A circle is defined in geometry to be the locus of all points equidistant from a given fixed point called the *center* of the circle. The distance between the center and any point of the circle is called the *radius* of the circle. Hence to specify a circle it is sufficient to specify the coordinates of its center, which we denote by (h,k), and its radius, which we denote by r.

Theorem 2.12: *The circle with center at the point (h,k) and with radius r has or an equation*

$$(x - h)^2 + (y - k)^2 = r^2.$$

Proof: According to Definition 2.11, we must first show that if $P_1(x_1,y_1)$ is on the circle, then its coordinates satisfy this equation, i.e., that

$$(x_1 - h)^2 + (y_1 - k)^2 = r^2.$$

But if P_1 is on the circle, the distance between P_1 and (h,k) is r. By Theorem 2.3,

$$\sqrt{(x_1 - h)^2 + (y_1 - k)^2} = r.$$

Squaring,

$$(x_1 - h)^2 + (y_1 - k)^2 = r^2.$$

Next, we must show that if $P_2(x_2,y_2)$ is not on the circle, then its coordinates do not satisfy our equation. But if P_2 is not on the circle, then the distance between P_2 and (h,k) is some number $s \neq r$. By Theorem 2.3,

$$\sqrt{(x_2 - h)^2 + (y_2 - k)^2} = s$$

or

$$(x_2 - h)^2 + (y_2 - k)^2 = s^2.$$

Since $s \neq r$, and both are positive, $s^2 \neq r^2$. Thus the coordinates of P_2 do not satisfy our equation.

If we expand the equation $(x - h)^2 + (y - k)^2 = r^2$ of Theorem 2.12, we obtain

$$x^2 - 2hx + h^2 + y^2 - 2ky + k^2 = r^2$$

which we can write as

$$x^2 + y^2 + dx + ey + f = 0.$$

This is a second-degree equation, but it is not true that every second-degree equation is an equation of a circle. We shall investigate the general second-degree equation in Chapter 6.

Note that each of the above equations contains three constants. This corresponds to the geometric theorem that three points determine a circle.

PROBLEMS

1. Write, in the form $x^2 + y^2 + dx + ey + f = 0$, an equation for the circle which has

   a) center at $(2,2)$, radius 1.

      (*Hint:* Use first the formula in Theorem 2.12.)   Ans. $x^2 + y^2 - 4x - 4y + 7 = 0$.

   b) center at $(2,-2)$, radius 2.
   c) center at $(3,4)$, radius 5.
   d) center at $(0,4)$, radius 3.   Ans. $x^2 + y^2 - 8x + 7 = 0$.
   e) center at $(6,0)$, radius 1.
   f) center at $(1,-1)$, radius $\sqrt{2}$.
   g) center at (a,b), radius $a + b$.

2. Find an equation for the circle which has its center at $(2,3)$ and passes through the point $(-1,-1)$.

   Solution: The radius of the circle is the distance from the center $(2,3)$ to any point, in particular $(-1,-1)$, on the circle, and so is

   $$\sqrt{(2 + 1)^2 + (3 + 1)^2} = 5.$$

   By Theorem 2.12, an equation for the circle is

   $$(x - 2)^2 + (y - 3)^2 = 5^2,$$
   or
   $$x^2 + y^2 - 4x - 6y - 12 = 0.$$

3. Find an equation for the circle which

   a) has its center at $(1,2)$ and passes through $(4,5)$.

      Ans. $x^2 + y^2 - 2x - 4y - 13 = 0$.

   b) has the points $(2,-4)$ and $(6,3)$ as ends of a diameter.
   c) has its center at $(-2,4)$ and is tangent to the x-axis.   (*Hint:* Draw a figure.)
   d) has its center on the line $y = 2x + 2$ and is tangent to the x-axis at the point $(3,0)$.   Ans. $x^2 + y^2 - 6x - 16y + 9 = 0$.
   e) has radius 3 and is tangent to both axes.

4. Find an equation for the circle which passes through the points $(2,3)$, $(-1,-6)$, and $(3,-4)$.

   Solution: We use the form $x^2 + y^2 + dx + ey + f = 0$.   Since $(2,3)$ is on the circle, its coordinates must satisfy the equation of the circle:

   $$2^2 + 3^2 + 2d + 3e + f = 0,$$
   or
   $$2d + 3e + f + 13 = 0.$$

Using the other two points, we obtain the equations

$$-d - 6e + f + 37 = 0$$

$$3d - 4e + f + 25 = 0.$$

Solving these equations simultaneously, we obtain $d = 2$, $e = 2$, and $f = -23$. Therefore the equation of our circle is

$$x^2 + y^2 + 2x + 2y - 23 = 0.$$

5. Find an equation for the circle which passes through the points:

   a) $(1,-3)$, $(4,6)$, $(-4,2)$.   Ans. $x^2 + y^2 - 2x - 4y - 20 = 0$.
   b) $(6,-1)$, $(-3,-4)$, $(2,3)$.   Ans. $x^2 + y^2 - 2x + 2y - 23 = 0$.
   c) $(5,0)$, $(-2,7)$, $(-2,17)$.   Ans. $x^2 + y^2 - 20x - 24y + 75 = 0$.
   d) $(8,1)$, $(4,9)$, $(-10,-5)$.   Ans. $x^2 + y^2 + 4x - 2y - 95 = 0$.
   e) $(7,0)$, $(0,7)$, $(-5,8)$.   Ans. $x^2 + y^2 + 10x + 10y - 119 = 0$.

6. Find the radius and the center of the circle whose equation is $x^2 + y^2 - 4x + 6y + 9 = 0$.

   Solution: By completing the square in x and in y, we rewrite this equation in the form $(x - h)^2 + (y - k)^2 = r^2$ as follows:

   $$x^2 - 4x \qquad + y^2 + 6y \qquad = -9.$$

   $$x^2 - 4x + 4 + y^2 + 6y + 9 = -9 + 4 + 9.$$

   $$(x - 2)^2 \qquad + (y + 3)^2 \qquad = 2^2.$$

   Comparing this with $(x - h)^2 + (y - k)^2 = r^2$, we see that $h = 2$, $k = -3$, $r = 2$. By Theorem 2.12, our equation is an equation for the circle with center at $(2,-3)$ and with radius 2.

7. Find the center and radius of the circle whose equation is

   a) $x^2 + y^2 = 25$.
   b) $(x - 1)^2 + (y + 2)^2 = 3$.
   c) $x^2 + y^2 - 2x + 4y + 2 = 0$.
   d) $x^2 + y^2 - 4x - 6y = 0$.   Ans. $\sqrt{13}$, $(2,3)$.
   e) $x^2 + y^2 + x = 0$.
   f) $x^2 + y^2 - y = 0$.

   g) $4x^2 + 4y^2 + x + y = 1$.   Ans. $\dfrac{3\sqrt{2}}{8}$, $(-\frac{1}{8},-\frac{1}{8})$.

   h) $12x^2 + 12y^2 = 50x$.

8. Find the points where the line $x - 2y = 2$ meets the circle $x^2 + y^2 + 2x + 3y + 2 = 0$.

9. Draw the graphs of the equations:

    a) $x^2 + y^2 = 25$.   b) $x^2 + y^2 = 1$.
    c) $x^2 + y^2 = 0$.   d) $x^2 + y^2 = -1$.
    e) $x^2 + y^2 - 2x + 4y = 20$.   f) $x^2 + y^2 - 2x + 4y = -4$.
    g) $x^2 + y^2 - 2x + 4y = -5$.   h) $x^2 + y^2 - 2x + 4y = -6$.

10. What relation must hold between d, e, and f if the graph of $x^2 + y^2 + dx + ey + f = 0$ is to be   a) a circle?   b) a point?   c) vacuous?

REVIEW PROBLEMS

1. Solve the inequalities

    a) $\sqrt{x} < 2$.   b) $\dfrac{1}{1-x} \le 1 + 2x$.

2. Show by the methods of this chapter that

    a) If A, B, C, and D are collinear points, then $(d_{AD}d_{BC}) + (d_{BD}d_{CA}) + (d_{CD}d_{AB}) = 0$, where d_{AD} is the directed distance from A to D, and similarly for d_{BC}, etc.
    b) The line segment joining the midpoints of two opposite sides of a quadrilateral and the line segment joining the midpoints of the diagonals bisect each other.
    c) If the diagonals of a parallelogram are perpendicular, the parallelogram is a rhombus.
    d) In any triangle, the ratio of the sum of the squares of the sides to the sum of the squares of the medians is $\frac{4}{3}$.
    e) The line segment from one vertex of a parallelogram to a midpoint of an opposite side meets the opposite diagonal in a trisection point of each.
    f) If the sum of the squares of the distances from any point in the plane to two opposite vertices of a quadrilateral equals the sum of the squares of the distances to the other two vertices, the quadrilateral is a rectangle.

3. The point $(\frac{8}{3}, \frac{5}{3})$ trisects the line segment joining $(2,3)$ to $(4,k)$. What is k?

4. Find the vertices of a triangle if the midpoints of its sides are

    a) $(1,0)$, $(3,4)$, and $(-1,-2)$.   Ans. $(1,2)$, $(5,6)$, $(-3, -6)$.
    b) $(-1,-2)$, $(3,5)$, and $(6,1)$.

5. The vertices of a triangle are $A(3,2)$, $B(4,3)$, and $C(-2,6)$. Find the coordinates of the point on the median from A which is three-fourths of the way from A to the opposite side.

6. The slopes of two lines are 3 and 5. Find the slope of each of the lines which bisects the angles between the two lines.

7. If ABC is a triangle and if X, Y, and Z divide the segments AB, BC, and CA in the ratio r, show that the medians of the triangle XYZ meet at the same point as the medians of the triangle ABC.

8. Find the area of the quadrilateral whose vertices are $(1,3)$, $(4,1)$, $(0,-5)$, and $(6,-8)$.   Ans.   37.

9. If $Ax + By + C = 0$ is an equation for a line, and if (a,b) is a point not on this line, find the perpendicular distance from the point to the line.

10. Find equations for the lines through the origin which, together with $2x + 3y = 4$, form an isosceles triangle with a right angle at the origin.

11. Find a value for a such that the lines $3x + y = 2$, $2x - y = 3$, and $5x + 2y = a$ are concurrent.   Ans.   3.

12. If (a,b) and (b,a) are on the lines $x + 2y = 3$ and $3x - 2y = 4$ respectively, find a and b.

13. Find an equation for the line which passes through $(1,1)$ and forms, together with the axes, a triangle of area 10.

14. The vertices of a triangle are the points $(1,1)$, $(3,-1)$, and $(0,-4)$. Find an equation for the inscribed circle.

15. The vertices of a square are $(3,4)$, $(-1,2)$, $(1,-2)$, and $(5,0)$. Find an equation for the inscribed circle.   Ans. $x^2 + y^2 - 4x - 2y = 0$.

16. Show, by use of the methods of this chapter, that an angle inscribed in a semicircle is a right angle.

17. Find an equation for the circle which has $x + 2y = 0$ and $3x - 4y = 7$ as diameters and which passes through the point $(2,6)$.

18. Find an equation for the circle which circumscribes the triangle whose vertices are $(1,3)$, $(5,1)$, and $(3,-3)$.

19. Find an equation for a circle which circumscribes the triangle formed by the line $x + 2y = 4$ and the axes.

20. Show, by use of the methods of this chapter, that the length of a perpendicular from a point on a circle to a diameter is a mean proportional between the lengths of the segments into which the diameter is divided by the foot of the perpendicular.

21. A band of pirates buried their treasure on an island. They chose a spot at which to bury it in the following manner: Near the shore there were two large rocks and a large pine tree. One pirate started out from one rock along a line at right angles to the line between this rock and the tree. He marched a distance equal to the distance between this rock and the tree. Another pirate started out from the second rock along a line at right angles to the line between this second rock and the tree and marched a distance equal to the distance between this rock and the tree.

     The rest of the band of pirates then found the spot midway between these two and there buried the treasure.

Many years later, these directions came to light and a party of treasure-seekers sailed off to find the treasure. When they reached the island, they found the two rocks with no difficulty. But the tree had long since disappeared, so they did not know how to proceed. All seemed lost till the cabin boy, who had just finished his freshman year at Yale, spoke up. Remembering the analytic geometry he had studied, he calculated where the treasure must be, and a short spell of digging proved him correct. How did he do it?

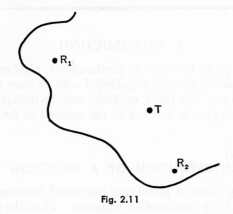

Fig. 2.11

Functions

1. INTRODUCTION

There are three main branches of mathematics: algebra, geometry, and analysis. The reader is already acquainted with at least the rudiments of the first two of these. The third, analysis, may be defined as the study of functions. This chapter is devoted to the concept of function and to related concepts.

2. DEFINITION OF A FUNCTION

There are many ways of specifying numerical information. Probably the most common is by means of an equation. Thus the equation

$$F = \tfrac{9}{5}C + 32$$

tells us that the numerical reading of the temperature on the Fahrenheit scale is obtained from that on the centigrade scale by multiplying by $\frac{9}{5}$ and adding 32.

Another method of specifying numerical information is by means of a graph. In this example, the graph tells us the number of students failing a certain course in each of certain years.

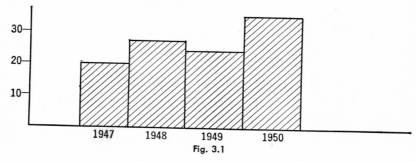

Fig. 3.1

A third method is by means of a table, such as a table of tangents. Such a table gives us, in the right-hand column, the value of the tangent of the angle whose magnitude, in degrees, is the number in the left-hand column.

The common feature of these three methods of specifying numerical information is that in each one a correspondence is set up between two collections of numbers. In the first example above, the correspondence is between the readings of a centigrade thermometer and those of a Fahrenheit thermometer. In the second example, the correspondence is between the collection of four integers, 1947, $\cdots$, 1950, and the number of failures in each of those years. In the last example, the correspondence is between the numerical measure of angles and the tangents of those angles.

The definition of a function which we now give is abstracted from this common property of these examples:

Definition 3.1: *A **function** consists of two things:*

1. *A collection of numbers, called the **domain of definition**,*
2. *A rule which assigns to each number in the domain of definition one and only one number.*

The *range of values* of a function is the collection of all the numbers which the rule of the function assigns to the numbers in the domain of definition of the function.*

3. NOTATIONS AND TERMINOLOGY FOR FUNCTIONS

We shall use the letters f, g, h, φ, etc., to designate the rule part of a function, and also to designate the function itself. As the reader will see, this use of the same name for two different objects will not cause confusion, since it will always be clear from the context which is meant, the rule or the function.

We shall use letters at the end of the alphabet, such as x, y, z, w, t, $\cdots$, to stand for numbers in the domain of definition or the range of values.

If f is a function and x a number in its domain of definition, we designate by $f(x)$ that number which the rule f assigns to the number x. The number $f(x)$ is called the value of the function f at the number x.

To specify a particular function, it is necessary to specify its domain of definition and its rule. As an example, consider the particular function whose domain of definition consists of all the numbers in the interval $[-1,1]$ and whose rule is: to each number x in the domain assign the number obtained by squaring x, subtracting this from 1, and taking the positive square root of the result.

To specify this function we write

$$f(x) = \sqrt{1 - x^2}, \quad -1 \leq x \leq 1.$$

---

* It is possible, and in advanced mathematics necessary, to make a similar definition for a domain of definition or range of values which consists, not of real numbers, but of other quantities. However, we shall not be concerned in this book with such situations, and the word "function" will always have for us the meaning given in Definition 3.1.

The reader should convince himself, keeping in mind the notation explained above, that this does indeed specify the function described above.

If it happens that the domain of definition is the largest collection of numbers for which the rule is meaningful, then, by convention, we agree that the domain of definition need not be specifically indicated. In the case of the function specified above, the expression $\sqrt{1 - x^2}$ is meaningful only when $-1 \leq x \leq 1$ (Why?), so we can specify this function merely by writing

$$f(x) = \sqrt{1 - x^2}.$$

However, to specify the function whose rule is the same as that of the function above but whose domain of definition is the interval $[0,1]$, we must indicate the domain specifically:

$$f(x) = \sqrt{1 - x^2}, \quad 0 \leq x \leq 1.$$

Definition 3.2: *Two functions are* **equal** *if*

a) *They have the same domain of definition.*

b) *They have the same rule, i.e., to each number in the common domain of definition the rules of the two functions assign the same number.*

According to this definition, the functions f, g, and h, specified by

$$f(x) = \sqrt{1 - x^2}, \qquad 0 \leq x \leq 1.$$

$$g(t) = \sqrt{1 - t^2}, \qquad 0 \leq t \leq 1.$$

$$h(z) = \tfrac{1}{2}\sqrt{4 - 4z^2}, \quad 0 \leq z \leq 1.$$

are all equal, since for each one the domain of definition is the interval $[0,1]$, and they all have the same rule. Thus we see that it is immaterial which symbol we use to indicate a number in the domain of definition.

The reader must not assume that all functions are as simple as those above. For one thing, the domain of definition may consist of more than one interval. Thus if f is specified by

$$f(x) = \sqrt{x^2 - 1},$$

the domain of definition of f consists of the two separate intervals $(-\infty, -1]$ and $[1, \infty)$. Also, the rule may behave in different ways on different parts of the domain of definition. Thus

$$f(x) = \begin{cases} 1 - 2x, & 0 \leq x \leq 1 \\ 4x, & 1 < x \leq 2. \end{cases}$$

specifies, according to Definition 3.1, a single function, whose domain of definition is the interval $[0,2]$.

As another example, consider the function whose domain of definition consists of all positive numbers and whose rule is: to each number x in the domain of definition assign the number of one cent stamps needed to mail a letter weighing x ounces. To specify this function in the manner used above, we need an infinite number of equations:

$$f(x) = \begin{cases} 3, & 0 < x \le 1 \\ 6, & 1 < x \le 2 \\ 9, & 2 < x \le 3 \\ \quad \cdot \qquad \cdot \\ \quad \cdot \qquad \cdot \\ \quad \cdot \qquad \cdot \end{cases}$$

Further examples will be found in Section 6.

For some purposes a convenient analogy to a function is a mechanical process. The rule of the function corresponds to a machine, equipped with

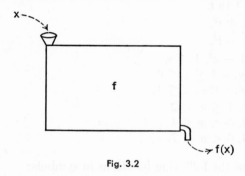

Fig. 3.2

a hopper at the top, and a spout at the bottom. The domain of definition corresponds to the raw materials which can be fed into the machine, and the range of values to the products of the machine. If we drop x into the machine, $f(x)$ comes out of the spout.

For some simple functions it is possible actually to construct such a machine, but in general it is not possible, so this is not a perfect analogy.

PROBLEMS

1. For each of the following functions, state the domain of definition and write out in words the rule of the function.

   a) $f(x) = 1 + 2x$. Ans. domain is all numbers; rule is: to each number x in domain assign the number obtained by adding 1 to the product of 2 and x.

   b) $f(x) = 1 + 2x, 0 \le x < 3$.

   c) $f(x) = 1 + 2/x$. Ans. domain is all numbers but 0; rule is: to each number x in domain assign the number obtained by adding 1 to the quotient of 2 by x.

d) $g(x) = 1 + x^2 + x^3$.

e) $g(x) = (1 + x^2)/(1 - x^3)$.

f) $h(x) = \begin{cases} 1 - 2x, & 0 \le x \le 1 \\ 4x, & 1 < x \le 2. \end{cases}$ Ans. domain is the interval [0,2]; rule is: assign to x the number obtained by subtracting the product of 2 and x from 1 if x is in [0,1], but assign to x the number obtained by multiplying 4 by x if x is in (1,2].

g) $h(x) = \begin{cases} x + 1, & 0 \le x \le 1 \\ x - 1, & 3 \le x \le 4 \\ 5, & x = 9. \end{cases}$

h) $\varphi(x) = x + 1$.

i) $f(t) = \sqrt{1 + t}$. Ans. domain is the interval $[-1, \infty)$; rule is: to each number t assign the positive square root of the number obtained by adding 1 to t.

j) $f(t) = \sqrt{1 + t^2}$.

k) $f(t) = \sqrt{1 - t^2}$.

l) $g(s) = \sqrt{1 - s^2}, \ 1 \le s$.

m) $g(y) = \begin{cases} y, & -1 \le y \le 0 \\ |y|, & 0 < y \le 1. \end{cases}$

n) $\varphi(w) = \begin{cases} 1, & 1 \le w < 2 \\ 2, & 3 < w \le 4 \\ 3, & 6 < w < 7. \end{cases}$

2. Specify each of the following functions in symbols:

a) domain of definition is $1 \le x \le 2$, rule is: for each x in the domain, add 3 to x and divide result by 2. Ans. $f(x) = (x + 3)/2$, $1 \le x \le 2$.

b) domain of definition is $0 \le x$, rule is: for each x in domain, take cube root of sum of x and twice the square of x.

c) domain of definition is $0 \le y \le 2$, rule is: for each y in domain, take midpoint of segment joining y to -1.

d) rule is: for each s, take half the area of square of side s. Ans. $f(s) = \frac{1}{2}s^2, \ 0 < s$.

Remark: The domain is the interval $(0, \infty)$ since a square whose side has negative or zero length is not meaningful.

e) rule is: for each s, take average of volume of cube of side twice s and area of circle of radius one half s.

f) domain is $0 \le t \le 1$ together with $2 < t < 3$, rule is: the number assigned to any t in the domain is $2t$.

g) domain is $-2 \le x \le -1$ together with $1 \le x \le 2$, rule is: number assigned to any x in first interval is $1 - x$, in second interval is 5.

3. For each of the functions in Problem 1, find the value, if any, of the function at

   a) 0.   Ans.   a) 1, d) 1.
   b) 1.
   c) -1.   Ans.   a) -1, d) 1.
   d) 3.
   e) p.
   f) $p + q$.   Ans.   a) $1 + 2p + 2q$.

4. For each of the functions of Problem 1

   a) find the value of the function at 1 plus the value of the function at 3, whenever these are defined.
   b) find the value of the function at 4, whenever it is defined.
   c) compare your answers to a) and b) to see when they are equal.

5. For which of the functions in Problem 1 is the number 0 in the range of values?

6. For each of the following functions find all the numbers in the domain of definition at which the value of the function is 2.

   a) $f(x) = 1 + 2x$.   Ans. $\frac{1}{2}$.   b) $f(x) = 2 - x^2$.
   c) $f(x) = \sqrt{1 - x^2}$.   Ans.   None.   d) $f(x) = \sqrt{9 - x^2}$.
   e) $f(x) = 1 - 2x,\ 0 \leq x \leq 1$.   f) $f(x) = x^3,\ -1 \leq x \leq 1$.

7. Describe a machine which corresponds to the rule of each of the following functions:

   a) $f(x) = x$.   b) $f(x) = x,\ 0 \leq x \leq 1$.
   c) $f(x) = 1$.   d) $f(x) = |x|$.

4. GRAPH OF A FUNCTION

A convenient way of visualizing some of the properties of a function is to construct its graph.

Definition 3.3: *The **graph** of a function f consists of all points on the graph of the equation*

$$y = f(x)$$

for which the x-coordinate is in the domain of definition of f.

According to the definition of the graph of an equation, in Section 8 of Chapter 2, this means that the graph of a function f consists of those points in the plane for which the y-coordinate is the value of the function at the x-coordinate.

For example, the graph of the function f defined by

$$f(x) = 2x + 3$$

is seen to be the straight line of slope 2 crossing the y-axis at the point $(0,3)$, for this line, by Section 9 of Chapter 2, is the graph of the equation

$$y = 2x + 3.$$

At the present, we can construct the graph of a function if the corresponding equation is of the first degree, or if it is derived from an equation of a circle; for example, if $f(x) = \sqrt{1 - x^2}$, the graph is the upper half of the circle with center at the origin and radius 1. However, in any case, we can always construct as many points on the graph as we wish, merely by choosing various values for x, calculating the corresponding values of the function at these points, and then plotting the points $(x,f(x))$. We may then join these points by a curve. This is rarely the graph of our function, but it does coincide with the graph at the points we have plotted. We shall find, by experiment, that often this curve is a good approximation to the graph of the function if we plot enough points and if the rule for the function is not too complicated. We shall return later to these problems of constructing or approximating the graph of a function, but until then it will be sufficient to plot a number of points on the graph and to join them by a curve.

The graphs of all functions have one property in common. On any vertical line there can be at most one point of the graph. (Why?) Thus the circle, for example, whose equation is $x^2 + y^2 = 1$ is not the graph of any function whatsoever. But it can be regarded as the combination of the graphs of the two functions $f(x) = \sqrt{1 - x^2}$ and $g(x) = -\sqrt{1 - x^2}$. The graph of f is the upper half of the circle and that of g is the lower half.

We should notice here that another way of specifying a function is to specify its graph. For if we have the graph, then the domain of definition consists of all points of the x-axis lying under the graph, and the rule is essentially given, since we can find the number in the range which corresponds to any particular number in the domain; it is the y-coordinate of that point of the curve lying over the point in the domain. Thus the line joining the points $(1,2)$ and $(3,-4)$ is the graph of the function $f(x) = 5 - 3x$, for an equation of this line is $y = 5 - 3x$.

PROBLEMS

1. Draw the graph of each of the following functions:

a) $f(x) = 2x$.
c) $f(x) = 2x, 0 \leq x \leq 1$.
e) $f(x) = x/2$.
g) $f(x) = 0$.
i) $g(x) = |x|$.
k) $g(x) = |x + 1|$.

b) $f(x) = 2x + 1$.
d) $f(x) = x$.
f) $f(x) = x/10$.
h) $g(x) = 1$.
j) $g(x) = |x| + 1$.
l) $h(x) = \sqrt{4 - x^2}$.

m) $h(x) = -\sqrt{4 - x^2}$.

n) $h(x) = 1 + \sqrt{4 - x^2}$.

o) $f(t) = t^2$.

p) $f(t) = 1 - 2t^2$.

q) $f(y) = y^3$.

r) $f(y) = \dfrac{1}{y}$.

s) $f(s) = \begin{cases} s, & 0 \le s \le 1 \\ 2s - 1, & 1 < s \le 2. \end{cases}$

t) $\varphi(z) = \begin{cases} z, & 0 \le z \le 1 \\ 1 - z, & 1 < z \le 2. \end{cases}$

u) $\varphi(t) = \begin{cases} t, & 0 \le t \le 1 \\ 1, & 1 < t \le 2. \end{cases}$

v) $f(w) = \begin{cases} w, & 0 \le w \le 1 \\ 1, & 2 \le w \le 3. \end{cases}$

w) $g(x) = \begin{cases} x, & 0 \le x \le 1 \\ 2x, & 2 < x \le 3 \\ x/2, & 3 < x \le 4. \end{cases}$

2. Specify the functions for which the following are the graphs:

a) the line through the origin with slope -2.　Ans.　$f(x) = -2x$.

b) the line through $(1,2)$ with slope 3.　Ans.　$f(x) = 3x - 1$.

c) the line joining $(1,2)$ and (p,q).

d) the upper half of the circle with center at $(1,2)$ and radius 3.

e) the segment joining $(-1,2)$, to $(2,-1)$.　　　Ans.　$f(x) = 1 - x$, $-1 \le x \le 2$.

f) the part of the circle $x^2 + y^2 = 4$ which lies in the second quadrant.

g) the segment joining $(0,0)$ to $(1,1)$ and the segment joining $(1,1)$ to $(2,0)$.

h) the segment joining $(0,0)$ to $(1,1)$ and the segment joining $(1,1)$ to $(2,1)$.

5. EXAMPLES OF FUNCTIONS

One reason for the importance of the concept of function is that functions appear so often, not only in mathematics, but also in other fields. For whenever there is a relationship between two quantities, it defines a function, and before we can study this relationship it is usually necessary to disentangle the function from the verbiage in which it is first presented, the problem being to find as simple an expression for it as possible. There are no fixed rules for doing this, but the problems below illustrate some of the methods which can be used.

PROBLEMS

1. The area of a circle is related to its radius. What is the function which expresses this relationship?　Ans.　$f(x) = \pi x^2$, $0 < x$.

Remark: Another way of stating the above problem is "Find the area of a circle as a function of its radius." This terminology, while often used, is not really satisfactory because it lays stress on the value of the function, in this case the area, instead of on the function itself. While we shall use this terminology occasionally, the reader must remember that it is always the function itself which is required.

2. Find the area of a semicircle as a function of its perimeter.

Solution: The perimeter p of a semicircle is half the circumference of the circle plus the diameter, or $p = \pi r + 2r$, where r is the radius. Hence $r = p/(\pi + 2)$, and the area of the semicircle is $\pi r^2/2 = \pi p^2/2(\pi + 2)^2$. Therefore the function is $f(x) = \pi x^2/2(\pi + 2)^2$, $0 < x$.

3. Express the surface area of a cube as a function of its edge.

4. A taxi charges 20 cents for the first $\frac{1}{4}$ mi. and 15 cents for each succeeding $\frac{1}{4}$ mi. What is the function which relates cost to distance traveled?

5. From a rectangular piece of paper, 10 in. by 20 in., equal squares are cut out at each corner and the edges are folded up to make a box. Find the volume of the box in terms of the size of the squares.

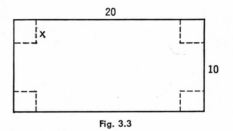

20

10

Fig. 3.3

Solution: Denote the side of the squares by x. Then the base of the box will be $10 - 2x$ in. by $20 - 2x$ in. The height will be x in. Therefore the volume will be $x(10 - 2x)(20 - 2x)$, and the function is $f(x) = x(10 - 2x)(20 - 2x)$, $0 < x < 5$.

6. A rectangular box with a cover is to have a square base. The volume is to be 10 cu. ft. Find the surface area of the box in terms of the side of the base.

Solution: Let x represent the side of the base. Then x^2 is the area of the base. Since the volume is 10, the height must be $10/x^2$. Each side has area $x10/x^2 = 10/x$. There are four sides, a top and a bottom, so the total surface is $40/x + 2x^2$. The function is $f(x) = 40/x + 2x^2$, $0 < x$.

7. If the material for the base of the box of Problem 6 costs 10 cents per sq. ft., for the sides 20 cents and for the top 5 cents, find the cost of the box as a function of the side of the base.

8. A rectangle is inscribed in a circle of radius R. Find its area as a function of the length of one side. Ans. $f(x) = x\sqrt{4R^2 - x^2}$, $0 < x < 2R$.

9. A window has the shape of a rectangle surmounted by a semicircle. If the perimeter is 100 in., find the function which relates the area of the window to the length of the base of the rectangle.

10. 1000 yds. of fencing are to be used to enclose two plots, one a square and one a circle. Find the total area enclosed in terms of the side of the square.

11. The cost per hour for fuel to run a boat is proportional to the cube of the speed and is $10 for a speed of 5 mph. Other costs are $20 per hour. Find the cost of going 10 mi. as a function of the speed. Ans.
$$f(x) = \frac{4}{5}x^2 + \frac{200}{x}, \ 0 < x.$$

12. The strength of a beam is proportional to the breadth and the square of the depth. Find the strength of beams which can be cut from a circular log as a function of their breadths.

13. A triangle has two of its vertices at the points $(0,0)$ and $(4,0)$. Its third vertex is on the graph of the equation $x^2y = 1$. Find the function which gives the area of the triangle in terms of the x-coordinate of the third vertex. Ans. $f(x) = 2/x^2$.

14. A right circular cylinder is inscribed in a sphere of radius 1. Find its volume as a function of the radius of its base.

15. A tank has the form of a right circular cylinder with hemispherical ends. Its volume is A. Find its total length as a function of its radius.

16. A right circular cylinder is inscribed in a right circular cone of height H and radius R. Find the function which relates the volume of the cylinder to the radius of its base.

17. A radio manufacturer spends $200 a week for rent and upkeep of his plant. His production cost is $10 per radio set. At a selling price of p dollars per set, he can sell $200 - p$ sets per week. Find the function which expresses his weekly profit as a function of selling price.

Solution: His income is $(200 - p) \ p$ dollars and his total cost is $200 + 10(200 - p)$. Hence his profit is $210p - p^2 - 2200$. But his selling price must be a positive number (we assume he does not pay people to carry his sets away), so $p > 0$. Also, the number of sets he sells, $200 - p$, must be non-negative, so $200 - p \geq 0$. Hence $p \leq 200$, so p must be in the interval $(0,200]$. Finally, he can sell only a whole number of sets, so $200 - p$ and hence p itself, must be an integer. Therefore the domain of definition of our function consists of the integers in the interval $(0,200]$ and the rule is

$$f(p) = 210p - p^2 - 2200.$$

18. The same as Problem 17 except that he can sell only $200 - 4p$ at a selling price of p.

19. The same as Problem 18 except that the manufacturer has other costs of $n^2/100$ dollars if he produces n radios per week.

20. The same as Problem 19 except that the government imposes an excise tax of q dollars per radio.

21. Along a street 3 mi. long potential customers are evenly distributed. One mile from one end of the street is a dime store. A new and similar store is located on this street. Each customer will trade at the store nearest him. Find the function which expresses the share of business the new store does in terms of its distance from the end of the street.

6. MORE EXAMPLES OF FUNCTIONS

The only functions that we have seen so far are all rather simple and do not illustrate the generality of the concept of a function. Hence we devote this section to a number of examples which illustrate some of the types of behavior of functions.

All the functions seen so far have been defined by a simple rule or a few equations. There is nothing in the definition which requires this simplicity, and the following specifies a perfectly good function:

Example 1:

$$f(x) = \begin{cases} 0, & x \text{ rational} \\ 1, & x \text{ irrational.} \end{cases}$$

The graph of this function consists of the rational points on the x-axis and the irrational points on the line $y = 1$, and we cannot draw the graph.

We see from the above that the graph of a function can be quite complicated. This is still true even if the equation specifying the function is relatively simple.

Example 2:

$$f(x) = \sin\left(\frac{180}{x}\right)^{\circ}, \quad x > 0.$$

The graph of this function is indicated by the following figure.

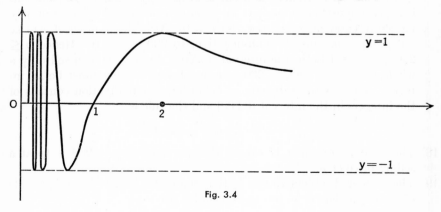

Fig. 3.4

This function is not defined when $x = 0$, so there is no point of the graph on the y-axis. The nearer x gets to 0, the more rapidly the graph oscillates. There is an infinite number of places where the graph touches the line $y = 1$, and the same is true for the line $y = -1$.

Example 3:

$$f(x) = \begin{cases} x \sin \left(\dfrac{180}{x}\right)^\circ, & x \neq 0 \\ 0, & x = 0. \end{cases}$$

The graph of this function is indicated by the following figure.

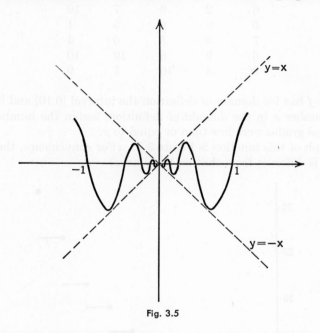

Fig. 3.5

As in Example 2, this graph oscillates infinitely often and touches each of the lines $y = x$ and $y = -x$ an infinite number of times.

These examples show us that the graph of a function can be fairly complicated. It can have sharp corners, it can consist of more than one piece, and it can fluctuate rather violently. These examples may seem somewhat artificial, but our last two examples show that simple everyday situations can give rise to similar functions.

Example 4: Let us consider a gram of ice, at a temperature of $-10°$ Centigrade. Let the function f be defined by the rule: for each x, $f(x)$ is the temperature, on the centigrade scale, of our gram of H_2O after x calories have been absorbed.

The graph of this function is

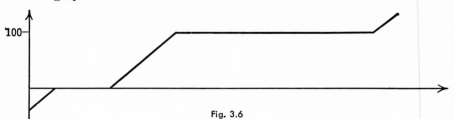

100—

Fig. 3.6

Example 5: On a certain quiz, a class of 25 students received the following grades:

6	2	9	7	10
0	9	6	5	1
7	8	5	6	4
6	9	6	10	10
8	3	10	1	9

A function f has for domain of definition the interval [0,10] and its rule is: to each number x in the domain of definition, assign the number of students whose grades were less than or equal to x.

The graph of this function is Figure 3.7. (For convenience, the scale on the y-axis is different from that on the x-axis.)

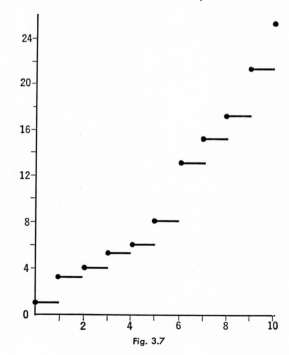

Fig. 3.7

This function is called the *cumulative frequency function* for the collection of 25 numbers listed above. Such functions are of considerable interest to statisticians. This graph can be used to find, for example, the median grade. This grade is at the middle of the list when the grades are arranged in increasing order, i.e., in the thirteenth place. Inspection of the graph shows that $f(6) = 13$, so 6 is the median grade.

PROBLEMS

1. Draw the graphs of

   a) $f(x) = |x|/x$.

   b) $f(x) = |x \sin (180/x)°|$.

   c) $f(x) = x|\sin (180/x)°|$.

   d) $f(x) = x^2 \sin (180/x)°$.

2. By the greatest integer in x, denoted by $[x]$, we mean the largest integer n such that $n \leq x$. Thus $[x] \leq x < [x] + 1$. Draw the graphs of

   a) $f(x) = [x]$.

   b) $f(x) = 2[x]$.

   c) $f(x) = [2x]$.

3. Draw the graph of the function, defined in Section 3, giving the postage required to mail a letter.

4. Draw the graph of f, where f is defined by

$$f(x) = 3 + 3[x], \ 0 < x.$$

   Is this the same function as the one in Problem 3?

5. Draw the graph of

$$f(x) = \begin{cases} 0, & 0 \leq x < 3 \\ 1, & 3 \leq x < 6 \\ 2, & 6 \leq x < 9. \end{cases}$$

   Write an equation for $f(x)$ in terms of the greatest integer function.

6. Draw the graph of the function defined as in Example 5 above for the following collection of numbers.

16	9	20	12
20	16	11	10
7	5	4	11
16	16	0	13
8	10	19	18
2	7	2	6
19	5	8	15
18	6	13	8
19	10	4	3
3	11	17	20

7. ALGEBRAIC COMBINATIONS OF FUNCTIONS

Many functions can be thought of as being built up from other functions by means of algebraic operations.

Definition 3.4: *If f and g are two functions, the* **sum** *of these functions is the function, denoted by $\{f + g\}$, whose domain of definition consists of those numbers which belong both to the domain of definition of f and to that of g, and whose rule is*

$$\{f + g\}(x) = f(x) + g(x).$$

In terms of machines, a machine for $\{f + g\}$ can be constructed by using the machines for f and for g together with two auxiliary machines, a duplicator, D, which furnishes two copies of any number dropped into it, and an adding machine, symbolized by $+$ in the diagram.

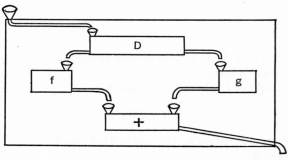

Fig. 3.8

The reader can now write down for himself the definitions of the functions symbolized by $\{f - g\}$, $\{f \cdot g\}$, and $\{f/g\}$. In the last case it should be noticed that the domain of $\{f/g\}$ consists of those numbers in the common part of the domains of f and of g except for those numbers x for which $g(x) = 0$.

Note that the domain of definition of $\{f + g\}$, say, can be much smaller than that of either f or g. For example, if the domain of f is [0,1] and that of g is [1,2], then $\{f + g\}$ is defined only at the single number 1.

PROBLEMS

1. State the domain of definition and the rule of $\{f + g\}$ if

    a) $f(x) = x$; $g(x) = 1$.   Ans. $\{f + g\}(x) = 1 + x$, all numbers.
    b) $f(x) = x^2$; $g(x) = 2x$, $0 \leq x$.   Ans. $\{f + g\}(x) = x^2 + 2x$, $0 \leq x$.

    c) $f(x) = 1 - x^2$, $\frac{1}{2} \leq x \leq 2$; $g(x) = \dfrac{1}{x}.$

d) $f(x) = \dfrac{1}{|x|}$, $2 \le x \le 4$; $g(x) = x^3$, $1 \le x \le 3$.

e) $f(x) = x$, $-1 \le x \le 1$; $g(x) = 2 - x$, $0 \le x \le 10$.

f) $f(x) = \sqrt{1 - x^2}$; $g(x) = |x|$, $0 \le x$. Ans. $\{f + g\}(x) = |x| + \sqrt{1 - x^2}$, $0 \le x \le 1$.

g) $f(x) = \sqrt{4 - x^2}$; $g(x) = \sqrt{x^2 - 1}$.

h) $f(x) = \sqrt{1 + x}$; $g(x) = \sqrt{9 - x^2}$.

i) $f(x) = \begin{cases} 1 - x, & 0 \le x \le 1 \\ 4x, & 1 < x \le 2. \end{cases}$ $g(x) = \begin{cases} x^2, & 0 \le x \le 1 \\ x^3, & 1 < x \le 2. \end{cases}$

   Ans. $\{f + g\}(x) = \begin{cases} 1 - x + x^2, & 0 \le x \le 1 \\ 4x + x^3, & 1 < x \le 2. \end{cases}$

j) $f(x) = \begin{cases} x, & -2 \le x < 0 \\ x + 1, & 0 \le x \le 2; \end{cases}$ $g(x) = \begin{cases} 1, & -2 \le x < 0 \\ x, & 0 \le x \le 2. \end{cases}$

k) $f(x) = \begin{cases} x, & -1 \le x \le 0 \\ x + 1, & 0 < x \le 2; \end{cases}$ $g(x) = \begin{cases} 1, & -1 \le x \le 1 \\ x, & 1 < x \le 2. \end{cases}$

l) $f(x) = \begin{cases} |x|, & 0 \le x < 2 \\ \sqrt{1 + x^2}, & 2 \le x \le 4; \end{cases}$ $g(x) = \begin{cases} x^2, & 0 \le x \le 1 \\ x^3, & 1 < x \le 3. \end{cases}$

m) $f(x) = \begin{cases} x, & 1 \le x \le 2 \\ x^2, & 2 < x \le 3; \end{cases}$ $g(x) = \begin{cases} 1, & 1 \le x < 2 \\ \dfrac{1}{x}, & 2 \le x \le 3. \end{cases}$

n) $f(x) = \begin{cases} x, & 0 \le x < 1 \\ x^2, & 1 \le x < 2 \\ \dfrac{1}{x}, & 2 \le x \le 3; \end{cases}$ $g(x) = \begin{cases} \sqrt{1 - x^2}, & 0 \le x \le 1 \\ x, & 1 < x \le 4. \end{cases}$

2. Find g in each of the following cases:

a) $f(x) = x$; $\{f + g\}(x) = 1 + 2x$.

b) $f(x) = x$; $\{f + g\}(x) = 1$.

c) $f(x) = |x|$, $\{f + g\}(x) = 1 + x$.

d) $f(x) = \begin{cases} 1 - x, & 0 \le x \le 1 \\ 4x, & 1 < x \le 2, \end{cases}$ $\{f + g\}(x) = \begin{cases} -x, & 0 \le x \le 1 \\ x^2, & 1 < x \le 2. \end{cases}$

e) $f(x) = \begin{cases} x, & -1 \le x \le 0 \\ x + 1, & 0 < x \le 2, \end{cases}$ $\{f + g\}(x) = \begin{cases} 0, & -1 \le x \le 1 \\ 1, & 1 < x \le 2. \end{cases}$

f) $f(x) = x$, $\{f - g\}(x) = x^2$. Ans. $g(x) = x - x^2$.

g) $f(x) = x$, $\{f - g\}(x) = 1$.

h) $f(x) = |x|$, $\{f - g\}(x) = x + x^2$.

i) $f(x) = x$, $\{fg\}(x) = x^3$. Ans. $g(x) = x^2$.

j) $f(x) = x^2$, $\{fg\}(x) = \dfrac{1}{x}$.

k) $f(x) = \sqrt{1 - x^2}$, $\{fg\}(x) = |x|$.

l) $f(x) = \sqrt{1 - x^2}$, $\{f/g\}(x) = x$. Ans. $g(x) = \dfrac{\sqrt{1 - x^2}}{x}$.

m) $f(x) = x$, $\{f/g\}(x) = 1 - x$.

n) $f(x) = |x|$, $\{f/g\}(x) = |1 - x|$.

o) $f(x) = \begin{cases} x, & 0 \le x \le 1 \\ \sqrt{1+x}, & 1 < x \le 2; \end{cases}$ $\{fg\}(x) = \begin{cases} x^2 - x^3, & 0 \le x \le 1 \\ x, & 1 < x \le 2. \end{cases}$

p) $f(x) = \begin{cases} x, & 0 \le x < 1 \\ x^2, & 1 \le x < 2 \\ \dfrac{1}{x}, & 2 \le x \le 4; \end{cases}$ $\{f/g\}(x) = \begin{cases} 1, & 0 \le x \le 1 \\ 1/x, & 1 < x \le 2 \\ 1 + x, & 2 < x \le 3 \\ x^2 - 1, & 3 < x \le 4. \end{cases}$

3. If $g(x) = x$, $h(x) = |x|$, write equations for and draw the graphs of $\{g + h\}$, $\{g - h\}$, $\{g \cdot h\}$, and $\{g/h\}$.

4. If $\varphi(x) = x + \sqrt{1 - x^2}$, write φ in the form $\{f + g + h\}$.

5. One way of making a sketch of the graph of $\{f + g\}$ is to start with the graphs of f and g and to remember that $\{f + g\}(x) = f(x) + g(x)$. For any point x on the x-axis, $f(x)$ can be read off from the graph of f and $g(x)$ from the graph of g. The sum of these is then $\{f + g\}(x)$, and the point $(x, \{f + g\}(x))$ is on the graph of $\{f + g\}$. As many such points as necessary can be plotted and joined by a curve which is then an approximation to the graph of $\{f + g\}$. The same method can be used to sketch the graphs of $\{f - g\}$, $\{fg\}$, and $\{f/g\}$. Use this method to sketch the graphs of

a) $\{f + g\}$ if $f(x) = x$, $g(x) = 1$.

b) $\{f + g\}$ if $f(x) = x$, $g(x) = [x]$.

c) $\{f - g\}$ if $f(x) = x$, $g(x) = 2|x|$.

d) $\{fg\}$ if $f(x) = \sqrt{1 - x^2}$, $g(x) = x$.

e) $\{f/g\}$ if $f(x) = x$, $g(x) = 1 + x$.

8. LIMITS

After the concept of function, the most important concept in calculus is that of a limit. Indeed, calculus can be considered as a collection of methods for calculating limits.

The reader is already somewhat familiar with this concept. For example, in elementary geometry, the circumference of a circle is defined as the limit of the perimeters of inscribed polygons as the sides of the polygons approach zero in length. Similarly, the area of the circle is defined to be the limit of the areas of the polygons.

This concept of limit arises in the following way. Quite often we will be faced with a function which is defined everywhere in a certain interval except at one point, $x = a$. Examples are $f(x) = \sin (180/x)°$, Fig. 3.4, and

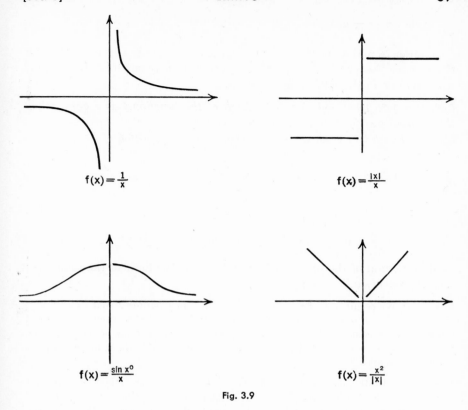

$$f(x) = \frac{1}{x}$$

$$f(x) = \frac{|x|}{x}$$

$$f(x) = \frac{\sin x^0}{x}$$

$$f(x) = \frac{x^2}{|x|}$$

Fig. 3.9

Each of these functions is defined everywhere except at $x = 0$.

In such a case, the graph of the function can behave in one of two ways near the point where the function is not defined. The graph may settle down toward one particular point on the line $x = a$, as in the last two examples above, or the graph may fail to settle down toward any one point. The first three examples above show this second kind of behavior.

We are interested in the first kind of behavior, and in particular we are interested in the y-coordinate of the point on the line $x = a$ toward which the graph points. This number we call the limit of the values of the function, or, more briefly, the limit of the function, as x approaches a, in symbols

$$\lim_{x \to a} f(x).$$

Remembering that the y-coordinate of the point on the graph of f over the point x is $f(x)$, we see that a number A is the limit, as x approaches a, or f, if whenever x is near enough to a then $f(x)$ is as close as we please to A. More briefly,

$$A = \lim_{x \to a} f(x)$$

if, whenever $|x - a|$ is sufficiently small, then $|f(x) - A|$ is as small as we please.

In order to make this precise, we must explain exactly what we mean by the phrases "as small as we please" and "sufficiently small." This is just what is done in the following definition.

Definition 3.5: *The number A is the* **limit of the function f as x approaches the number** *a if for each number e > 0, no matter how small, there is a number d > 0 such that whenever x is in the domain of definition of f and*

$$0 < |x - a| < d,$$

then

$$|f(x) - A| < e.$$

We shall use the symbols

$$A = \lim_{x \to a} f(x) \quad \text{or} \quad A = \lim f(x) \quad \text{as} \quad x \to a$$

as abbreviation of the phrase "the number A is the limit of the function f as x approaches a."

Remark I: We recall from Problem 4 in Section 2 of Chapter 2 that $|x - a| < d$ means $a - d < x < a + d$. Hence we see that if $|x - a| < d$, then x lies in the interval whose center is at a and which reaches out a distance d on each side. Similarly, $|f(x) - A| < e$ means that $f(x)$ is in the interval whose midpoint is at A and whose total length is $2e$.

Remark II: In the definition above, we wrote $0 < |x - a|$, which means that $x \neq a$, since the functions we were interested in were not defined at a. But even if f is defined at a, the definition, as it stands, still makes sense. However, the reader must be careful not to confuse $\lim f(x)$ as $x \to a$ with $f(a)$. They may not be the same number. See Example 2, p. 61.

Remark III: If there are no numbers near a in the domain of definition of f, it does not make much sense to talk about $\lim f(x)$ as $x \to a$. Thus, for example, if $f(x) = \sqrt{-|x|}$, then it is pointless to talk about $\lim f(x)$ as $x \to 0$, since f is defined only at the single number 0. Therefore we make the blanket hypothesis, for all the theorems of this chapter, that for each function f appearing in the theorem, whenever $\lim f(x)$ as $x \to a$ is considered, then every open interval containing a contains at least one number, different from a, which belongs to the domain of definition of f.

We shall be faced with various kinds of problems involving limits. In one kind of problem we are given a function f and numbers a and A and we are asked to show that $A = \lim f(x)$ as $x \to a$. This is a relatively easy kind of problem, and the examples below illustrate the methods. In another kind of problem, we are given a function f and a number a and we are asked to find the number A, if it exists, such that $A = \lim f(x)$ as $x \to a$. This kind of problem is generally more difficult. Some aspects of it are treated in later sections of this chapter.

Example 1: Let us consider the following function:

$$f(x) = \begin{cases} 2x, & 0 \leq x \leq 1 \\ 5 - 3x, & 1 < x \leq 2. \end{cases}$$

We shall show that $\lim f(x) = 2$ as $x \to 1$. Given any number $e > 0$, choose d to be $e/3$. Now, if $|x - 1| < d$, and if $x < 1$, then $f(x) = 2x$, so $|f(x) - 2| = |2x - 2| = 2|x - 1| < 2d = 2e/3 < e$. On the other hand, if $x > 1$, then $f(x) = 5 - 3x$, so $|f(x) - 2| = |5 - 3x - 2| = |3 - 3x| = 3|1 - x| = 3|x - 1| < 3 \cdot d = 3 \cdot e/3 = e$. Thus we have found, for any $e > 0$, a number $d > 0$, namely $e/3$, so that when $|x - 1| < d$, $|f(x) - 2| < e$, so we have shown that $2 = \lim f(x)$ as $x \to 1$.

Example 2: Consider now the following modification of the function of Example 1.

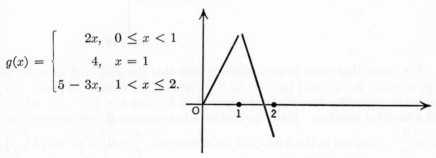

$$g(x) = \begin{cases} 2x, & 0 \leq x < 1 \\ 4, & x = 1 \\ 5 - 3x, & 1 < x \leq 2. \end{cases}$$

Fig. 3.11

We can show that $\lim g(x) = 2$ as $x \to 1$. In fact, the argument used in Example 1 can be repeated exactly. It is only necessary to observe that in our definition, we require $|f(x) - A| < e$, when $0 < |x - a| < d$, i.e., when $|x - a| < d$ and $x \neq a$. Thus the value of the function at a has no bearing on the value of the limit. In this particular case, $f(x) = g(x)$ whenever $x \neq 1$, so they must have the same limit.

In some cases, for a given function f and a given number a, there may be no number A such that $\lim f(x) = A$ as $x \to a$. In order to discuss this kind of situation, let us see what it means to say that the statement "$\lim f(x) = A$ as $x \to a$" is false. According to Definition 3.5, if this statement is false, then there is some particular number $e > 0$ for which it is false that there is a number $d > 0$ such that whenever x is in the domain of definition of f and $0 < |x - a| < d$, then $|f(x) - A| < e$. Then for this particular number $e > 0$ and for every number $d > 0$ it is false that for each x in the domain with $0 < |x - a| < d$, $|f(x) - A| < e$. This in turn means that for this particular number $e > 0$ and for any number $d > 0$ there is a number x in the domain such that $0 < |x - a| < d$ but at the same time $|f(x) - A| \geq e$.

Thus we see that to show that $\lim f(x) = A$ as $x \to a$ is false, we need to exhibit a number $e > 0$ such that no matter what number $d > 0$ is given, there is a number x in the domain of definition of f such that $0 < |x - a| < d$ and at the same time $|f(x) - A| \geq e$.

Example 3: Let

$$h(x) = \begin{cases} -1, & x < 0 \\ 1, & x > 0. \end{cases}$$

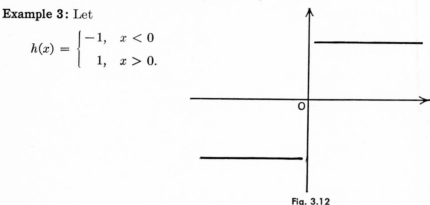

Fig. 3.12

We assert that there is no number A such that $\lim h(x) = A$ as $x \to 0$, or, in other words, that $\lim h(x)$ as $x \to 0$ does not exist. To prove this assertion, consider first the case where $A \neq 1$. Let $e = \frac{1}{2}|1 - A|$, which is a positive number. Now, no matter what number $d > 0$ is given, let $x = \dfrac{d}{2}$. Then x is in the domain of definition and $\left|\dfrac{d}{2} - 0\right| < d$. But $h\left(\dfrac{d}{2}\right) = 1$, so $\left|h\left(\dfrac{d}{2}\right) - A\right| = |1 - A| > \dfrac{1}{2}|1 - A| = e$. The case $A = 1$ can be handled in a similar fashion. Consequently $\lim h(x)$ as $x \to 0$ does not exist.

PROBLEMS

1. Prove that if $f(x) = 5 - 2x$, then $\lim_{x \to 4} f(x) = -3$.
2. Prove that if $f(x) = |x|$, then $\lim_{x \to 1} f(x) = 1$ and $\lim_{x \to -1} f(x) = 1$.
3. Prove that if $f(x) = x^2/|x|$, then $\lim_{x \to 0} f(x) = 0$.
4. It is true that $\lim_{x \to 2} f(x) = 4$ if $f(x) = x^2$. Substantiate this by finding a number $d > 0$ such that when $0 < |x - 2| < d$, then $|f(x) - 4| < \frac{1}{10}$.

Solution: To have $|x^2 - 4| < \frac{1}{10}$, we must have $3.9 < x^2 < 4.1$, (Why?) or $\sqrt{3.9} < x < \sqrt{4.1}$. Let d be any positive number which is less than the distance between 2 and $\sqrt{3.9}$ and also less than the distance between 2 and $\sqrt{4.1}$. (For example, since $\sqrt{3.9} = 1.9748$ (approximately) and $\sqrt{4.1} = 2.0248$ (approximately), we could choose $d = .02$.) Then, when $|x - 2| < d$, $2 - d < x < 2 + d$ and so $\sqrt{3.9} < x < \sqrt{4.1}$, from which we have $|x^2 - 4| < \frac{1}{10}$.

5. For the function of Problem 4, find a number $d > 0$ such that when $0 < |x - 2| < d$, then $|x^2 - 4| < \frac{1}{100}$.
6. For the function of Problem 4, find a number $d > 0$ such that when $0 < |x - 3| < d$, then $|x^2 - 9| < \frac{1}{10}$.
7. Show that if f is defined by the equation $f(x) = \sqrt{x}, 0 \leq x$, then, for any number $a \geq 0$, $\lim_{x \to a} f(x) = \sqrt{a}$.

   Hint: For any number $e > 0$, choose $d = e\sqrt{a}$ and observe that $\sqrt{x} - \sqrt{a} = (x - a)/(\sqrt{x} + \sqrt{a})$.

8. Finish the proof that for the function h of Example 3, $\lim h(x)$ as $x \to 0$ does not exist. Let $e = 1$ and take $x = \dfrac{-d}{2}$.

9. Let the function f be defined by the equation

$$f(x) = \begin{cases} 1, & 0 \leq x < 1 \\ 2, & 1 \leq x \leq 2. \end{cases}$$

Show that $\lim f(x)$ as $x \to 1$ does not exist.

10. Let the function f be defined by the equation

$$f(x) = \begin{cases} 3x, & 0 \leq x \leq 1 \\ 5 - 3x, & 1 < x \leq 2. \end{cases}$$

Show that $\lim f(x)$ as $x \to 1$ does not exist.

11. If $f(x) = 1/x$, show that $\lim f(x)$ as $x \to 0$ does not exist.
12. Returning to the function of Example 3, define a new function φ which has the same rule as h but whose domain consists of that part of the domain of h to the right of 0, i.e., $\varphi(x) = 1, 0 < x$. Show that $\lim \varphi(x) = 1$ as $x \to 0$.

    We say that a number A is the *right-hand* limit of a function f as $x \to a$ if $\lim \varphi(x) = A$ as $x \to a$ where φ is the function whose rule is that of f but whose domain of definition consists of that part of the domain of f to the right of a. The definition of a *left-hand* limit is analogous.

13. Find the right-hand and left-hand limits of the function of Problem 10 as $x \to 1$.
14. Show that the function of Problem 11 does not have either a right-hand or a left-hand limit as $x \to 0$.

9. VELOCITY

Before continuing with our discussion of limits, it is worth while to pause for a moment to consider why we are concerned with this notion. The reason is that there are numerous interesting and important problems which lead naturally to the concept of a limit. Such problems are found in various parts of mathematics and also in many of the sciences. We shall study some of these later, but at the moment we shall look at a physical problem, namely that of finding out how fast a falling weight is moving at any instant.

Suppose a weight falls under the influence of gravity and suppose, by performing a physical experiment, we find that in t seconds the weight falls $s = g(t)$ feet. If the weight falls in a vacuum, we know that $g(t) = 16t^2$, approximately, and we shall use this formula in our calculations below.

Now we can ask how fast the weight is moving at any particular time. In particular we might ask what the velocity of the weight is at the end of one second. But this immediately raises the question as to what we mean by "the velocity at a particular time." We can, of course, calculate the average velocity of the weight over the first second, i.e., the distance it falls divided by the time elapsed. This turns out to be

$$\frac{16 \cdot 1^2}{1 - 0} = 16 \text{ ft./sec.}$$

But we would not like to say that this is the velocity when $t = 1$. For the average velocity is the speed at which the weight would have to move in order to fall 16 ft. in one second moving at a constant rate. But we can see, by watching the experiment, that the velocity of the weight increases as time goes on, no matter how we use the word "velocity." Indeed, the average velocity over the first half-second is

$$\frac{16 \cdot (\frac{1}{2})^2}{\frac{1}{2}} = 8,$$

while over the last half-second it is

$$\frac{16 \cdot 1^2 - 16 \cdot (\frac{1}{2})^2}{1 - \frac{1}{2}} = 24.$$

We would not like to say that its velocity when $t = 1$ is 24 ft./sec., because a further calculation shows that the average velocity over the interval from $\frac{1}{2}$ sec. to $\frac{3}{4}$ sec. is 20, while over the interval from $\frac{3}{4}$ sec. to 1 sec. it is 28.

But by now it is apparent that it would be reasonable to define the velocity when $t = 1$ as the limit, as t approaches 1, of the average velocity over the interval from t seconds to 1 second. Thus the velocity at $t = 1$ is

$$\lim_{t \to 1} \frac{16 \cdot 1^2 - 16t^2}{1 - t}.$$

In a more general situation, say when the weight falls in air or through a viscous fluid, the function g which gives the distance fallen in terms of the elapsed time will not be so simple as in the case where $g(t) = 16t^2$. Nevertheless, if we ask for the velocity at the end of a seconds, we can go through the same discussion as above. At the end of t seconds, the weight has fallen $g(t)$ feet, so from time t to time a it moves $g(a) - g(t)$ feet. Thus the average velocity over this interval of time is

$$\frac{g(a) - g(t)}{a - t}.$$

Hence it is reasonable to define the velocity at the end of a seconds to be

$$\lim_{t \to a} \frac{g(a) - g(t)}{a - t},$$

which can also be written

$$\lim_{t \to a} \frac{g(t) - g(a)}{t - a}.$$

Thus a reasonable definition of velocity is in terms of limits, and the problem of calculating velocities is one of calculating limits.

10. THEOREMS ON LIMITS

The calculations of limits worked out in Section 8 suggest that such problems may become quite involved, especially if the function in question is at all complicated. This is indeed the case. Furthermore, certain other questions about limits were slurred over or neglected entirely. For example, it was not indicated why, in the first example, we decided to try to prove that $\lim f(x)$ as $x \to 1$ was 2, rather than some other number.

In view of all this, we would like to have other and easier methods for finding limits. The following theorems furnish one such method which is often useful.

Theorem 3.1: *If the function f is defined by the equation*

$$f(x) = c,$$

where c is a number, then for any number a,

$$\lim_{x \to a} f(x) = c.$$

Theorem 3.2: *If the function f is defined by the equation*

$$f(x) = x,$$

then, for any number a,

$$\lim_{x \to a} f(x) = a.$$

Exercise: Prove these two theorems by the methods of Section 8.

These two theorems give us complete information about the limits of two particular functions. Our next theorem will allow us to calculate limits for algebraic combinations of these functions.

Theorem 3.3: *If f and g are two functions, and if*

$$\lim_{x \to a} f(x) = M \quad \text{and} \quad \lim_{x \to a} g(x) = N,$$

then

α) $\qquad\qquad \lim_{x \to a} \{f + g\}(x) = M + N.$

β) $\qquad\qquad \lim_{x \to a} \{f - g\}(x) = M - N.$

γ) $\qquad\qquad \lim_{x \to a} \{f \cdot g\}(x) = M \cdot N.$

δ) $\qquad\qquad \lim_{x \to a} \{f/g\}(x) = M/N,$ provided that $N \neq 0$.

Before proceeding to the proof of this theorem, let us illustrate how we can use these three theorems.

Example: Find $\lim_{x \to 2} f(x)$ if $f(x) = \dfrac{2x}{1 - x}.$

Solution: Let the functions g, h, and φ be defined by the equations $g(x) = 2$, $h(x) = x$, and $\varphi(x) = 1$. Then $f = \{\{gh\}/\{\varphi - h\}\}$. Now

1) $\lim_{x \to 2} g(x) = 2$	Theorem 3.1.
2) $\lim_{x \to 2} h(x) = 2$	Theorem 3.2.
3) $\lim_{x \to 2} \{gh\}(x) = 2 \cdot 2 = 4.$	Theorem 3.3γ and steps 1 and 2.
4) $\lim_{x \to 2} \varphi(x) = 1$	Theorem 3.1.
5) $\lim_{x \to 2} \{\varphi - h\}(x) = 1 - 2$ $\quad = -1$	Theorem 3.3β and steps 2 and 4.
6) $\lim_{x \to 2} \{\{gh\}/\{\varphi - h\}\}(x)$ $\quad = 4/-1 = -4$	Theorem 3.3δ and steps 3 and 5.
7) $\lim_{x \to 2} f(x) = -4$	Step 6 and $f = \{\{gh\}/\{\varphi - h\}\}$.

Remark: In more complicated problems the number of auxiliary functions needed may be very large. Hence it is customary to abbreviate the working of this kind of problem by not writing down the definitions of these functions, and to do the work thus:

1) $\lim_{x \to 2} 2 = 2$	Theorem 3.1.
2) $\lim_{x \to 2} x = 2$	Theorem 3.2.
3) $\lim_{x \to 2} 2x = 2 \cdot 2 = 4$	Theorem 3.3γ and steps 1 and 2.

4) $\lim_{x \to 2} 1 = 1$ Theorem 3.1.

5) $\lim_{x \to 2} 1 - x = 1 - 2 = -1$ Theorem 3.3β and steps 2 and 4.

6) $\lim_{x \to 2} \dfrac{2x}{1-x} = \dfrac{4}{-1} = -4$ Theorem 3.3δ and steps 3 and 5.

Before we can prove Theorem 3.3, it is necessary to make a remark about the definition of limit. It is easy to see that for a given function f and a given number a, different values of e require different values for d. In general, the smaller e, the smaller d must be. But also d depends on the number a. For a fixed e, the d corresponding to a need not be the same as the d at a different number b. Finally, d depends on the function. For the same e and a, the d for a function f need not be the same as the d for another function g.

In order to emphasize all this, we shall, in the following proof of Theorem 3.3, write $d(e,a,f)$, instead of just d, for a number such that when x is in the domain of definition of f and

$$0 < |x - a| < d(e,a,f),$$

then

$$|f(x) - M| < e.$$

Proof of Theorem 3.3, Part α.

Let $e > 0$ be any positive number. Then $e/2$ is also a positive number. Since $\lim f(x) = M$ as $x \to a$, there is a number $d(e/2,a,f)$ such that when x is in the domain of definition of f and

$$0 < |x - a| < d(e/2,a,f),$$

then

$$|f(x) - M| < e/2.$$

Since $\lim g(x) = N$ as $x \to a$, there is a number $d(e/2,a,g)$ such that when x is in the domain of definition of g and

$$0 < |x - a| < d(e/2,a,g),$$

then

$$|g(x) - N| < e/2.$$

Now let $d(e,a,\{f + g\})$ be the smaller of $d(e/2,a,f)$ and $d(e/2,a,g)$. Then, if x is in the domain of definition of $\{f + g\}$ and

$$0 < |x - a| < d(e,a,\{f + g\}),$$

we have

$$|f(x) - M| < e/2,$$

and

$$|g(x) - N| < e/2. \quad \text{(Why?)}$$

But

$$|f(x) + g(x) - (M + N)| \leq |f(x) - M| + |g(x) - N| < e/2 + e/2 = e,$$

so

$$|\{f + g\}(x) - (M + N)| < e.$$

Hence, according to Definition 3.5, we have shown that

$$\lim_{x \to a} \{f + g\}(x) = M + N.$$

It is possible to give direct proofs of Theorem 3.3 parts γ and δ, but the calculations become quite complicated. Therefore we separate out these difficulties into a number of simpler theorems.

Theorem 3.4: *If f is a function and M a number, and if $\lim f(x) = M$ as $x \to a$, then $\lim \{f(x) - M\} = 0$ as $x \to a$. Conversely, if $\lim \{f(x) - M\} = 0$ as $x \to a$, then $\lim f(x) = M$ as $x \to a$.*

Exercise: Prove this theorem.

Theorem 3.5: *If f is a function and if $\lim f(x) = M$ as $x \to a$, then there is a number $d > 0$ such that when x is in the domain of definition of f and*

$$0 < |x - a| < d,$$

then

$$|f(x)| < 2|M| + 1$$

and if $M \neq 0$,

$$\frac{|M|}{2} < |f(x)|.$$

Proof: If $M \neq 0$, $|M|$ is a positive number. Hence $|M|/2$ is also a positive number. Since, by hypothesis, $\lim f(x) = M$ as $x \to a$, there is a number $d\left(\dfrac{|M|}{2}, a, f\right) > 0$ such that when x is in the domain of definition of f and

$$0 < |x - a| < d\left(\frac{|M|}{2}, a, f\right),$$

then

$$|f(x) - M| < \frac{|M|}{2}.$$

By Theorem 1.18,

$$\left||f(x)| - |M|\right| \leq |f(x) - M|.$$

Hence

$$\left||f(x)| - |M|\right| < \frac{|M|}{2},$$

or

$$|M| - \frac{|M|}{2} < |f(x)| < |M| + \frac{|M|}{2}.$$

This completes the proof for the case $M \neq 0$, since $|M| - |M|/2 = |M|/2$ and $|M| + |M|/2 < 2|M| < 2|M| + 1$.

If $M = 0$, then when x is in the domain of definition of f and

$$0 < |x - a| < d(1,a,f),$$

we have

$$|f(x)| = |f(x) - 0| < 1 = 2|M| + 1.$$

Thus in either case we have shown that the required number d does exist.

Definition 3.6: *A function f is **bounded on an interval**, I, if there is a positive number, M, such that for each number x in I, and in the domain of definition of f, $|f(x)| \le M$.*

Thus, for example, if $\lim f(x)$ exists as $x \to a$, f is bounded in some interval I containing a. For let $\lim f(x) = M$ as $x \to a$ and let $d > 0$ be the number given by Theorem 3.5. Let I be the interval $(a - d, a + d)$. Then for each x in I, except perhaps for $x = a$, we have $|f(x)| \le 2|M| + 1$. Let N be the larger of $2|M| + 1$ and $|f(a)|$. Then for each x in I, we have $|f(x)| \le N$, so f is bounded on I.

Theorem 3.6: *If $\lim f(x) = 0$ as $x \to a$, and if g is a function which is bounded in some open interval containing a, then $\lim \{fg\}(x)$ exists and equals 0 as $x \to a$.*

Proof: Since, by hypothesis, g is bounded in some open interval I containing a, there is a number $M > 0$ such that for each x in I belonging to the domain of definition of g, $|g(x)| \le M$. Since I is an open interval, there is a number $d_1 > 0$ such that when $|x - a| < d_1$, then x is in I. (Why?)

Now if e is any positive number, e/M is also a positive number. Since $\lim f(x) = 0$ as $x \to a$, there is a number $d(e/M,a,f) > 0$ such that when x is in the domain of definition of f and

$$0 < |x - a| < d(e/M,a,f),$$

then

$$|f(x) - 0| = |f(x)| < e/M.$$

Now let d_2 be a positive number which is smaller than d_1 and at the same time smaller than $d(e/M,a,f)$. Then whenever x is in the domain of $\{fg\}$ and

$$0 < |x - a| < d_2,$$

we have

$$0 < |x - a| < d_1,$$

and at the same time

$$0 < |x - a| < d(e/M,a,f).$$

Because of the first inequality,

$$|g(x)| \le M.$$

Because of the second inequality, we have

$$|f(x)| < e/M.$$

Consequently

$$|\{fg\}(x)| = |f(x)g(x)| = |f(x)||g(x)| < M(e/M) = e.$$

Thus we have shown that for any positive number e there is a positive number d, namely d_2 above, such that when x is in the domain of definition of $\{fg\}$ and

$$0 < |x - a| < d,$$

then

$$|\{fg\}(x)| < e.$$

But this, by definition, means that $\lim \{fg\}(x) = 0$ as $x \to a$.

Now that we have these three theorems, we are in a position to finish the proof of Theorem 3.3.

Proof of Theorem 3.3, Part γ:

We are given that $\lim f(x) = M$ and $\lim g(x) = N$ as $x \to a$. We are to show that $\lim \{fg\}(x) = MN$ as $x \to a$. By Theorem 3.4, we merely need to show that $\lim (\{fg\}(x) - MN) = 0$ as $x \to a$.

We can write (and it is this ingenious device which is the essence of the proof)

$$\{fg\}(x) - MN = f(x)g(x) - MN = f(x)g(x) - f(x)N + f(x)N - MN,$$

or

$$\{fg\}(x) - MN = f(x)(g(x) - N) + N(f(x) - M).$$

Now, by Theorem 3.4,

$$\lim_{x \to a} (g(x) - N) = 0,$$

and by Theorem 3.5, $f(x)$ is bounded in some open interval containing a. Hence, by Theorem 3.6,

$$\lim_{x \to a} f(x)(g(x) - N) = 0.$$

Similarly,

$$\lim_{x \to a} (f(x) - M) = 0,$$

and since N can be considered as a function, which is of course bounded,

$$\lim_{x \to a} N(f(x) - M) = 0.$$

Now, by Theorem 3.3, part α,

$$\lim_{x \to a} (f(x)(g(x) - N) + N(f(x) - M)) = 0.$$

Thus we have shown that $\lim (\{fg\}(x) - MN) = 0$ as $x \to a$.

Proof of Theorem 3.3, Part δ: We first show that if $\lim g(x) = N \neq 0$ as $x \to a$, then $\lim 1/g(x) = 1/N$ as $x \to a$. By Theorem 3.4, it is enough to show that $\lim (1/g(x) - 1/N) = 0$ as $x \to a$. Now we can write

$$\frac{1}{g(x)} - \frac{1}{N} = \frac{N - g(x)}{Ng(x)} = \frac{-1}{Ng(x)}(g(x) - N).$$

By Theorem 3.5, there is an open interval I such that when x is in I,

$$|g(x)| > \frac{|N|}{2},$$

or

$$\frac{1}{|g(x)|} < \frac{2}{|N|}.$$

Then, for any x in I,

$$\left| \frac{-1}{N(g(x))} \right| < \frac{2}{N^2}.$$

Consequently $-1/Ng(x)$ is bounded on the interval I. Since $\lim (g(x) - N) = 0$ as $x \to a$, by Theorem 3.4, we have

$$\lim_{x \to a} \left(\frac{-1}{Ng(x)} \right) (g(x) - N) = 0.$$

Since $\dfrac{-1}{N(g(x))} (g(x) - N) = \dfrac{1}{g(x)} - \dfrac{1}{N}$, we see that

$$\lim 1/g(x) = 1/N \text{ as } x \to a.$$

Now, suppose $\lim f(x) = M$ and $\lim g(x) = N \neq 0$ as $x \to a$. We can write

$$\{f/g\}(x) = f(x)(1/g(x)).$$

By the above argument,

$$\lim_{x \to a} 1/g(x) = 1/N.$$

By part γ,

$$\lim_{x \to a} f(x)(1/g(x)) = \lim_{x \to a} f(x) \lim_{x \to a} (1/g(x)) = M(1/N) = M/N,$$

which finishes the proof.

PROBLEMS

1. Write out in full the proof of Theorem 3.3, part β. (*Hint:* Follow the pattern of the proof of part α.)

2. a) It is true that if $f(x) = \dfrac{1}{x}$, then $\lim f(x) = \frac{1}{10}$ as $x \to 10$. Take $e = 1$ and show that if $d(1,10,f) = 9$, then when $0 < |x - 10| < d$, we have $\left| f(x) - \frac{1}{10} \right| < 1$.

b) It is also true that $\lim f(x) = 1$ as $x \to 1$. Take $e = 1$ and find a number $d(1,1,f) > 0$ such that when $0 < |x - 1| < d$, then $|f(x) - 1| < 1$.

c) It is also true that $\lim f(x) = 10$ as $x \to \frac{1}{10}$. Take $e = 1$ and find a suitable $d(1,\frac{1}{10},f) > 0$ for this case.

3. Find, using Theorem 3.3,

a) $\lim_{x \to 3} 4x + 3$. Ans. 15.
b) $\lim_{x \to 3} x^2$. Ans. 9.
c) $\lim_{x \to 2} 4x^2 - 2$.
d) $\lim_{x \to -1} 1 - x^3$.
e) $\lim_{x \to 0} x(1 + 2x)$.
f) $\lim_{x \to 10} x^2 - 2x + 3$.

g) $\lim_{x \to 4} 2x + \sqrt{x}$. (*Hint:* Use Problem 7 of Section 8.) Ans. 10.
h) $\lim_{x \to 2} x^2\sqrt{x} + 2\sqrt{x}$.
i) $\lim_{x \to 0} 3\sqrt{x} + x\sqrt{3}$.
j) $\lim_{x \to 9} (x^2 + 2)(\sqrt{x} - 1)$.
k) $\lim_{x \to 2} (2x^2 + x + 1)(1 - x - x^3)$. Ans. -99.
l) $\lim_{x \to 4} (x^3(x + 2))(1 - 3(x - \sqrt{x}))$.
m) $\lim_{x \to -3} (x^4 - x^3 + x^2 - 1)(1 + 2x - 3x^2)$.

n) $\lim_{x \to 1} \dfrac{x^2 + 1}{2 - x}$. Ans. 2.

o) $\lim_{x \to 3} \dfrac{2x^2 - x + 3}{1 - x}$.

p) $\lim_{x \to -10} \dfrac{1 - x^2}{2x + 3}$.

q) $\lim_{x \to 5} \dfrac{(1 + x)(1 - x^2)(2 + \sqrt{x})}{(1 - 2x)(2 - x)}$.

r) $\lim_{x \to 1} 1 + |x|$. (*Hint:* Use Problem 2 of Section 8.) Ans. 2.

s) $\lim_{x \to -1} \dfrac{1 + |x|}{x^2}$.
t) $\lim_{x \to 1} \dfrac{2 + 3\sqrt{x}}{4 + 5|x|}$.

u) $\lim_{x \to -1} \dfrac{|x| - x^2}{(1 + 2x)(3 - x^2)}$.
v) $\lim_{x \to a} \dfrac{a\sqrt{x} + x\sqrt{a}}{a + x}$.

4. If $f(x) = (x^2 - x)/(x - 1)$, find $\lim_{x \to 1} f(x)$.

Solution: The procedure used above fails, since the limit of the denominator is 0, so Theorem 3.3, part δ, cannot be used. But if we write $f(x) = x(x - 1)/(x - 1)$, we see that $f(x) = x$ except when $x = 1$. Since, by Definition 3.5, it makes no difference what happens when $x = 1$, as far as the limit as $x \to 1$ is concerned, we see that $\lim f(x)$ as $x \to 1$ is the same as $\lim g(x)$ as $x \to 1$ where $g(x) = x$. By Theorem 3.2, $\lim g(x)$ as $x \to 1$ is 1, so $\lim_{x \to 1} f(x) = 1$.

5. Find

a) $\lim\limits_{x \to 1} \dfrac{2x - 2x^2}{1 - x}$.   Ans. 2.

b) $\lim\limits_{x \to 3} \dfrac{x^3 - 3x^2}{x - 3}$.   Ans. 9.

c) $\lim\limits_{x \to -2} \dfrac{2x + x^2}{x + 2}$.

d) $\lim\limits_{x \to 2} \dfrac{x - 2}{2 - x}$.

e) $\lim\limits_{x \to 0} \dfrac{x^2 - x}{2x}$.   Ans. $-\frac{1}{2}$.

f) $\lim\limits_{x \to 1} \dfrac{x^3 - 1}{x - 1}$.

g) $\lim\limits_{x \to 1} \dfrac{x^2 - 2x + 1}{1 - x}$.

h) $\lim\limits_{x \to 1} \dfrac{1 - x^2}{x - x^2}$.

i) $\lim\limits_{x \to 1} \dfrac{2x^2 - x - 1}{x^2 + x - 2}$.   Ans. 1.

j) $\lim\limits_{x \to 3} \dfrac{x^2 - 2x - 3}{x^2 - 4x + 3}$.

k) $\lim\limits_{x \to -2} \dfrac{x^2 + 2x}{x^2 + 4x + 4}$.

l) $\lim\limits_{x \to 4} \dfrac{x - 4}{x^2 - 16}$.

6. Find $\lim\limits_{x \to 4} \dfrac{\sqrt{x} - 2}{x - 4}$.

Solution: As in Problem 4, the limit of the denominator is 0, so we cannot use Theorem 3.3, part δ.   However, we can rationalize the numerator:

$$\frac{\sqrt{x} - 2}{x - 4} = \frac{(\sqrt{x} - 2)(\sqrt{x} + 2)}{(x - 4)(\sqrt{x} + 2)} = \frac{x - 4}{(x - 4)(\sqrt{x} + 2)} = \frac{1}{\sqrt{x} + 2}$$

whenever $x \neq 4$.   Hence

$$\lim\limits_{x \to 4} \frac{\sqrt{x} - 2}{x - 4} = \lim\limits_{x \to 4} \frac{1}{\sqrt{x} + 2} = \frac{1}{4}.$$

7. Find

a) $\lim\limits_{x \to 1} \dfrac{\sqrt{x} - 1}{3x - 3}$.   Ans. $\frac{1}{6}$.

b) $\lim\limits_{x \to 1} \dfrac{1 - x}{1 - \sqrt{x}}$.

c) $\lim\limits_{x \to \sqrt{3}} \dfrac{x^2 - 3}{x - \sqrt{3}}$.   Ans. $2\sqrt{3}$.

d) $\lim\limits_{x \to 2} \dfrac{\sqrt{x} - \sqrt{2}}{x^2 - 2x}$.

e) $\lim\limits_{x \to 3} \dfrac{3 - \sqrt{x}}{x - 9}$.

8. If $f(x) = x^2$, find $\lim\limits_{x \to 2} \dfrac{f(x) - f(2)}{x - 2}$.

Solution: $f(x) - f(2) = x^2 - 4$, so we are asked to find $\lim\limits_{x \to 2} \dfrac{x^2 - 4}{x - 2}$.

By the method of Problem 4, we find the answer to be 4.

9. Find $\lim\limits_{x \to a} \dfrac{f(x) - f(a)}{x - a}$ for the indicated functions and values of a.

a) $f(x) = 2x + 6$, $a = 3$.   Ans.   2.
b) $f(x) = 2x - x^2$, $a = -1$.
c) $f(x) = x^3$, $a = 2$.   Ans.   12.
d) $f(x) = x^3 + x + 10$, $a = 1$.
e) $f(x) = x^3 - x^2$, $a = 0$.

f) $f(x) = \dfrac{1}{x}$, $a = 2$.   Ans. $-\frac{1}{4}$.

g) $f(x) = \dfrac{x}{1 + x}$, $a = 5$.

h) $f(x) = \sqrt{x} - x$, $a = 4$.

10. A weight falls under the influence of gravity. At the end of t seconds, it has fallen $g(t) = 16.1t^2$ ft. How fast is it falling at the end of 2 sec.?

Solution: We saw in Section 9 that a reasonable definition of the velocity of the weight at the end of 2 sec. is

$$\lim_{t \to 2} \frac{g(t) - g(2)}{t - 2}.$$

By the method of Problem 8 we find that the velocity is 64.4 ft. per sec.

11. Find the velocity at the indicated time of a falling weight if at the end of t seconds it has fallen $g(t)$ feet.

a) $g(t) = 4t$, $t = 2$.   Ans.   4.   b) $g(t) = t^2 - 2t$, $t = 3$.
c) $g(t) = t^3$, $t = 1$.   Ans.   3.   d) $g(t) = t^3$, $t = 2$.

e) $g(t) = \dfrac{t}{1 + t}$, $t = 5$.   f) $g(t) = \sqrt{t}$, $t = 100$.

11. FURTHER THEOREMS ON LIMITS

In this section we collect a few more theorems concerning limits which will be useful in later work.

Theorem 3.7: *If* $\lim_{x \to a} f(x) = A$ *and* $\lim_{x \to a} f(x) = B$, *then* $A = B$.

Theorem 3.8a: *If $\lim f(x) = A$ as $x \to a$ and if $A > 0$, then there is some interval I containing a such that $f(x) > 0$ for each x in I and in the domain of definition of f, with the possible exception of a.*

Theorem 3.8b: *If $\lim f(x) = A$ as $x \to a$ and if $A < 0$, then there is some interval I containing a such that $f(x) < 0$ for each x in I and in the domain of definition of f, with the possible exception of a.*

Theorem 3.9: *If there is an interval I containing a such that for any x in I, $f(x) \le g(x)$, and if $\lim_{x \to a} f(x) = A$ and $\lim_{x \to a} g(x) = B$, then $A \le B$.*

Theorem 3.10: *If there is an interval I containing a such that for any x in I, $f(x) \le h(x) \le g(x)$, and if $\lim_{x \to a} f(x) = \lim_{x \to a} g(x) = A$, then $\lim_{x \to a} h(x)$ exists and equals A.*

PROBLEMS

1. Construct a complete proof of Theorem 3.7 by expanding the following outline. Give a reason for each step of your proof.

   If $A \ne B$, then $|A - B| = e$ is a positive number. There is a $d > 0$ such that when $0 < |x - a| < d$, then $|f(x) - A| < e/2$ and $|f(x) - B| < e/2$. But $e/2 + e/2 > |f(x) - A| + |f(x) - B| = |A - f(x)| + |f(x) - B| \ge |A - B| = e$, which is impossible, so A must be equal to B.

   Remark: This is another indirect proof. See page 5.

2. Construct a complete proof of Theorem 3.8a by expanding the following outline. Give a reason for each step of your proof.

   Since $e = A/2 > 0$, there is a number $d > 0$ such that when $0 < |x - a| < d$, $|f(x) - A| < e$. When x is in the interval $I = (a - d, a + d)$, and $x \ne a$, then $f(x) > A - e = A/2 > 0$.

3. Construct a proof of Theorem 3.8b.

4. We give below all the steps in the proof of Theorem 3.9. Fill in the reasons for each step:

   Assume $A > B$.

   1) $e = \dfrac{A - B}{2} > 0.$

   2) There is a number $d > 0$ such that when $0 < |x - a| < d$, then x is in I and $|f(x) - A| < e$ and $|g(x) - B| < e$.

   3) When $0 < |x - a| < d$, then $A - e < f(x)$.

   4) When $0 < |x - a| < d$, then $g(x) < B + e$.

   5) $B + e = B + \dfrac{A - B}{2} = \dfrac{A + B}{2} = A - e.$

   6) When $0 < |x - a| < d$, then $g(x) < f(x)$.

   7) $A \le B$.

5. Fill in a reason for each step in the proof below of Theorem 3.10.

1) Given any $e > 0$, there is a $d(e,a,f) > 0$ such that when $0 < |x - a| < d(e,a,f)$, then $|f(x) - A| < e$.

2) Given any $e > 0$, there is a $d(e,a,g) > 0$ such that when $0 < |x - a| < d(e,a,g)$, then $|g(x) - A| < e$.

3) There is a number d^* such that when $|x - a| < d^*$, then x is in I.

4) If $d(e,a,h)$ is a positive number less than $d(e,a,f)$, $d(e,a,g)$, and d^*, then when $0 < |x - a| < d(e,a,h)$, we have $A - e < f(x)$ and $g(x) < A + e$.

5) When $0 < |x - a| < d(e,a,h)$, we have $h(x) \geq f(x) > A - e$ and $A + e > g(x) \geq h(x)$.

6) When $0 < |x - a| < d(e,a,h)$, we have $|h(x) - A| < e$.

7) $\lim_{x \to a} h(x) = A$.

12. CONTINUITY

We have seen that the limit of a function, as x approaches a given number, does not depend at all on the value of the function at the number, but only on the value of the function at nearby numbers. In fact, the limit can exist even if the function is not defined at the number, and if it is defined there, the limit need not equal the value of the function.

We shall have use for functions for which neither of these things can happen.

Definition 3.7: *A function f is* **continuous at a number** *a if*

1) *f is defined at a,*
2) $\lim_{x \to a} f(x) = f(a)$.

If a function f is continuous at each number in an interval I, we shall say that f is continuous on I.

The function g defined in Example 2 of Section 8 is not continuous at the number 1. (Why?) The function h defined in Example 3 of Section 8 is not continuous at the number 0. (Why?) The function f defined by the equation $f(x) = x^2/|x|$ is not continuous at the number 0. (Why?)

The intuitive idea of a function being continuous on an interval I is that the part of the graph of the function over this interval has no jumps or breaks. This, of course, cannot serve as a definition, since "jump" and "break" are not defined. A little reflection will show that any attempt to define them leads back to the concept of a limit and to the definition above.

The following theorem, however, shows that the intuitive idea of a continuous function is not misleading. It says that such a function cannot "jump" from one value to another since it takes on, between any two numbers a and b, all values between $f(a)$ and $f(b)$.

Theorem 3.11: *If f is continuous at each point of an interval $[a,b]$, if $f(a) \neq f(b)$, and if K is a number between $f(a)$ and $f(b)$, then there is a number c in the interval $[a,b]$ such that $f(c) = K$.*

Proof: There are two cases: $f(a) < f(b)$ and $f(a) > f(b)$. We consider only the first case, the proof for the other case being quite similar. Then $f(a) < K < f(b)$. Let us denote by M the collection of all numbers x in the interval $[a,b]$ such that $f(x) < K$. The collection M contains at least one point, namely a, and it has an upper bound, namely b. Therefore, by the Least Upper Bound Axiom, M has a least upper bound. Call this least upper bound c. We shall show that $f(c) = K$.

Since f is continuous at the number c, $\lim_{x \to c} f(x) = f(c)$. Therefore, for any number $e > 0$, there is a number $d > 0$ such that whenever x is in $[a,b]$ and

$$c - d < x < c + d,$$

then

$$f(c) - e < f(x) < f(c) + e. \quad \text{(Why?)}$$

Now, since c is the *least* upper bound of the collection M, no number to the left of c is an upper bound of M, and in particular $c - d$ is not. Therefore there is some number x such that $c - d < x \leq c$ and $f(x) < K$. But for this number x, $f(c) - e < f(x)$, so $f(c) - e < K$.

On the other hand, if x is any number in $[a,b]$ such that $c < x$, then $K \leq f(x)$, for otherwise x would be in M and c would not be an upper bound of M. If $c < b$, then there is a number x in $[a,b]$ with $c < x < c + d$, and since, for this x, $f(x) < f(c) + e$, we have $K < f(c) + e$. If $c = b$, then, since $K < f(b)$, we again have $K < f(c) + e$.

Thus we have $f(c) - e < K < f(c) + e$, or $|f(c) - K| < e$. But this holds for any number $e > 0$, so we must have $f(c) = K$. (Why?)

Remark: This is the first time we have made use of the Least Upper Bound Axiom. As we shall see, whenever we prove a general theorem which asserts the existence of a number having a special property, we find it necessary to appeal to this axiom.

Exercise: Carry out the proof of this theorem for the case $f(a) > f(b)$.

The basic properties of continuous functions are expressed in the next theorem.

Theorem 3.12: *If f and g are continuous at a point a, then so are $\{f + g\}$, $\{f - g\}$, $\{f \cdot g\}$, and $\{f/g\}$, if $g(a) \neq 0$.*

The proof of this theorem follows quickly from Theorem 3.3. We consider only the case of $\{f + g\}$. Since f and g are both continuous at a, they are both defined at a, because of part 1 of the definition. Hence $\{f + g\}$ is also defined at a. Also, by part 2 of the definition, $\lim_{x \to a} f(x) = f(a)$

and $\lim_{x \to a} g(x) = g(a)$. Now, by Theorem 3.3, part α

$$\lim_{x \to a} \{f + g\}(x) = f(a) + g(a) = \{f + g\}(a),$$

which proves that $\{f + g\}$ is continuous at a.

An important class of function consists of those of the form

$$f(x) = a_n x^n + a_{n-1} x^{n-1} + \cdots + a_1 x + a_0,$$

where the coefficients a_n, a_{n-1}, $\cdots$, a_1, a_0 are constants and n is a non-negative integer. Such a function is called a *polynomial*. Any expression which can be built up by starting with x's and constants and applying the operations of addition, subtraction, and multiplication is a polynomial. (Why?) If we also allow the operation of division, the result can always be written as the quotient of two polynomials, and is called a *rational* function. It follows easily from Theorem 3.3 that every polynomial is continuous at every number and every rational function is continuous at every number in its domain of definition.

PROBLEMS

1. Show that $f(x) = x^2 + 2x - 1$ is continuous at $x = 1$.
2. For each of the following functions, draw the graph and tell where the function does not have a limit and also where it is not continuous.

a) $f(x) = \dfrac{|x|}{2x}$.   Ans.   No limit at 0, not continuous at 0.

b) $f(x) = \begin{cases} |x|, & -1 \le x \le 0 \\ 2, & 0 < x \le 1. \end{cases}$

c) $f(x) = \begin{cases} x, & -1 \le x < 0 \\ 1, & x = 0 \\ 2, & 0 < x \le 1. \end{cases}$

d) $f(x) = \begin{cases} x, & -1 \le x < 0 \\ 1, & x = 0 \\ 2x, & 0 < x \le 1. \end{cases}$ Ans.   Limit at each number where defined. Not continuous at 0.

e) $f(x) = \begin{cases} -1, & -1 \le x < 0 \\ x, & 0 \le x < 1 \\ 2 - x, & 1 \le x < 2 \\ 3, & x = 2 \\ x - 3, & 2 < x \le 3. \end{cases}$

f) $f(x) = 1/x$.

3. The domain of definition of each of the following functions is to be the interval $[-2, +2]$. Specify a function and draw its graph if

a) it has a limit at each point and is continuous at each point;

b) it has a limit at each point, but is not continuous at $x = 0$ and $x = 1$;

c) it has no limit when $x = 0$ and is not continuous when $x = 0, 1, 2$.

4. For each of the examples of Section 6, state where the function is not continuous.

5. Prove that any polynomial is continuous at every number.

6. Prove that any rational function is continuous at each number in its domain of definition.

13. FUNCTION OF A FUNCTION

Given two functions, f and g, we saw, in Section 7, how we could combine them algebraically to form new functions, $\{f + g\}$, etc. There is another way of combining two functions which is of the utmost importance.

Definition 3.8: *If f and g are two functions, then the function $\{f(g)\}$ is defined by the equation*

$$\{f(g)\}(x) = f(g(x)).$$

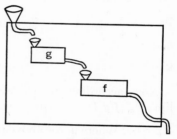

Fig. 3.13

This function is easily pictured in terms of machines. The machines for f and g are arranged as shown in the diagram and enclosed in one box. The resulting combination is the machine for $\{f(g)\}$.

The domain of definition of $\{f(g)\}$ consists of those numbers x in the domain of definition of g for which $g(x)$ is in the domain of definition of f. Even for fairly simple functions f and g, the domain of $\{f(g)\}$ may be unfortunately small or complicated, and it may not even contain one number. Consequently, theorems about limits or continuity of $\{f(g)\}$ are somewhat complicated. The following theorem is sufficient for our purposes.

Theorem 3.13: *If the range of values of g is contained in the domain of definition of f, if g is continuous at a, and if f is continuous at $b = g(a)$, then $\{f(g)\}$ is continuous at a.*

Proof: Since f is continuous at b, $\lim f(x) = f(b)$ as $x \to b$. Hence, given any number $e > 0$, there is a number $d = d(e,b,f) > 0$ such that

1) $|f(x) - f(b)| < e$

when

2) $|x - b| < d.$

Since g is continuous at a, $\lim g(x) = g(a)$ as $x \to a$. So, for the number d above, there is a number $d' = d'(d,a,g) > 0$ such that

3) $|g(x) - g(a)| < d$

when

4) $|x - a| < d'.$

Now $g(a) = b$, so whenever

5) $|x - a| < d',$

then

6) $|g(x) - b| < d.$

So, by 2) and 1) above, we have

7) $|f(g(x)) - f(b)| < e,$

or

8) $|\{f(g)\}(x) - \{f(g)\}(a)| < e.$

Now, according to Definition 3.5, it follows from 5) and 8) that $\lim_{x \to a} \{f(g)\}(x) = \{f(g)\}(a)$, i.e., $\{f(g)\}$ is continuous at a.

Exercise: Where in the above proof did we use the hypothesis that the range of g is contained in the domain of f?

PROBLEMS

1. Give the domain of definition of and an equation for $\{f(g)\}$ if

   a) $f(x) = x^2 - 3x$, $g(x) = 1 - x$.   Ans.   Domain consists of all numbers. $\{f(g)\}(x) = x^2 + x - 2$.
   b) $f(x) = 1 - x$, $g(x) = x^2 - 3x$.
   c) $f(x) = \sqrt{x}$, $g(x) = x^3$.   Ans. $\{f(g)\}(x) = x^{3/2}$, $0 \le x$.

   d) $f(x) = \sqrt{x}$, $g(x) = x^4$.   e) $f(x) = \dfrac{|x|}{x}$, $g(x) = 2 + x$.

   f) $f(x) = g(x) = x$.   g) $f(x) = g(x) = x^2$.
   h) $f(x) = x^2$, $g(x) = 1$.   i) $f(x) = 1$, $g(x) = x^2$.

   j) $f(x) = x$, $0 \le x \le 1$; $g(x) = 2x$, $0 \le x \le 1$.   Ans. $\{f(g)\}(x) = 2x$, $0 \le x \le \frac{1}{2}$.
   k) $f(x) = 2x$, $0 \le x \le 1$; $g(x) = x$, $0 \le x \le 1$.
   l) $f(x) = 2x$, $0 \le x \le 1$; $g(x) = 2x$, $0 \le x \le 1$.

m) $f(x) = \begin{cases} -x, & x < 0 \\ x + \dfrac{1}{x}, & 0 < x; \end{cases}$ $g(x) = \begin{cases} x^2, & x < 0 \\ -1, & 0 \le x. \end{cases}$

2. Specify and draw the graph of $\{f(g)\}$ if

    a) $f(x) = \sqrt{x}$, $g(x) = 1 - x^2$.   Ans. $\{f(g)\}(x) = \sqrt{1 - x^2}$.
    b) $f(x) = 1 - x^2$, $g(x) = \sqrt{x}$.
    c) $f(x) = 2 + x$, $g(x) = 4 - x$.
    d) $f(x) = 2 + x$, $g(x) = 2 - x$.

3. Specify $f(x)$ if

    a) $g(x) = 1 - x^2$, $\{f(g)\}(x) = \sqrt{1 - x^2}$.   Ans. $f(x) = \sqrt{x}$.
    b) $g(x) = x^2$, $\{f(g)\}(x) = \sqrt{1 - x^2}$.
    c) $g(x) = x$, $\{f(g)\}(x) = \sqrt{1 - x^2}$.
    d) $g(x) = 1 - x$, $\{f(g)\}(x) = x$.
    e) $g(x) = 2x + 3$, $\{f(g)\}(x) = 4x^2 + 12x + 9$.

4. Specify g if

    a) $f(x) = x^2$, $\{f(g)\}(x) = x^2 + 2x + 1$.   Ans. $g(x) = x + 1$.
    b) $f(x) = x + 1$, $\{f(g)\}(x) = x^2$.
    c) $f(x) = 1 - x$, $\{f(g)\}(x) = x$.
    d) $f(x) = 1 + x + x^2$, $\{f(g)\}(x) = x^2 - 3x + 3$.

5. What is the domain of definition of $\{f(g)\}$ if
    a) $f(x) = \sqrt{x}$, $g(x) = 1 + x$.   Ans. $-1 \le x$.
    b) $f(x) = \sqrt{x}$, $g(x) = 1 - x^2$.
    c) $f(x) = \sqrt{x}$, $g(x) = 1 + x^2$.
    d) $f(x) = \sqrt{x}$, $g(x) = -x^2$.

6. Use Problem 7 of Section 8 and Theorem 3.13 to find

    a) $\lim_{x \to 0} \sqrt{1 - x}$.   Ans.   1.   b) $\lim_{x \to 0} \sqrt{1 - x^2}$.

    c) $\lim_{x \to 1} \sqrt{x^2 - 1}$.   d) $\lim_{x \to 2} \sqrt{\dfrac{x^2 - 4}{x - 2}}$.

REVIEW PROBLEMS

1. If the function f is defined by the equation $f(x) = x + 1/x$, show that

$$(f(x))^2 = f(x^2) + 2,$$

and

$$(f(x))^3 = f(x^3) + 3f(x).$$

2. A function f is to be defined by an equation of the form

$$f(x) = ax + b.$$

If we require that
$$\{f(f)\}(x) = 4x - 9,$$
what are possible values for a and b? Ans. $a = 2, b = -3$ or $a = -2, b = 9$.

3. A function g is defined by the equation
$$g(x) = x^n,$$
where n is an integer. For which values of n is it true that
$$g(-x) = -g(x)?$$

4. If h is defined by the equation
$$h(t) = t/(1 - t),$$
show that
$$h(t^2) = \tfrac{1}{2}(h(t) + h(-t)).$$

5. For which values of a and b, if any, do the points $(1,2)$, $(-3,-1)$, and $(2,4)$ all lie on the graph of f if
$$f(x) = ax + b/x?$$

6. The vertices of a triangle are $(-3,-1)$, $(2,2)$, and $(5,0)$. A function f is defined as follows: The domain of definition of f is the interval $(-3,5)$. For each x in the domain, $f(x)$ is the length of the part of the vertical line through x which lies inside the triangle. Write equations which specify f.

7. Postal regulations prescribe that the sum of the length and girth of a package must not exceed 100 in. Consider rectangular boxes with square ends which come just within the rule and express the volume as a function of the side of the square end.

   (*Hint:* The length of a parcel is the length of the largest side.)

8. A tank holds 50 qt. It is filled with a 30 per cent solution of alcohol in water. A certain amount of the solution is removed and replaced with pure alcohol. Express the concentration of the final solution as a function of the amount removed. Ans. $f(x) = 30 + \tfrac{7}{5}x$.

9. A unit segment is divided into equal segments, each of length r. On each segment as a diameter a semicircle is constructed. Denote by L_r the sum of the lengths of these semicircles. What is
$$\lim_{r \to 0} L_r?$$

10. Show that the equation
$$4x^3 - 9x^2 - 6x + 2 = 0$$
has a root in each of the intervals $(-1,0)$, $(0,1)$, and $(2,3)$.

   (*Hint:* Remember Theorem 3.11.)

11. The function f is defined by the equations

$$f(x) = \begin{cases} x, & x \text{ a rational number} \\ 0, & x \text{ an irrational number.} \end{cases}$$

Show that

$$\lim_{x \to 0} f(x) = 0.$$

Is f continuous at 0?　Show that f is not continuous at any number different from 0.

Derivatives

1. INTRODUCTORY DISCUSSION

In Section 9 of Chapter 3, we discussed the problem of the velocity of a falling body. We saw there that a reasonable definition of the velocity at the end of a seconds is

$$\lim_{t \to a} \frac{g(t) - g(a)}{t - a}$$

where $g(t)$ is the distance fallen in t seconds.

Let us now consider another problem, this time a problem from geometry. If we are given a curve and a point on it, how can we find the tangent line to the curve at the given point? As in the velocity problem, we must first decide what we mean by a tangent line to a curve. In plane geometry a

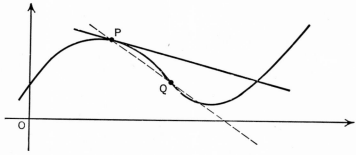

Fig. 4.1

tangent line to a circle was defined as a line through the end of a radius and perpendicular to it. But for any curve not a circle this definition is useless. We might try to define a tangent to a curve to be a line which meets the curve at just one point. But the accompanying figure shows that this definition is not satisfactory. We would like to call the solid line through P a tangent to the curve, but this line meets the curve at more than one point.

Now suppose we consider the line through P and another point Q on the curve. Suppose Q moves along the curve toward P. Then, in the above figure, the line through P and Q will swing around and approach the solid line through P. This suggests that we might define the tangent line to the curve at P to be the limit of a line through P and another point Q as Q approaches P along the curve.

This, of course, is not very satisfactory as a definition of a tangent line, since we have not said what is meant by the limit of a line. Neither have we said what is meant by Q approaching P along the curve. It is possible to make these concepts precise, but for convenience we shall do so only in the special case where the curve in question is the graph of a function continuous at P.

Let f be a function, P a point on its graph, with coordinates $(a, f(a))$, and suppose that f is continuous at a. For any number $x \neq a$, $Q = (x, f(x))$ is another point on the graph. As x approaches a, the distance between P and Q approaches 0 (why?), and this is what we mean when we say that Q approaches P along the curve.

Let $m(x)$ be the slope of the line joining P and Q. Then we define the limit of the line PQ, as Q approaches P along the curve, to be the line through P whose slope is equal to $\lim_{x \to a} m(x)$.

The slope of the line joining P and Q is $\dfrac{f(x) - f(a)}{x - a}$. Therefore it is reasonable to define the tangent line to this curve at P to be the line through P whose slope is

$$\lim_{x \to a} \frac{f(x) - f(a)}{x - a},$$

provided, of course, that this limit exists.

With this definition, the problem of finding the tangent line to the graph of a function reduces to the problem of calculating a limit, and in fact the same kind of limit we encountered in the velocity problem.

2. DERIVATIVES

In the preceding section, we saw that two diverse problems both led to limits of the same form. This particular type of limit also turns up in other problems, and it is so important that we propose to study it abstractly, i.e., without reference to the problems which suggested it originally. These problems we will come back to later.

Definition 4.1: *If f is a function, then the function f', whose value at any number (or point) a is*

$$f'(a) = \lim_{x \to a} \frac{f(x) - f(a)}{x - a},$$

*whenever this limit exists, is called the **derivative** of f. The function f is said* to be **differentiable** *at a number (or point) a if*

$$f'(a) = \lim_{x \to a} \frac{f(x) - f(a)}{x - a}$$

exists.

Another notation for the derivative of f, instead of f', is $D\{f\}$. Ordinarily we shall abbreviate this to Df, but it must be remembered that this is not the product of D and f, but rather the new function defined by the equation in Definition 4.1. In this notation, the value of the derivative of f at the point a is $Df(a)$.

The domain of definition of f' consists of those numbers a in the domain of f for which the above limit exists. The function

$$f(x) = |x|$$

shows that the domain of f' can be smaller than that of f, for f is defined at 0, but f' is not (see Problem 4 below).

The above example shows that a function can be continuous at a certain point without being differentiable there. However, it is a useful fact that differentiability does imply continuity.

Theorem 4.1: *If a function f is differentiable at a point a, then it is continuous at a.*

Proof: To show that f is continuous at a, we must show that

$$\lim_{x \to a} f(x) = f(a).$$

For this it is sufficient to show that

$$\lim_{x \to a} (f(x) - f(a)) = 0. \quad \text{(Why?)}$$

We are given that

$$\lim_{x \to a} \frac{f(x) - f(a)}{x - a} = f'(a),$$

where $f'(a)$ is some number. Also,

$$\lim_{x \to a} (x - a) = 0.$$

By Theorem 3.3, part γ, we have

$$\lim_{x \to a} \frac{f(x) - f(a)}{x - a} \cdot (x - a) = f'(a) \cdot 0 = 0.$$

Hence

$$\lim_{x \to a} (f(x) - f(a)) = 0. \quad \text{(Why?)}$$

Given a particular function f, the problem of finding f' or Df explicitly is not an easy one. The problems below show a few of the methods which can be applied to this problem. In a later section we shall undertake a systematic attack on the problem.

PROBLEMS

1. Find f' if $f(x) = 3x^2$.

Solution: To specify f', we must tell what $f'(x)$ is for any value of x. Let a be a value of x. Then, for all $x \neq a$,

$$\frac{f(x) - f(a)}{x - a} = \frac{3x^2 - 3a^2}{x - a} = \frac{3(x - a)(x + a)}{x - a} = 3(x + a).$$

Therefore

$$f'(a) = \lim_{x \to a} \frac{f(x) - f(a)}{x - a} = \lim_{x \to a} 3(x + a) = 6a. \quad \text{(Why?)}$$

Since a could be any value of x, f' is specified by the equation

$$f'(x) = 6x.$$

2. Find Df if $f(x) = \sqrt{1 - x^2}$, $|x| \leq 1$.

Solution: For any number a such that $|a| < 1$, and for any $x \neq a$, $|x| \leq 1$, we have

$$\frac{f(x) - f(a)}{x - a} = \frac{\sqrt{1 - x^2} - \sqrt{1 - a^2}}{x - a}$$

$$= \frac{(\sqrt{1 - x^2} - \sqrt{1 - a^2})(\sqrt{1 - x^2} + \sqrt{1 - a^2})}{(x - a)(\sqrt{1 - x^2} + \sqrt{1 - a^2})}$$

$$= \frac{(1 - x^2) - (1 - a^2)}{(x - a)(\sqrt{1 - x^2} + \sqrt{1 - a^2})}$$

$$= -\frac{(x - a)(x + a)}{(x - a)(\sqrt{1 - x^2} + \sqrt{1 - a^2})}$$

$$= -\frac{x + a}{\sqrt{1 - x^2} + \sqrt{1 - a^2}}.$$

Therefore

$$Df(a) = \lim_{x \to a} -\frac{x + a}{\sqrt{1 - x^2} + \sqrt{1 - a^2}} = \frac{-a}{\sqrt{1 - a^2}}. \quad \text{(Why?)}$$

Hence

$$Df(x) = \frac{-x}{\sqrt{1 - x^2}}, \quad |x| < 1.$$

Exercise: Why did we have to assume $|a| < 1$?

3. Find Df if

a) $f(x) = 2x - 3$. Ans. $Df(x) = 2$.   b) $f(x) = 1 - x^2$.

c) $f(x) = x^3$.   d) $f(x) = 2x - x^2$.

e) $f(x) = \dfrac{1}{x}$. Ans. $Df(x) = \dfrac{-1}{x^2}$.   f) $f(x) = \dfrac{x}{1 + x}$.

g) $f(x) = \sqrt{x}$.

4. Find $f'(x)$ for all values of x for which $f'(x)$ exists if $f(x) = |x|$.

   Solution: For all $x \neq a$,

$$\frac{f(x) - f(a)}{x - a} = \frac{|x| - |a|}{x - a} = \begin{cases} -1 \text{ for } a < 0 \text{ and } x \leq 0 \\ +1 \text{ for } 0 < a \text{ and } 0 \leq x. \end{cases}$$

   Hence

$$f'(a) = \lim_{x \to a} \frac{f(x) - f(a)}{x - a} = \begin{cases} -1, a < 0 \\ +1, a > 0. \end{cases}$$

   However, if $a = 0$, then

$$\frac{f(x) - f(a)}{x - a} = \frac{|x|}{x} = \begin{cases} -1, x < 0 \\ +1, x > 0. \end{cases}$$

   Therefore $f'(0)$ does not exist. (Why?)

5. Find Df for all values of x for which Df is defined if

a) $f(x) = |x - 2|$.   b) $f(x) = x|x|$.

c) $f(x) = |1 - x^2|$.   d) $f(x) = |x^3|$.

6. In which of the following cases does $f'(0)$ exist?

a) $f(x) = \begin{cases} \sin\left(\dfrac{180°}{x}\right), & x \neq 0 \\ 0, & x = 0. \end{cases}$

b) $f(x) = \begin{cases} x \sin\left(\dfrac{180°}{x}\right), & x \neq 0 \\ 0, & x = 0. \end{cases}$

c) $f(x) = \begin{cases} x^2 \sin\left(\dfrac{180°}{x}\right), & x \neq 0 \\ 0, & x = 0. \end{cases}$

3. HIGHER DERIVATIVES

According to Definition 4.1, the derivative f' of a given function f is another function. Therefore it too can have a derivative, which we denote by f'' or D^2f and call the second derivative of f. Similarly, the derivative of the second derivative of f is called the third derivative of f, and is denoted by f''' or D^3f, etc.

PROBLEMS

1. Find the second derivative of each of the following functions:

a) $f(x) = 3(x - 2)$.   Ans. $f''(x) = 0$.   b) $f(x) = x^2$.
c) $f(y) = y^5$.   d) $g(y) = y^3 - y^4$.

e) $f(t) = t^{-1}$.   Ans. $f''(t) = \dfrac{2}{t^3}$.   f) $h(w) = \sqrt{w}$.

g) $\varphi(s) = \sqrt{1 - s}$.

2. Find the third derivative of each of the following functions:

a) $f(x) = 4 - 7x$.   b) $f(x) = x^2 + 2x$.
c) $f(x) = x^3$.   Ans. $f'''(x) = 6$.   d) $g(x) = 2x - 2$.
e) $h(x) = x^2 - 2x - 3$.   f) $\varphi(x) = x^3 - 3x^2 - 9x + 9$.

4. THEOREMS ON DERIVATIVES

The following theorems will make it easy for us to differentiate, i.e., to find the derivatives of, a large number of functions.

Theorem 4.2: *If $f(x) = c$, where c is a number, then f is differentiable everywhere and $Df(a) = 0$ for each a.*

Proof: By definition

$$Df(a) = \lim_{x \to a} \frac{f(x) - f(a)}{x - a},$$

and in this case $f(x) = f(a) = c$, so

$$\frac{f(x) - f(a)}{x - a} = \frac{c - c}{x - a} = 0 \text{ when } x \neq a.$$

Hence

$$\lim_{x \to a} \frac{f(x) - f(a)}{x - a} = 0.$$

Theorem 4.3: *If $f(x) = x$, then f is differentiable everywhere and $Df(a) = 1$ for each a.*

Proof: For any $x \neq a$,

$$\frac{f(x) - f(a)}{x - a} = \frac{x - a}{x - a} = 1.$$

Therefore

$$Df(a) = \lim_{x \to a} \frac{f(x) - f(a)}{x - a} = \lim_{x \to a} 1 = 1. \quad \text{(Why?)}$$

Theorem 4.4: *If f and g are both differentiable at a point a, then* $\{f + g\}$ *is also differentiable at a and*

$$D\{f + g\}(a) = \{Df + Dg\}(a),$$

i.e.,

$$D\{f + g\} = \{Df + Dg\}.$$

Proof: $\{f + g\}(x) - \{f + g\}(a) = f(x) + g(x) - f(a) - g(a) = f(x) - f(a) + g(x) - g(a).$
Hence

$$\frac{\{f + g\}(x) - \{f + g\}(a)}{x - a} = \frac{f(x) - f(a)}{x - a} + \frac{g(x) - g(a)}{x - a}$$

By hypothesis,

$$\lim_{x \to a} \frac{f(x) - f(a)}{x - a} = Df(a) \quad \text{and} \quad \lim_{x \to a} \frac{g(x) - g(a)}{x - a} = Dg(a).$$

Therefore, by Theorem 3.3, Part α,

$$\lim_{x \to a} \frac{\{f + g\}(x) - \{f + g\}(a)}{x - a} = Df(a) + Dg(a) = \{Df + Dg\}(a).$$

Theorem 4.5: *If f and g are both differentiable at a point a, then* $\{f - g\}$ *is also differentiable at a, and*

$$D\{f - g\}(a) = \{Df - Dg\}(a),$$

i.e.,

$$D\{f - g\} = \{Df - Dg\}.$$

The proof of this is so similar to that of the preceding theorem that we do not bother to write it out.

Theorem 4.6: *If f and g are both differentiable at a point a, then so is* $\{f \cdot g\}$ *differentiable at a, and*

$$D\{f \cdot g\}(a) = \{g \cdot Df\}(a) + \{f \cdot Dg\}(a),$$

i.e.,

$$D\{f \cdot g\} = \{g \cdot Df\} + \{f \cdot Dg\}.$$

Proof: $\{f \cdot g\}(x) - \{f \cdot g\}(a) = f(x) \cdot g(x) - f(a) \cdot g(a) = f(x) \cdot g(x) - f(a) \cdot g(x) + f(a) \cdot g(x) - f(a) \cdot g(a) = g(x)(f(x) - f(a)) + f(a)(g(x) - g(a)).$
Hence

$$\frac{\{f \cdot g\}(x) - \{f \cdot g\}(a)}{x - a} = g(x) \cdot \frac{f(x) - f(a)}{x - a} + f(a) \cdot \frac{g(x) - g(a)}{x - a}.$$

By hypothesis,

$$\lim_{x \to a} \frac{f(x) - f(a)}{x - a} = Df(a) \quad \text{and} \quad \lim_{x \to a} \frac{g(x) - g(a)}{x - a} = Dg(a).$$

By Theorem 4.1, g is continuous at a, so

$$\lim_{x \to a} g(x) = g(a).$$

By Theorem 3.1,

$$\lim_{x \to a} f(a) = f(a).$$

Then, by Theorem 3.3, Parts α and γ,

$$\lim_{x \to a} \frac{\{f \cdot g\}(x) - \{f \cdot g\}(a)}{x - a} = g(a) \cdot Df(a) + f(a) \cdot Dg(a)$$

$$= \{g \cdot Df\}(a) + \{f \cdot Dg\}(a).$$

Remark: If f is a function, if c is a number, and if g is the function defined by the equation $g(x) = c$, then common abbreviations for the function $\{g \cdot f\}$ are $\{cf\}$ or cf.

Theorem 4.7: *If f is differentiable at a point a, and if c is a number, then cf is differentiable at a, and*

$$D(cf)(a) = cDf(a), \quad i.e., \quad D(cf) = cDf.$$

Exercise: Show that this theorem is a consequence of Theorems 4.2 and 4.6.

Theorem 4.8: *If n is a positive integer, and if f is the function defined by $f(x) = x^n$, then f is differentiable everywhere, and $Df(a) = n \cdot a^{n-1}$, for each a.*

Proof: We shall prove this theorem by mathematical induction, i.e., we shall first show that the theorem is true when $n = 1$, and then we shall show that if the theorem is true for a particular integer m, then it is also true for the next integer, $m + 1$. Hence the theorem will be true for every integer.

For the case where $n = 1$, $f(x) = x^1 = x$. By Theorem 4.3, $Df(x) = 1$. But $n \cdot x^{n-1} = 1 \cdot x^0 = 1$ when $n = 1$, so this theorem is true when $n = 1$.

Now suppose that the theorem is true for a particular integer m, and consider $f(x) = x^{m+1}$. We can write $f = \{gh\}$, where $g(x) = x^m$ and $h(x) = x$. By Theorem 3.6,

$$Df = \{(Dg) \cdot h\} + \{g \cdot Dh\}.$$

By Theorem 4.3,

$$Dh(x) = 1.$$

Since we have assumed that our theorem is true for the integer m,

$$Dg(x) = m \cdot x^{m-1}.$$

Substituting, we have

$$Df(x) = m \cdot x^{m-1} \cdot x + x^m \cdot 1 = mx^m + x^m = (m + 1)x^m.$$

Therefore the theorem is also true for the integer $m + 1$.

Theorem 4.9: *If f and g are both differentiable at a point a, and if $g(a) \neq 0$, then $\{f/g\}$ is also differentiable at a, and*

$$D\{f/g\}(a) = \frac{\{g \cdot Df\}(a) - \{f \cdot Dg\}(a)}{(g(a))^2},$$

i.e.,

$$D\{f/g\} = \{\{g \cdot Df\} - \{f \cdot Dg\}\}/g^2.$$

Proof:

$$\{f/g\}(x) - \{f/g\}(a) = f(x)/g(x) - f(a)/g(a)$$

$$= \frac{f(x) \cdot g(a) - g(x) \cdot f(a)}{g(x) \cdot g(a)}$$

$$= \frac{f(x) \cdot g(a) - f(a) \cdot g(a) - g(x) \cdot f(a) + f(a) \cdot g(a)}{g(x) \cdot g(a)}$$

$$= \frac{g(a)(f(x) - f(a)) - f(a)(g(x) - g(a))}{g(x) \cdot g(a)}.$$

Hence

$$\frac{\{f/g\}(x) - \{f/g\}(a)}{x - a} = \frac{1}{g(x)g(a)}\left(g(a)\frac{f(x) - f(a)}{x - a} - f(a)\frac{g(x) - g(a)}{x - a}\right).$$

Now, by Theorem 4.1, g is continuous at a, so

$$\lim_{x \to a} g(x) = g(a).$$

By hypothesis,

$$\lim_{x \to a} \frac{f(x) - f(a)}{x - a} = Df(a) \quad \text{and} \quad \lim_{x \to a} \frac{g(x) - g(a)}{x - a} = Dg(a).$$

By Theorem 3.1,

$$\lim_{x \to a} f(a) = f(a) \quad \text{and} \quad \lim_{x \to a} g(a) = g(a).$$

Then, by Theorem 3.3,

$$\lim_{x \to a} \frac{\{f/g\}(x) - \{f/g\}(a)}{x - a} = \frac{Df(a) \cdot g(a) - f(a) \cdot Dg(a)}{(g(a))^2}$$

$$= \frac{\{Df \cdot g\}(a) - \{f \cdot Dg\}(a)}{(g(a))^2}.$$

It is now clear that any function which is built up from constants and powers of x by means of the algebraic operations of addition, subtraction, multiplication, and division, i.e., any rational function, is differentiable, and its derivative can be obtained by means of the theorems above.

Theorem 4.8, which gives a formula for Df when $f(x) = x^n$, n an integer, is also true when n is any number at all. We cannot prove this at present, partly because we are not sure what x^n means in some cases. (For example, what does the symbol $3^{\sqrt{2}}$ mean?) However, in Chapter 9 we shall show how to define x^n for $x > 0$ and any n, and we shall prove that the formula in Theorem 4.8 is valid in this general case. In the meantime, we shall allow ourselves to use Theorem 4.8 in this extended form.

PROBLEMS

1. Find Df it $f(x) = 2x^2 + 4x - 8$.

Solution: Let g, h, and φ be the functions defined by the equations $g(x) = x^2$, $h(x) = x$, and $\varphi(x) = 8$. Then $f = \{2g + 4h - \varphi\}$. Now

1) $Dg(x) = 2x$	Theorem 4.8.
2) $D(2g)(x) = 2 \cdot Dg(x) = 4x$	Theorem 4.7 and Step 1.
3) $Dh(x) = 1$	Theorem 4.3.
4) $D(4h)(x) = 4 \cdot Dh(x) = 4$	Theorem 4.7 and Step 3.
5) $D\{2g + 4h\}(x) = 4x + 4$	Theorem 4.4 and Steps 2 and 4.
6) $D\varphi(x) = 0$	Theorem 4.2.
7) $D\{2g + 4h - \varphi\}(x) = 4x + 4$	Theorem 4.5 and Steps 5 and 6.
8) $Df(x) = 4x + 4$	Step 7, and $f = \{2g + 4h - \varphi\}$.

Therefore Df is the function defined by the equation $Df(x) = 4x + 4$.

Remark: It would become excessively tedious were we to work all derivative problems in such detail. Hence it is customary to abbreviate the solution in the manner below. However, the student must always be able to write out the solution in full, as above, if called on to do so.

Abbreviated form of solution:

1) $D(2x^2 + 4x - 8) = D(2x^2) + D(4x)$ $+ D(-8)$	Theorem 4.4.
2) $D(2x^2) = 2 \cdot D(x^2) = 2.2x = 4x$	Theorems 4.7 and 4.8.
3) $D(4x) = 4 \cdot D(x) = 4.1 = 4$	Theorems 4.7 and 4.3.
4) $D(-8) = 0$	Theorem 4.2.
5) $D(2x^2 + 4x - 8) = 4x + 4$	Steps 1, 2, 3, and 4.

Remark: We must mention at this point the convention which allows the above problem to be stated "Find the derivative of $2x^2 + 4x - 8$." The word "derivative" can only be used with reference to functions, and the expression $2x^2 + 4x - 8$ does not specify a unique function. $2x^2 + 4x - 8$ is the number corresponded to x by the function f defined by the equation $f(x) = 2x^2 + 4x - 8$. But it is also the value of other functions. If $g(t) = 2t^4 + 4t^2 - 8$, for example, then g assigns to the number $\sqrt{x}$ the number $2x^2 + 4x - 8$. Similarly, if h is defined by the equation $h(t) = t$, then h assigns to the number $2x^2 + 4x - 8$ the number $2x^2 + 4x - 8$.

We shall occasionally use this convention in stating problems, but nowhere else.

2. Find Df if

 a) $f(x) = 3x^2 - 2x + 1$.   Ans. $Df(x) = 6x - 2$.
 b) $f(x) = x^3 + x^2 + x + 1$.
 c) $f(x) = ax^3 + bx^2 + cx + d$.
 d) $f(t) = 1 - t - t^4$.   Ans. $Df(t) = -1 - 4t^3$.
 e) $f(t) = t^{10} - t^{20}$.   f) $f(z) = \frac{1}{2}z^2 + \frac{1}{3}z^3$.
 g) $f(w) = 3(1 - w^5) + 5(w^3 - 1)$.   h) $f(y) = 9y^{10} - 10y^9 + y^{90}$.

3. Find the first and second derivatives of each of the following functions:

 a) $g(x) = 127x - 43x^3$.   Ans. $g'(x) = 127 - 129x^2,\ g''(x) = -258x$.

 b) $g(t) = at^{10} + bt^{30}$.   c) $\varphi(y) = (y^3 - 10y)/100$.

 d) $v(s) = \pi\left(as^2 - \dfrac{s^3}{3}\right)$.   e) $h(r) = \dfrac{r^4}{4} + 2\left(r - \dfrac{1}{2}\right)$.

 f) $\varphi(z) = 2(z + z^2) - 3(z^3 - z^4)$.

4. Find f' if

 a) $f(x) = \sqrt{x}$.   *Solution:* $\sqrt{x} = x^{\frac{1}{2}}$, so, using Theorem 4.8, we have

$$f'(x) = \tfrac{1}{2}x^{-\frac{1}{2}} = \frac{1}{2\sqrt{x}}.$$

 b) $f(x) = x^{\frac{5}{2}} + x^{\frac{3}{2}}$.   Ans. $f'(x) = \frac{5}{2}x^{\frac{3}{2}} + \frac{3}{2}x^{\frac{1}{2}}$.

 c) $f(x) = \dfrac{1}{x}$. $\left(Hint: \dfrac{1}{x} = x^{-1}.\right)$ Ans. $f'(x) = -x^{-2} = \dfrac{-1}{x^2}$.

 d) $f(x) = \dfrac{1}{\sqrt{x}}$.

 e) $f(x) = x^{\frac{3}{2}} + \dfrac{1}{x^{\frac{3}{2}}}$.

 f) $f(t) = t^2 + \dfrac{1}{t^2}$.

 g) $f(z) = z^{10} + z^{\frac{1}{10}} + \dfrac{1}{z^{10}} + \dfrac{1}{z^{\frac{1}{10}}} + 10$.

 h) $f(x) = \dfrac{1 - x}{\sqrt{x}}$.

 i) $f(t) = \dfrac{1 - \sqrt{t}}{t}$.

5. State the domain of definition of f' for each part of Problem 4.

6. Find the derivative of each of the following functions:

a) $f(x) = (x^2 + 2)(x^3 + 3)$.   *Solution:* This is a product. Using Theorem 4.6, we have $f'(x) = 2x(x^3 + 3) + 3x^2(x^2 + 2) = 5x^4 + 6x^2 + 6x$.

b) $f(x) = (1 - x)(x^2 - 3x + 1)$.   Ans. $f'(x) = -3x^2 + 8x - 4$.

c) $f(x) = \sqrt{x}\left(1 - \dfrac{x^3}{3}\right)$.   Ans. $f'(x) = \dfrac{3 - 7x^3}{6\sqrt{x}}$.

d) $g(t) = (3t^2 + 4)\left(\sqrt{t} + \dfrac{1}{\sqrt{t}}\right)$.

e) $g(y) = (1 + y^2)^2$.

f) $g(x) = (x^4 + 4x^2 + 8)(1 - x^3)$.

g) $g(s) = (s^{1/3} + s^{2/3})(s^{1/4} - s^{1/3})$.

h) $f(w) = (1 - w^2)(1 - w^3)(1 - w^4)$.

i) $f(s) = (1 - s)^3$.

j) $g(w) = (\sqrt{w} + 1)(\sqrt[3]{w} - 1)$.

k) $\varphi(w) = (w^{100} + w^{50} + w)\left(\dfrac{1}{w} + \dfrac{2}{w^2}\right)$.

7. Find the second derivative of each of the following functions:

a) $f(y) = (y^2 - 3y^3)(y^4 + 1)$.   Ans. $f''(y) = -126y^5 + 30y^4 - 18y + 2$.

b) $\varphi(t) = \sqrt[3]{t}\left(1 + \dfrac{1}{t}\right)$.

c) $g(x) = \left(x + \dfrac{1}{x}\right)\left(x^2 + \dfrac{1}{x^2}\right)$.

d) $h(w) = (w^{10} - 10)(w^5 + 5)(w^2 - 2)$.

8. Find Df if

a) $f(x) = \dfrac{x^2 - 1}{x + 2}$.   *Solution:* This is a quotient. Using Theorem 4.9,

we have
$$Df(x) = \frac{(x + 2)(2x) - (x^2 - 1)(1)}{(x + 2)^2} = \frac{x^2 + 4x + 1}{(x + 2)^2}.$$

b) $f(x) = \dfrac{x^3}{1 - x}$.   Ans. $Df(x) = \dfrac{3x^2 - 2x^3}{(1 - x)^2}$.

c) $f(y) = \dfrac{y^3 + y^2 + 1}{y^3 - y^2 - 1}$.

d) $f(t) = \dfrac{1 - \sqrt{t}}{1 + t^2}$.

e) $f(w) = \dfrac{w + w^2}{\sqrt{w} + \sqrt[3]{w}}$.

f) $f(s) = \dfrac{as^3 + bs^2 + cs + d}{es + f}$.

g) $f(z) = \dfrac{(1 - \sqrt{z})(1 + \sqrt{z})}{1 + z^2}.$ Ans. $Df(z) = \dfrac{z^2 - 2z - 1}{(1 + z^2)^2}.$

h) $f(x) = \dfrac{1 - \sqrt{x}}{(1 + x^2)(1 + \sqrt{x})}.$

i) $f(x) = \dfrac{(x^2 + 2)(x^3 + 3)}{(x^4 + 4)(x^5 + 5)}.$

9. Find f'' if

a) $f(x) = \dfrac{1 + x}{1 + x^2}.$ Ans. $f''(x) = \dfrac{2x^3 + 6x^2 - 6x - 2}{(1 + x^2)^3}.$

b) $f(s) = \dfrac{s}{1 - s}.$

c) $f(t) = \dfrac{t}{1 - \sqrt{t}}.$

d) $f(t) = \dfrac{1 - t}{1 + t + t^2}.$

10. Find Df, and state its domain of definition, if

a) $f(x) = \begin{cases} x^2 + 1, & -2 \le x < 0 \\ x^3 + x, & 0 \le x \le 2. \end{cases}$

b) $f(x) = \begin{cases} x(1 - x), & 0 \le x < 1 \\ x & , \ 1 \le x < 4 \\ \dfrac{x + 4}{4} & , \ 4 \le x \le 8. \end{cases}$

11. For each of the following functions, find Df, D^2f, and D^3f.

a) $f(x) = x^5 + x^4 + x^3 + x^2 + x + 1.$ b) $f(x) = x^{1/3} - 1/x^{1/3}.$

c) $f(x) = \dfrac{x^2 + 1}{x^3 - 1}.$ d) $f(x) = \dfrac{\sqrt{x} - 1}{\sqrt{x} + 1}.$

12. Find a formula for $D^n f$ if

a) $f(x) = x^{100}.$
b) $f(x) = 1/x.$

13. In each of the following cases, find a function f such that

a) $f'(x) = x^2.$ Ans. $f(x) = \dfrac{x^3}{3}.$ b) $f'(x) = x + 1.$

c) $f'(x) = 1/x^2.$ d) $f'(x) = \sqrt{x}.$
e) $f'(x) = 1/\sqrt{x}.$ f) $f'(x) = (x + 1)(x - 2).$

14. In each of the following cases, find a function f such that

   a) $D^2f(x) = x^2$

   b) $D^3f(x) = x^2 + x + \sqrt{x}$.

5. TANGENTS AND NORMALS

The introductory discussion, in the first section of this chapter, makes the following definitions appear quite reasonable.

Definition 4.2: *The **tangent line** to the graph of a function f at a point $(a, f(a))$ on the graph is the straight line through this point whose slope is $f'(a)$.*

Remark: According to this definition, if f' is not defined at a, there is no tangent line to the graph at the point $(a, f(a))$. This agrees with our intuition for such a

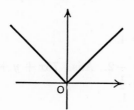

Fig. 4.2

case as the function f defined by $f(x) = |x|$. For this function, f' is not defined at 0, and there is no one unique line which we would like to call the tangent line to the graph at the point $(0,0)$.

On the other hand, if $f(x) = \sqrt{1 - x^2}$, then f' is not defined when $x = 1$. But in this case there is a line, namely the line $x = 1$, which we would like to call the tangent line to the graph at the point $(1,0)$. There are various methods for overcoming this difficulty, one of which we discuss in Chapter 9.

Definition 4.3: *The **normal line** to the graph of a function f at a point $(a, f(a))$ on the graph is the straight line through this point which is perpendicular to the tangent line to the graph at this point.*

We recall from Chapter 2, that since the slopes of perpendicular lines are negative reciprocals of each other, the slope of the normal line to the graph of a function f at the point $(a, f(a))$ is $-1/f'(a)$, provided that $f'(a) \neq 0$.

Definition 4.4: *The **slope of the graph** of a function f at a point $(a, f(a))$ on the graph is the slope of the tangent line there, i.e., $f'(a)$.*

PROBLEMS

1. Find the equations of the tangent lines to the graphs of the following functions at the indicated points.

   a) $f(x) = 2x^2 - 6x + 1$, $x = 1$.

Solution: $f'(x) = 4x - 6$, so $f'(1) = -2$. Also, $f(1) = -3$. By Theorem 2.9, an equation for the line through $(1,-3)$ with slope -2 is $y + 3 = -2(x - 1)$ or $2x + y + 1 = 0$.

b) $f(x) = 3 - 2x$, $x = -2$. Ans. $2x + y - 3 = 0$.

c) $f(x) = x^3 - 3x^2 + 1$, $x = 2$.

d) $g(x) = x^4 + 3x^2 - 6$, $x = 0$.

e) $f(y) = \sqrt{y}$, $y = 9$. Ans. $x - 6y + 9 = 0$.

f) $g(t) = t(1 + |t|)$, $t = 0$.

g) $h(t) = t^{15} - t^7 + 1$, $t = 1$.

h) $\varphi(z) = 2z^2 - \dfrac{2}{z^2}$, $z = -1$.

i) $g(y) = \dfrac{y}{1 + y}$, $y = 5$. Ans. $x - 36y + 25 = 0$.

j) $h(w) = \dfrac{\sqrt{w}}{1 + \sqrt{w}}$, $w = 4$.

k) $\varphi(x) = (1 - x^2)(1 + x + x^3)$, $x = -2$. Ans. $75x + y + 123 = 0$.

l) $f(z) = (1 - z^3)^2$, $z = \frac{1}{2}$.

m) $g(z) = (z^{1/2} + z^{1/4})(z^{3/4} + z^{5/4})$, $z = 1$.

n) $g(t) = \left(t - \dfrac{1}{t^2}\right)\left(t^2 + \dfrac{2}{t}\right)$, $t = -4$.

o) $h(t) = \dfrac{t^2}{1 + t^3}$, $t = 5$.

p) $h(y) = \dfrac{y^2 + 1}{y^2 - 4}$, $y = -1$.

q) $\varphi(y) = \dfrac{1 + \sqrt{y}}{y - \sqrt{y}}$, $y = 16$.

2. Find the equations of the normals in Problem 1.

3. For each of the following functions, find where the tangent line is horizontal.

a) $f(x) = x^3 - 3x^2 + 1$.   Ans. $(0,1)$ and $(2,-3)$.

b) $g(x) = x^4 - 8x^2 + 5$.

c) $h(t) = t^{4/3}$.

d) $f(y) = \dfrac{y}{4 - y}$.

e) $g(y) = \dfrac{y^2}{4 - y}$.   Ans. $(0,0)$ and $(8,-16)$.

f) $h(z) = \dfrac{1 - \sqrt{z}}{1 + \sqrt{z}}$.

4. Find all the points on the graph of $f(x) = x^3 + 2x^2 + 3x + 4$ where the slope of the tangent line is 2.

5. Find all points on the graph of $f(x) = x^3 - 3x^2 + 1$ where the tangent is parallel to the line $9x - y + 5 = 0$.

6. Find all points on the graph of $f(x) = \dfrac{x^2}{1+x}$ where the tangent is perpendicular to the line $x - 8y + 2 = 0$.

7. Show that the slope of the graph of $f(x) = ax^3 + bx + c$ is never 0 if $ab > 0$.

8. The tangent line to the graph of $f(x) = x^3 - 3x^2 + 3x$ at the point (2,2) meets the graph at another point. Find this point.

9. The graph of $f(x) = x^2 + ax + b$ is tangent to the line $y = 2$ at the point (4,2). Find a and b.

10. For which values of a, b, and c is it true that the graphs of $f(x) = x^2 + ax + b$ and $g(x) = x^2 + cx$ have the same tangent line at the point (2,2)?

11. Over which points of the x-axis are the tangents to the graphs of $f(x) = x^3 + 8$ and $g(x) = 3x^2 - 3x + 9$ parallel?

12. The graphs of $f(x) = x^3 + x$ and $g(x) = x^2$ meet at the origin. What is the angle between the tangents to the graphs of these functions at this point? (*Hint:* Use Definition 4.4 and Theorem 2.8.)   Ans.   45°.

Remark: The angle between the tangents to two curves at a point of intersection of the curves is often called the *angle of intersection* of the curves.

13. Find the points of intersection of the following pairs of curves and, at each such point, find the tangent of the angle of intersection.

a) $f(x) = x^3 + 3x + 1$, $g(x) = 3x$.   Ans. $(-1,-3)$; $\frac{3}{19}$.
b) $h(x) = x^2$, $\varphi(x) = \sqrt{x}$.

c) $f(t) = 4 - t^2$, $h(t) = 2 - \dfrac{t^2}{2}$.

d) $g(z) = \dfrac{z^2}{4} - 1$, $h(y) = 4 - \dfrac{y^2}{16}$.

14. Find the equations of the tangent lines to the graph of $f(x) = x^2$ which pass through the point $(0, -4)$.

Hint: It is necessary to find the points of tangency. If (a,b) is such a point, we have one equation connecting a and b from the fact that the point is on the curve. Another equation connecting these two unknowns comes from the fact that the slope of the tangent line is $f'(a)$ and is also $(b + 4)/a$. Ans. $4x - y - 4 = 0$ and $4x + y + 4 = 0$.

15. Find the equations of the tangent lines to the graph of $f(x) = x^2$ which pass through the point $(1, -3)$.

16. Find the equation of the normal line to the graph of $f(x) = x^2$ which passes through the point $(3,0)$.

17. Show that the two lines which pass through the point $(\frac{3}{2},0)$ and are tangent to the graph of the function $g(x) = \dfrac{x^2 + 4}{4}$ are perpendicular.

18. Find the slopes of the three lines which pass through the point $(4,8)$ and are normal to the graph of the function $h(x) = \dfrac{x^2 - 4x}{8}$.

6. FUNCTION OF A FUNCTION

If we are given two functions, f and g, for each of which we can find the derivative, then the theorems of Section 3 give us the derivatives of $\{f + g\}$, $\{f - g\}$, $\{f \cdot g\}$ and $\{f/g\}$. But these theorems give us no direct information about $\{f(g)\}$.

Theorem 4.10: *If the range of values of g is contained in the domain of definition of f, if g is differentiable at a, and if f is differentiable at $g(a)$, then $\{f(g)\}$ is differentiable at a, and*

$$\{f(g)\}'(a) = f'(g(a)) \cdot g'(a).$$

Proof: The natural way to prove this would be to write

$$\frac{f(g(x)) - f(g(a))}{x - a} = \frac{f(g(x)) - f(g(a))}{g(x) - g(a)} \cdot \frac{g(x) - g(a)}{x - a}.$$

Now the first factor on the right should have $f'(g(a))$ as a limit and the second $g'(a)$. The trouble with this argument is that $g(x) - g(a)$ might very well be zero for values of x in every interval around a (consider the function $f(x) = x \sin \left(\dfrac{180}{x}\right)^\circ$ near 0), and then the first term on the right is not defined at these values of x. Hence a more complicated proof is needed.

Let $b = f(a)$, and let ψ be the function defined by

$$\psi(x) = \begin{cases} \dfrac{f(x) - f(b)}{x - b} - f'(b), & x \neq b \\ 0 & , x = b. \end{cases}$$

Since f is differentiable at b, $\lim_{x \to b} \psi(x) = 0$. Therefore, since g is continuous at a, and since $b = g(a)$, we have $\lim_{x \to a} \psi(g(x)) = 0$ by Theorem 3.13.

Now, from the definition of ψ, we have

$$\frac{f(g(x)) - f(g(a))}{x - a} = f'(g(a)) \frac{g(x) - g(a)}{x - a} + \psi(g(x)) \frac{g(x) - g(a)}{x - a}.$$

Since

$$\lim_{x \to a} \frac{g(x) - g(a)}{x - a} = g'(a),$$

and

$$\lim_{x \to a} \psi(g(x)) = 0,$$

we have, by Theorem 3.3,

$$\lim_{x \to a} \frac{f(g(x)) - f(g(a))}{x - a} = f'(g(a)) \cdot g'(a).$$

PROBLEMS

1. Find the derivative of each of the following functions:

a) $h(x) = (2 - 3x^2)^3$. *Solution:* If we let $f(x) = x^3$ and $g(x) = 2 - 3x^2$, then $h = \{f(g)\}$. Now $f'(x) = 3x^2$, so $f'(g(x)) = 3(2 - 3x^2)^2$. Also, $g'(x) = -6x$. Therefore, by Theorem 4.10,

$$h'(x) = f'(g(x)) \cdot g'(x) = -18x(2 - 3x^2)^2.$$

b) $h(x) = (3x^2 - 2x + 1)^5$. Ans. $h'(x) = 5(6x - 2)(3x^2 - 2x + 1)^4$.
c) $\varphi(x) = (x^3 + x^2 + x + 1)^{17}$.
d) $\varphi(y) = (y^{10} - y^{20})^{30}$.

e) $h(t) = t^{3/2} + \left(\dfrac{1}{t^{3/2}}\right)^3$.

f) $h(x) = (1 - x - x^4)^{-3}$. Ans. $h'(x) = 3(1 + 4x^3)(1 - x - x^4)^{-4}$.

g) $h(y) = \sqrt{y^2 + 1}$. Ans. $h'(y) = \dfrac{y}{\sqrt{y^2 + 1}}$.

h) $f(x) = \left(\dfrac{x}{1 + x}\right)^{3/2}$.

i) $f(t) = \left(\dfrac{t + 1}{t - 1}\right)^{1/3}$.

j) $f(x) = (x^2 + 1)^3(x^3 - 1)^2$.

k) $\varphi(t) = \sqrt{t^3 - 1} \cdot \sqrt[3]{t^2 + 1}$.

l) $g(z) = \dfrac{\sqrt{1 - z^{10}}}{(10 + z^2)^5}$.

m) $f(t) = \dfrac{\sqrt{t + \dfrac{1}{t}}\left(t^2 + \dfrac{1}{t^2}\right)^3}{\sqrt[3]{t^3 - 3(t^5 + 5t^4)^6}}$.

n) $\varphi(x) = \sqrt{1 + \sqrt{1 - x}}$.

Hint: $\varphi = \{f\{g(h)\}\}$, where $f(x) = \sqrt{x}$, $g(x) = 1 + \sqrt{x}$, and $h(x) = 1 - x$. Ans. $\varphi'(x) = \dfrac{-1}{4\sqrt{1 + \sqrt{1 - x}}\,\sqrt{1 - x}}$.

o) $f(y) = (1 + (2 + x^2)^3)^4$.

p) $g(t) = (x + \sqrt{1 - x^2})^{2/3}$.

q) $h(s) = \left(\sqrt{4 + s^2} + \dfrac{1}{\sqrt{1 - s^3}}\right)^{1/4}$.

2. Find the second derivative of each of the following functions:

a) $h(x) = \sqrt{4 - x}$.   Ans. $h''(x) = \dfrac{-1}{4(4 - x)^{3/2}}$.

b) $h(y) = \sqrt{4 - y^2}$.   Ans. $h''(y) = \dfrac{-1}{(4 - y^2)^{1/2}} + \dfrac{-y^2}{(4 - y^2)^{3/2}}$.

c) $\varphi(t) = (4 - t^2)^{-1/2}$.

d) $\varphi(z) = (z - z^2)^{-2}$.

e) $f(z) = \left(\dfrac{1}{1 + z}\right)^4$.

3. Find an equation for the tangent line to the graph of each of the following functions at the indicated points.

a) $h(x) = \sqrt{8 + x^2}$, $x = 1$.   Ans. $x - 3y + 8 = 0$.

b) $h(x) = \dfrac{1}{\sqrt{8 + x^2}}$, $x = -1$.   c) $g(y) = \dfrac{1}{\sqrt[3]{y^2 + 7}}$, $y = 1$.

d) $\varphi(t) = \left(\dfrac{t^3 + 3}{4 - t}\right)^4$, $t = 0$.   e) $f(x) = \dfrac{\sqrt{10 - x^2}}{(x^2 + 2)^3}$, $x = 1$.

4. In many of the problems above, the functions in question could be written as $\{f(g)\}$ where f has the special form $f(x) = x^n$, n some number. For this special case, Theorem 4.10 can be written as

Theorem 4.11: *If g is a function and n a number, then*

$$D(g^n) = ng^{n-1}Dg.$$

Prove this theorem.

5. As we shall see in Chapter 10, if $f(x) = \sin x$, then $f'(x) = \cos x$. Accepting this, find the derivative of each of the following functions.

a) $\varphi(x) = \sin(x^2 + 1)$.   Ans. $\varphi'(x) = 2x \cos(x^2 + 1)$.

b) $f(t) = (\sin t)^2$.   Ans. $f'(t) = 2 \sin t \cos t$.

c) $h(y) = \sin \sqrt{y}$.   d) $\varphi(z) = \sqrt{\sin z}$.

e) $f(x) = x^2 \sin x^2$.   f) $g(x) = \dfrac{\sin\left(\dfrac{1}{x}\right)}{x}$.

g) $f(s) = \dfrac{\sin \sqrt{1 + s}}{\sin(1 - s^2)}$.

6. In each of the following cases, find a function f such that

a) $f'(x) = 3(x + 1)^2$.   Ans. $f(x) = (x + 1)^3$.

b) $f'(x) = 6(2x - 1)^2$.   c) $f'(x) = \sqrt{x + 1}$.

d) $f'(x) = \dfrac{1}{2\sqrt{x + 1}}$.   e) $f'(x) = \dfrac{1}{\sqrt{2x + 1}}$.

f) $f'(x) = \dfrac{x}{\sqrt{x^2 + 1}}$.

7. Find formulas for D^2h and D^3h if $h = \{f(g)\}$.
8. Find a formula for $D^2\varphi$ if $\varphi = \{f\{g(h)\}\}$.
9. Let (a,b), with $b \neq 0$, be a point on the circle whose equation is $x^2 + y^2 = r^2$. Find an equation for the tangent line to the circle at this point, first by using Definition 4.2 and then by using the definition from plane geometry. (See the third paragraph of Section 1 of this chapter.) Observe that the two definitions lead to the same result.
10. Let g be a function such that $g' = g$.

a) Find f' if $f(x) = 1/g(x^{-1})$.
b) Find a function f such that $f'(x) = 2g(x^2)x$.

7. IMPLICIT FUNCTIONS

Whenever we are given a function relating two quantities (cf. Sections 2 and 4 of Chapter 3), the derivative of this function can often give us useful information. It often happens, however, that instead of being given the function relating two particular quantities, we are merely given an equation connecting them.

It is convenient to use the symbol $F(x,y)$ for an expression * involving two quantities, x and y, such as $y + 2x - 4$ or $x^5 + x^2y^3 + 7y^9$, or $x^2y^2/(1 - x^{10} - y)$. Then $F(x,y) = 0$ stands for an equation in x and y. A function g is called a solution of an equation $F(x,y) = 0$ if, for any number x, the equation $F(x,g(x)) = 0$, obtained by replacing y by $g(x)$, is satisfied identically. We say that the function g is defined implicitly by the equation $F(x,y) = 0$.

Sometimes we can find an explicit expression for the function g. For example, if

$$F(x,y) = 2x^2y + 4y - 7x - 1,$$

then we can solve for y the equation

1) $$2x^2y + 4y - 7x - 1 = 0,$$

---

* We can think of F as a function whose domain of definition consists not of real numbers, but of *pairs* of real numbers. See the footnote in Section 2 of Chapter 3.

and we obtain

2) $$y = (7x + 1)/(2x^2 + 4).$$

Then the function g, defined by

3) $$g(x) = (7x + 1)/(2x^2 + 4)$$

is a solution of the equation 1), as we can see by direct substitution of 3) in 1), and so g is implicitly defined by the equation 1).

We should notice that an equation may define more than one function. Thus, solving $x^2 + y^2 - 1 = 0$, we get $y = \pm\sqrt{1 - x^2}$. We have then two functions, g and h, $g(x) = \sqrt{1 - x^2}$, $h(x) = -\sqrt{1 - x^2}$, both implicitly defined by the equation.

Sometimes, however, we may have no simple way of solving the given equation. Such is the case, for example, for

$$F(x,y) = x^5 - xy + y^5 = 0.$$

There are general theorems, which we cannot state here, which tell us when such an expression does define implicitly a function, even though we may not be able to find a simple expression for the function. These theorems also tell us when the solution is differentiable.

Suppose now that we are given an equation in x and y which implicitly defines a certain differentiable function. We ask how we can find the derivative of this function. One method is to solve the equation if possible and obtain an explicit expression for the function. Then we can apply to this expression the methods already developed in this chapter.

Another method is to differentiate each term of the original equation, and to remember that y, in this equation, stands for the value of the implicitly defined function g. The resulting equation can then be solved for y', the value of the derivative of this function. This method may give us y' even when the defining equation cannot be solved by elementary methods. The result will in general involve both x and y.

For example, if we consider again the equation

1) $$2x^2y + 4y - 7x = 1,$$

differentiating each term gives

4) $$(4xy + 2x^2y') + 4y' - 7 = 0. \quad \text{(Why?)}$$

Solving for y',

5) $$y' = g'(x) = (7 - 4xy)/(2x^2 + 4).$$

This expression for y' involves both x and y. But if we substitute in equation 5) the expression for y in equation 3), we see that this is the same as the expression for the derivative obtained in the usual manner from equation 3).

This method, which is called implicit differentiation, can also be applied even when we cannot find an explicit expression for a function implicitly defined by an equation. For example, the equation

$$x^5 - xy + y^5 = 0$$

does define a function g. If we differentiate implicitly, we have

$$5x^4 - y - xy' + 5y^4y' = 0.$$

Hence

$$y' = g'(x) = (y - 5x^4)/(5y^4 - x).$$

PROBLEMS

1. Find y' if

 a) $x^2 + y^2 - 1 = 0$. Ans. $y' = -\dfrac{x}{y}$.

 b) $4x^2 + 9y^2 - 36 = 0$.

 c) $\sqrt{x} + \sqrt{y} = 5$.

 d) $x^{2/3} + y^{2/3} = 1$.

 e) $x^3 + x^2y^2 + y^3 = 1$. Ans. $y' = -\dfrac{3x^2 + 2xy^2}{2x^2y + 3y^2}$.

 f) $x + 2\sqrt{xy} + \dfrac{x}{y} = x + y$.

 g) $\sqrt{1 + xy} = \left(1 + \dfrac{x}{y}\right)^3$.

 h) $\sqrt{x^2y^2 - 1} + x^3y^3 \left(\dfrac{1 + x}{y}\right)^2 = 0$.

2. Find the equations of the tangent lines at the indicated points to the graphs of the functions defined by the equations

 a) $x^2 + xy + 2y^2 = 28$, $(2,3)$. Ans. $x + 2y - 8 = 0$.

 b) $x^3 + 3xy^2 + y^3 = 1$, $(2,-1)$.

 c) $\sqrt{4x} - \sqrt{9y} + 5 = 0$, $(4,9)$. Ans. $x - y + 5 = 0$.

 d) $x\sqrt{xy} + 2y^2 - 3 = 0$, $(1,1)$.

 e) $\sqrt{3 + x^2y^2} - \dfrac{2x^2}{y^2} = 0$, $(1,1)$.

 f) $y^2 = 4px$, $(p,-2p)$.

 g) $\dfrac{\sqrt[3]{1 + xy^2}}{\sqrt[4]{1 + x^2y}} = \sqrt[12]{2}$, $(1,1)$.

3. Find the slope at the point $(3,5)$ of the graph of the function defined by the equation

$$\frac{27(y^2 - x^2)^{3/2}}{x^3} + 34\left(\frac{y}{x} + \frac{x}{y}\right)^{-1} = 79.$$

8. VELOCITIES AND RATES

The discussion in Section 9 of Chapter 3 leads us to the following definition:

Definition 4.5: *If a particle moves on a line, its position at any time t being given by the value $s(t)$ of a function s, then its **velocity** at any time a is $s'(a)$.*

The velocity of a particle may be either positive or negative. If it is negative, then the particle is moving in the negative direction on the line. (Why?)

Definition 4.6: *The **speed** of a particle moving on a line is the absolute value of its velocity.*

We were led to this definition of velocity by a consideration of average velocities, or, in other words, average rates of change of distance with respect to time. Now, there is no reason why we have to restrict ourselves to the case where the numbers in the domain of definition are measures of time rather than of some other quantity, such as distance, for example. There are many cases where two quantities can be related by a function, in the sense that the measure of one quantity is the value of the function for the corresponding measure of the other quantity. In such cases, we can call the ratio of the change in the value of the function over an interval $[a,b]$ to the length of $[a,b]$ the average rate of change of the first quantity with respect to the second. Then it is reasonable to make the following definition.

Definition 4.7: *If f is a function, and if we denote $f(x)$ by y, then the **rate of change** of y with respect to x at the number a is the number $f'(a)$.*

In particular, then, velocity is rate of change of distance with respect to time. In physics, acceleration is defined as rate of change of velocity with respect to time. Hence, if we have a particle moving on a line and if we denote its acceleration at any time t by $a(t)$, we have $a(t) = v'(t)$. Since $v(t) = s'(t)$, we also have $a(t) = s''(t)$.

PROBLEMS

1. A particle moves on a line, its position at any time t being $s(t) = t^3 - 6t^2 + 9t - 4$. Find where the velocity is zero, where it is positive and where it is negative.

   Solution: $v(t) = s'(t) = 3t^2 - 12t + 9 = 3(t - 3)(t - 1)$. Hence $v(t) = 0$ when $t = 3$ or $t = 1$, $v(t) < 0$ when $1 < t < 3$, and $v(t) > 0$ when $0 \leq t < 1$ and $3 < t$.

   The motion of the particle for $0 \leq t \leq 4$ can be represented graphically by the following figure.

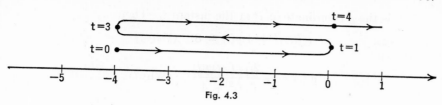

Fig. 4.3

2. For each of the following laws of motion, investigate the velocity as in Problem 1 and represent the motion graphically for the time range indicated.

a) $s(t) = t^2 + 4t + 3$, $-4 \le t \le 4$.
b) $s(t) = t^3 - 2t^2 - 4t + 4$, $-3 \le t \le 3$.
c) $s(t) = 64t - 16t^2$, $0 \le t \le 4$.
d) $s(t) = t - 4/\sqrt{t+1}$, $0 \le t \le 8$.

3. In each case of Problem 2, find when the acceleration is 0.
4. In each case in Problem 2, find the average velocity and average speed for the intervals $t = 0$ to $t = 1$, $t = 1$ to $t = 2$, and $t = 0$ to $t = 2$.
5. A cube is expanding in such a way that its edge is changing at a rate of 5 in./sec. When its edge is 4 in. long, find the rate of change of its volume.

Solution: We must consider two functions, one, say f, whose value $f(t)$ at any instant t is the volume of the cube at that instant, and another, say g, whose value $g(t)$ is the length of the edge of the cube at the instant t. We are given that $g'(t) = 5$ and we are asked for the value of f' when $g(t) = 4$. But

$$f(t) = (g(t))^3. \quad \text{(Why?)}$$

so

$$f'(t) = 3(g(t))^2 g'(t). \quad \text{(Why?)}$$

Now when $g(t) = 4$, $f'(t) = 3 \cdot 4^2 \cdot 5 = 240$.

6. A metal sphere is heated so that its radius increases at the rate of 1 mm. per sec. How fast is its volume changing when its radius is 3 cm.?
7. The area of an equilateral triangle is changing at the rate of 1 sq. in. per sec. How fast is its side changing when its area is $100\sqrt{3}$?

Ans. $\dfrac{\sqrt{3}}{30}$.

8. A point P moves along the graph of $(x^2 + 4)y = 8$ so that its abscissa is changing at a rate of 3 units per second. At what rate is the ordinate changing when $x = 2$?

Solution: Let f be the function whose value at any instant t is the x-coordinate of P at that instant, and let g be the function whose value

$g(t)$ is the y-coordinate of P at the instant t. Then

$$((f(t))^2 + 4)g(t) = 8. \quad (\text{Why?})$$

Hence

$$g'(t) = \frac{-2f(t)f'(t)g(t)}{(f(t))^2 + 4}. \quad (\text{Why?})$$

When $f(t) = 2$, then $g(t) = 1$ and $g'(t) = \dfrac{-3}{2}$.

9. In Problem 8, at what rate is the slope of the curve at P changing when $x = 2$?, when $x = 0$?

10. In Problem 8 consider the line PQ, where $Q = (0,4)$.

   a) At what rate is the distance between P and Q changing when $x = 2$?
   b) At what rate is the slope of the line PQ changing when $x = 2$?

11. Work Problem 10b if the ordinate, instead of the abscissa, is changing at a rate of -4 units per second.

12. A winch located at the end of a dock 6 ft. above the water hauls in a rope at the rate of 2 ft. per sec. How fast is a boat attached to the end of the rope approaching the dock when there are 10 ft. of the rope out?

13. Find the rate of change of the area of a circle with respect to

   a) its radius;
   b) its diameter;
   c) its circumference.

14. The radius r and altitude h of a right circular cylinder are changing respectively at the rates of 2 and 3 in./sec.

   a) At what rate is the volume changing when $r = 4$ and $h = 2$?
   b) At what rate is the total surface area changing when $r = 4$ and $h = 2$?

15. A particle moves on a line with a constant acceleration of α units per second.

   a) If it has a velocity of v_0 units per second at time $t = 0$, find the velocity at any time.
   b) If it is at the origin when $t = 0$, find its position at any time.

9. OTHER NOTATIONS FOR THE DERIVATIVE

For the derivative of a function f we have used the two symbols f' and Df interchangeably. The first of these is quite similar to the notation used by Newton, one of the two inventors of calculus, who would have written $\dot{f}$ instead of f'.

Another and still very commonly used notation was introduced by Leibnitz, the other inventor of calculus.

In order to explain Leibnitz's notation, let us return to the definition of the derivative:

$$f'(a) = \lim_{x \to a} \frac{f(x) - f(a)}{x - a}.$$

Let us denote the distance from the point a to the point x by the symbol h:

$$h = x - a.$$

Then

$$x = a + h,$$

and we can write

$$f'(a) = \lim_{h \to 0} \frac{f(a + h) - f(a)}{h},$$

or

$$f'(x) = \lim_{h \to 0} \frac{f(x + h) - f(x)}{h}.$$

Next we replace h by another much used symbol, Δx. This quantity is usually called the change in x. Then the corresponding change in the value of the function is denoted by Δf:

$$\Delta f = f(x + \Delta x) - f(x).$$

Using these symbols, we have

$$f'(x) = \lim_{\Delta x \to 0} \frac{\Delta f}{\Delta x}.$$

Finally, in order to remind ourselves that the value of the derivative at x is the limit of the quotient $\frac{\Delta f}{\Delta x}$, we use a symbol for the derivative, $\frac{df}{dx}$, which is similar to the symbol for this quotient:

$$f'(x) = \frac{df}{dx} = \lim_{\Delta x \to 0} \frac{\Delta f}{\Delta x}.$$

This is the symbolism introduced by Leibnitz, (although he arrived at it by a different method) and it is still in common use. For the benefit of those readers who may meet this symbol in other places, we shall use it from time to time in order to make it more familiar.

In a later chapter we shall use the symbols df and dx separately, but for the present we must think of the symbol $\frac{d}{dx}$ as a single symbol meaning the same thing as D or $'$. Accordingly, we denote the second derivative by the symbol

$$\frac{d^2f}{dx^2},$$

since the second derivative is the derivative of the first derivative:

$$\frac{d}{dx}\left(\frac{df}{dx}\right) = \frac{d^2f}{dx^2}.$$

REVIEW PROBLEMS

1. If $f(x) = x + c\sqrt{1 + x^2}$, where c is a number, show that

$$f'(x) = \frac{(xf(x) + 1)}{x^2 + 1}.$$

2. If $f(x) = (c + x)/(1 - cx)$, where c is a number, show that

$$f'(x) = \frac{1 + (f(x))^2}{1 + x^2}.$$

3. Find a formula for $D^2\{f \cdot g\}$.
4. Find y'' if $\sqrt{x} + \sqrt{y} = 1$.
5. Find where the normal at $(0,0)$ to the graph of $y = x^2 + x$ meets the tangent at $(1,2)$.   Ans. $(\frac{1}{4}, -\frac{1}{4})$.
6. For which values of the number c is the curve $y = x^2 + c$ tangent to $y = x$?
7. Does the tangent to $y = x^3 - 6x^2 + 8x$ at $(3, -3)$ meet the curve again? If so, where?
8. A tangent line to the graph of $xy = 1$, together with the axes, forms a triangle. Show that the area of the triangle is independent of the point of tangency.
9. A tangent line to the graph of $x^{2/3} + y^{2/3} = 1$ meets the x-axis at A and the y-axis at B. Show that the distance AB is independent of the point of tangency.
10. A point moves on the x-axis, its position at any time t being $s(t) = \sqrt{at + b}$, where a and b are numbers. Show that its acceleration is negative and inversely proportional to the cube of x.
11. A point moves on the graph of $y = x^2 + 6x - 3$. At which point do its x- and y-coordinates change at the same rate?
12. A light is on the ground 50 ft. from a high wall. A man 5 ft. tall starts at the light and walks directly toward the wall at the rate of 6 ft. per sec. How fast is the top of his shadow moving down the wall when he is halfway there?   Ans. $\frac{12}{5}$ ft. per sec.

13. A light is 10 ft. up. From a point equally high but 20 ft. away, a ball is dropped. How fast is the shadow of the ball moving along the ground at the end of $\frac{1}{4}$ sec.?

14. A particle starts at the origin and travels up the line $y = ax$ at a rate of p feet per second. A second particle starts from the origin w seconds later and travels up the line $y = bx$ at a rate of q feet per second. At what rate is the distance between the particles changing at the end of n seconds?

15. A triangular trough is 12 ft. long, 6 ft. wide at the top and 3 ft. deep. If water is poured in at the rate of 24 cu. ft. per minute, how fast is the water level rising when it is (a) 1 ft.? (b) 2 ft.?

16. Water is being withdrawn from a conical reservoir 8 ft. in diameter and 10 ft. deep at the constant rate of 5 cu. ft. per min. How fast is the water level falling when the depth of water is 5 ft. if (a) the vertex of the cone is up?   (b) the vertex of the cone is down?

   Hint: The volume of a cone of radius r and altitude h is $\dfrac{\pi r^2 h}{3}$.   Ans. (a) $\dfrac{5}{4\pi}$ ft. per min.

17. A swiming pool is 30 ft. long and 20 ft. wide. It is 4 ft. deep at one end and 8 ft. deep at the other. The pool is being filled at the rate of 100 cu. ft. per min. How fast is the water level rising when the greatest depth is (a) 1 ft.? (b) 3 ft.? (c) 4 ft.? (d) 5 ft.? (e) 6 ft.?

Extreme Values of Functions

---

1. INTRODUCTION

In all aspects of our everyday lives we are constantly faced with the problem of finding superlatives. We want to find the most efficient way of doing things; we want to get the most for our money; we want to expend the least amount of energy necessary to carry out a project; we want the biggest, the best, or, sometimes, the smallest, the least.

In many of these problems calculus can offer us some help. For many of these problems reduce to that of finding the highest or lowest points on the graph of a function. We shall see in this chapter how, using calculus, we can develop methods for locating these highest and lowest points. In fact, it will be convenient to do more, namely to find the relative maxima and relative minima of a function.

Definition 5.1: *A function f has an **absolute maximum value** at a number x_1 if $f(x_1) \geq f(x)$ for any number x in the domain of definition of f.*

Definition 5.2: *A function f has a **relative maximum value** at a number x_1 if there is an open interval (a,b) containing x_1 such that $f(x_1) \geq f(x)$ for any number x in the interval (a,b) and also in the domain of definition of f.*

Exercise: Write corresponding definitions of an absolute minimum value and a relative minimum value of a function.

Definition 5.3: *The **extreme values** of a function are the relative maximum values and the relative minimum values of the function.*

In order to find the extreme values of a given function, using nothing more than these definitions, it would be necessary to examine in turn each number in its domain of definition, comparing the value of the function at the number in question with the value at all other nearby points.

In some special cases it is possible to do this. Consider, for example, the function f defined by the equation

$$f(x) = \frac{1}{x^2 + 1}.$$

We assert that this function has an extreme value, namely an absolute maximum, when $x = 0$. It is easy to see that this is so, for when $x \neq 0$, then $x^2 + 1 > 0 + 1 = 1$, and so

$$f(x) = \frac{1}{x^2 + 1} < \frac{1}{1} = f(0).$$

However, in most cases it is not so easy to find where the extreme values are. (For example, can the reader see by inspection that

$$f(x) = x^3 + 2x^2 + x + 7$$

has an extreme value when $x = -\frac{1}{3}$?) Therefore we need a better scheme for locating these extreme values.

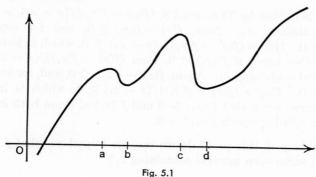

Fig. 5.1

Let us look at a graph of a function to see if it can suggest anything. At a and c in Figure 5.1, the function has relative maxima, and at b and d it has relative minima. We note that at these points the tangent lines to the graph seem to be horizontal, which would mean that the value of the derivative of the function would be zero at each of these points. Furthermore, if we return to the first function considered above, $f(x) = \dfrac{1}{x^2 + 1}$, we note that $f'(x) = \dfrac{-2x}{(x^2 + 1)^2}$, which has the value 0 when $x = 0$.

It would seem plausible then that the extreme values of a function are at just those points where the value of the derivative is zero. Unfortunately, things are not this simple. In the first place, we can perfectly well have an extreme value where the derivative does not even exist. Thus, if $f(x) = |x|$, $f(0)$ is a relative minimum value, but f' is not defined at 0. Also, the derivative may be different from zero at a point yielding an extreme value when this point is not inside any interval belonging to the domain of definition of the function. Thus, if $f(x) = x$, $0 \leq x \leq 1$, $f(0)$ is a relative minimum, and $f(1)$ is a relative maximum, but $f'(0) = f'(1) = 1$.

However, all is not lost, for we can show that these are the only exceptions to our original conjecture.

Theorem 5.1: *If f is a function, if $f(x_1)$ is an extreme value of f, if f is defined throughout some open interval containing x_1, and if f' is defined at x_1, then $f'(x_1) = 0$.*

Proof: Consider first the case where $f(x_1)$ is a relative maximum. Then there is an interval (a,b) containing x_1 such that $f(x)$ is defined for each x in (a,b) and such that $f(x_1) \geq f(x)$ for each such x. Now

$$\lim_{x \to x_1} \frac{f(x) - f(x_1)}{x - x_1} = f'(x_1).$$

If $f'(x_1) > 0$, then by Theorem 3.8, $(f(x) - f(x_1))/(x - x_1) > 0$ in some interval containing x_1. Now, $f(x) - f(x_1) \leq 0$, and for any $x > x_1$, $(x - x_1) > 0$. Hence $(f(x) - f(x_1))/(x - x_1) \leq 0$, which is impossible.

On the other hand, if $f'(x_1) < 0$, then $(f(x) - f(x_1))/(x - x_1) < 0$ in some interval containing x_1. Again, $f(x) - f(x_1) \leq 0$, and, for any $x < x_1$, $(x - x_1) < 0$. Hence $(f(x) - f(x_1))/(x - x_1) \geq 0$, which is impossible. Thus we have shown that $f'(x_1) > 0$ and $f'(x_1) < 0$ are both impossible. The only remaining case is $f'(x_1) = 0$.

Exercise: Where in this proof do we use the hypothesis that f is defined throughout some open interval containing x_1?

In view of this theorem, when we search for the extreme values of a function, we can restrict our attention to those points in the domain of definition of f of the following types:

Definition 5.4: *A **critical point** of a function f is a point c in the domain of definition of f such that either*

1) $f'(c) = 0$, *or*
2) f' *is not defined at c, or*
3) *c is not inside an open interval contained in the domain of definition of f. (Such points are called end points of the domain.)*

For, by Theorem 5.1, a function can have an extreme value only at points of these three types. Furthermore, as we shall see below in our problems, it is usually fairly easy to find these critical points.

Now, however, we run into another difficulty. Consider the function f defined by the equation $f(x) = x^3$. For this function $f'(0) = 0$, so 0 is a critical point of this function. But it is easy to see that $f(0)$ is not an extreme value of the function. (Why?) Thus we see that while each extreme value occurs at a critical point, the converse is not true in general. Hence, to find extreme values, we must first find the critical points and then test them one by one to find which ones yield extreme values.

In order to find such a test let us look back at Figure 5.1. We note that at a relative maximum the slope of the tangent line, and hence the value of the derivative, is positive to the left and negative to the right. At a relative minimum the reverse is true. For the example $f(x) = x^3$, for which 0 is a critical point but $f(0)$ is not an extreme value, the derivative is positive on each side. For the similar function $f(x) = -x^3$, it is negative on each side.

Fortunately for us, the test which these examples suggest is always valid.

Theorem 5.2: *If f is a continuous function, c a point inside an interval belonging to the domain of definition of f such that $f'(c) = 0$, and if there is an interval (a,b) containing c such that $f'(x) > 0$ for $a < x < c$ and $f'(x) < 0$ for $c < x < b$, then $f(c)$ is a relative maximum value for f. If $f'(x) < 0$ for $a < x < c$ and $f'(x) > 0$ for $c < x < b$, then $f(c)$ is a relative minimum value for f. If $f'(x) > 0$ for $a < x < c$ and $c < x < b$, or $f'(x) < 0$ for $a < x < c$ and $c < x < b$, then $f(c)$ is neither a relative maximum value nor a relative minimum value for f.*

The proof of this theorem is postponed to Section 2 of this chapter, but its use is illustrated in the problems below.

Note that this theorem gives us a test which can be applied to critical points of only the first kind. Methods for testing the other kinds of critical points are suggested in problems of Section 2.

PROBLEMS

1. Find the extreme values of the function $f(x) = x^3 - x^2 - 8x + 6$.

Solution: The domain of definition of this function consists of all numbers, so there are no critical points of type 3. Also,

$$f'(x) = 3x^2 - 2x - 8,$$

which is defined everywhere, so there are no critical points of type 2. Solving

$$f'(x) = 3x^2 - 2x - 8 = 0,$$

we obtain $x = -\frac{4}{3}$ and $x = 2$. These then are the only critical points. In order to test these, we first factor $f'(x)$, obtaining

$$f'(x) = (x - 2)(3x + 4).$$

It is easy to see that $f'(x)$ is positive if x is in $(-\infty, -\frac{4}{3})$ or $(2,\infty)$, and is negative if x is in $(-\frac{4}{3},2)$. (Cf. Problem 2, Section 2, Chapter 2.) By Theorem 5.2, then, $f(-\frac{4}{3})$ is a relative maximum and $f(2)$ is a relative minimum.

2. Find the extreme values of the functions:

   a) $f(x) = x^2 - 4x + 1$. Ans. $f(2) = 1$ is a relative minimum.
   b) $f(x) = (x - 1)^2(x + 2)$. Ans. $f(1) = 0$ is a relative minimum;
   $f(-1) = 4$ is a relative maximum.
   c) $f(x) = (x - 1)^3$. Ans. No extreme values.
   d) $f(x) = (x - 1)^3(x + 1)^2$.
   e) $f(x) = 1 - 7x + 3x^2$.
   f) $f(x) = 1 - 7x - 3x^2$.
   g) $f(t) = 2t^3 + 3t^2 - 36t$. Ans. $f(2)$ is a relative minimum, $f(-3)$ a
   relative maximum.

   h) $g(y) = 2y^3 - 3y^2 + 6y$.   i) $g(s) = s^4 - 4s^3 + 4s^2 - 4$.
   j) $\varphi(t) = t^3 - 6t^2 + 9t + 12$.   k) $\varphi(x) = x^4 - 2x^2 + 4$.
   l) $g(y) = y^4 - 4$.   m) $g(t) = t^4 - 4t + 4$.
   n) $f(z) = az^2 + bz + c$.

3. Find the extreme values of the functions:

   a) $f(x) = x^3 + \dfrac{3}{x}$. Ans. $f(1) = 4$ is a relative minimum value;

   $f(-1) = -4$ is a relative maximum value.

   b) $f(x) = x^2 + \dfrac{1}{x}$.   c) $f(x) = \dfrac{x^2 + 1}{x}$.

   d) $f(x) = \dfrac{x}{x^2 + 1}$.   e) $f(x) = \dfrac{x^2}{x + 1}$.

   f) $f(x) = \dfrac{x^2 + 2x - 23}{x - 4}$. Ans. $f(3)$ is a relative maximum, $f(5)$ a

   relative minimum.

   g) $h(x) = \dfrac{1 + x + x^2}{1 - x + x^2}$.   h) $\varphi(x) = \dfrac{1 - x + x^2}{1 + x + x^2}$.

   i) $h(y) = \dfrac{y^2 - 1}{1 + y + y^2}$.   j) $g(t) = \dfrac{1}{t} + \dfrac{1}{1 - t}$.

4. The sum of two numbers is 10. Find these numbers if their product
   is as large as possible.

   Hint: Denote these numbers by x and y. Since $x + y = 10$, $y = 10 - x$.
   Then their product is $x(10 - x)$. To finish the problem we need only find the
   maximum of the function $f(x) = x(10 - x)$. The methods used above can
   be applied.

5. The sum of two numbers is 10. Find these numbers if the sum of their
   squares is as small as possible. Ans. $x = y = 5$.

6. Find the positive number such that the sum of the number and its reciprocal is as small as possible.

7. Show that the sum of the square of any number and the square of its reciprocal is always greater than or equal to 2.

8. Of all rectangles with a given perimeter, find the one with the largest area.

> *Hint:* Denote the perimeter of the rectangle by P and lengths of the sides by x and y. Then $P = 2x + 2y$, so $y = (P - 2x)/2$. The area of the rectangle is $xy = x(P - 2x)/2$. Hence, to finish the problem we need to find the maximum of the function $f(x) = x(P - 2x)/2$. Ans. The square of side $P/4$.

9. The equal sides of an isosceles triangle are 10 in. long. What is the length of the base of the largest such triangle?

10. In Chapter 3, Section 5, Problem 5, find the dimensions of the largest box. Ans. $x = 5 - \dfrac{5\sqrt{3}}{3}$ in.

11. In Chapter 3, Section 5, Problem 7, find the dimensions of the cheapest box.

12. In Chapter 3, Section 5, Problem 9, find the area of the largest window.

13. In Chapter 3, Section 5, Problem 13, is there a largest or smallest triangle?

14. Chapter 3, Section 5, Problem 21, is there a best location for the new store?

15. An isosceles triangle has a base 10 units long and altitude 20. Rectangles are inscribed, with one side on the base of the triangle. What are the dimensions of the largest such rectangle?

> *Hint:* Let the length of the base of such a rectangle be $2x$ and its altitude y. Comparing the similar triangles FBD and ECD, we have $\frac{20}{5} = y/(5 - x)$. Hence $y = 4(5 - x)$. The area of the rectangle is then $8x(5 - x)$. We need to find then the maximum of the function $f(x) = 8x(5 - x)$.

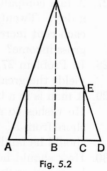

Fig. 5.2

16. Rectangles are inscribed in a circle of radius R. Find the dimensions of the rectangle whose perimeter has an extreme value. Is this extreme a relative maximum or minimum? Ans. The square with side $R\sqrt{2}$ has a maximum area.

17. Find the dimension of the largest right circular cylinder which can be cut from a solid sphere of radius R.

18. Find the dimensions of the largest right circular cylinder which can be cut from a solid right circular cone of height H and radius of base R.

19. A cylindrical tank, without a top, is to have a volume of A cubic feet. Show that for a minimum amount of metal, the radius of the base should equal the altitude.

20. Find the shortest segment which has its ends on the axes and is tangent to the graph of the equation $xy = 1$.

21. A tank has the form of a cylinder with hemispherical ends. If the volume is to be A cubic feet, what are its dimensions for a minimum amount of material? Ans. Radius of end is $(3A/4\pi)^{\frac{1}{3}}$.

22. A piece of wire 1 ft. long is cut into two pieces. One is bent into a square and the other into a circle. Where should cuts be made if the sum of the areas of the square and circle is to be an extreme? Which of these extremes are relative maxima and which relative minima?

23. What point on the curve $4y = x^2$ is nearest to the point $(0,4)$?

Hint: If (a,b) is any point, its distance from $(0,4)$ is

$$(a^2 + (b - 4)^2)^{\frac{1}{2}}.$$

If (a,b) is on the curve, $4b = a^2$. Hence the distance from $(0,4)$ is

$$(4b + (b - 4)^2)^{\frac{1}{2}}.$$

Thus we need to find the minimum of the function $f(x) = (4x + (x - 4)^2)^{\frac{1}{2}}$.

24. On the circle whose equation is $x^2 + y^2 = 25$, find the point nearest to the point $(6,8)$.

25. A rectangular poster is to contain 24 sq. in. of printed matter and is to have a margin at top and bottom of 2 in. and at the sides of 1 in. What are the dimensions of the poster using the least amount of paper? Ans. $2\sqrt{3}$ by $4\sqrt{3}$ in.

26. The demand for a certain article varies inversely as the cube of the selling price. If the articles cost 20 cents apiece to manufacture, find the selling price which yields a maximum profit.

27. A taxi company charges 15 cents a mile, and logs 600 passenger miles a day. Twenty-five fewer passenger miles a day would be logged for each cent increase in the rate per mile. What rate yields the greatest gross income?

28. In Problem 27, if the operating costs are 10 cents per mile, what rate yields the greatest net income?

29. A man is in a boat 1 mi. from the nearest point, A, of a straight shore. He wishes to arrive as soon as possible at a point B 3 mi. along the shore from A. He can row 2 mi. per hr. and walk 4 mi. per hr. Where should he land? Ans. $\sqrt{3}/3$ mi. from A.

30. How should he proceed in the above problem if he can row 5 mi. an hour and walk 4 mi. an hour?

31. A rectangular corral is to be built, using one side of a barn, B feet long, and L feet of fencing. What are the dimensions of the largest possible corral?

Hint: There are two cases: $L \leq B$ and $L > B$. In the second case, note that the side of the barn may form only part of a side of the corral. Also, in the second case there are three subcases: $B < L \leq 2B$, $2B < L \leq 3B$, and $3B < L$.

2. BASIC THEOREMS

In order to prove Theorem 5.2 we need to prove a number of other theorems. These theorems, however, will prove useful also in many other places in this and following courses in mathematics.

We remember that our aim in this chapter is to find relative maximum and minimum values of functions. A natural question to ask then is whether a given function has any maximum or minimum value at all. The example of the function f defined by the equation $f(x) = 1/x$, $0 < x$ shows that the answer is in the negative. In this case, if we restrict ourselves to a closed interval, the function does have a maximum and a minimum. But the function defined by the equations

$$f(x) = \begin{cases} \frac{1}{2}, x = 0 \\ x, 0 < x < 1 \\ \frac{1}{2}, x = 1 \end{cases}$$

has no maximum and no minimum. However, if we require the function to be continuous and if we restrict ourselves to a closed interval, then there is a maximum and a minimum.

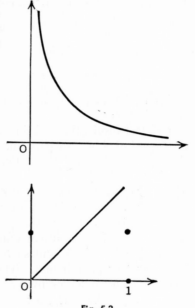

Theorem 5.3: *If the function f is continuous at each point of the closed interval $[a,b]$, then it has an absolute maximum value in this interval and also an absolute minimum value.*

Fig. 5.3

Proof: The proof consists of two parts. In the first part we show that any function, say φ, which is continuous over $[a,b]$ is bounded in the interval $[a,b]$. This means, according to Definition 3.6, that there is a number M such that $|\varphi(x)| \leq M$ for each x in $[a,b]$.

To prove this, let C be the collection of those numbers c in $[a,b]$ for which it is true that φ is bounded on the interval $[a,c]$. (A number c belongs to C if there is some number M_c, which may depend on c, such that $|\varphi(x)| \leq M_c$ for x in $[a,c]$.) Our problem is to show that b is in C. Now C contains at least the number a. Furthermore, since C is contained in the interval $[a,b]$, the number b is an upper bound for C. Therefore C has a least upper bound, which we denote by c^*.

We are going to show first that c^* is in C and then that $c^* = b$. Since φ is continuous, we can associate with the positive number $e = 1$ a number $d > 0$ such that, when $|x - c^*| < d$ and x is in $[a,b]$, then $|\varphi(x) - \varphi(c^*)|$

< 1. By Theorem 1.18 $\left| |\varphi(x)| - |\varphi(c^*)| \right| \leq |\varphi(x) - \varphi(c^*)|$, which gives $|\varphi(x)| < |\varphi(c^*)| + 1$ for each x in $[a,b]$ for which $|x - c^*| < d$.

Now, since c^* is the *least* upper bound of C, no number to the left of c^* is an upper bound of C, and in particular $c^* - d$ is not. Therefore, there is a number t in C such that $c^* - d < t \leq c^*$.

Next, consider any number w in $[a,b]$ such that $c^* \leq w < c^* + d$. If x is in the interval $[t,w]$, then $|x - c^*| < d$ (Why?) and so

$$|\varphi(x)| < |\varphi(c^*)| + 1.$$

But, since t is in C, there is a constant M_t such that, for any x in $[a,t]$,

$$|\varphi(x)| \leq M_t.$$

But then, for any x in $[a,w]$,

$$|\varphi(x)| < M_t + |\varphi(c^*)| + 1.$$

This shows that φ is bounded in the interval $[a,w]$, and hence that w is in the collection C.

This last result, that w is in C, holds for any number w in $[a,b]$ such that $c^* \leq w < c^* + d$. In particular it holds for $w = c^*$, so c^* is in C. Furthermore, we have $c^* = b$. For if not, then $c^* < b$ and we can choose a number w in $[a,b]$ such that $c^* < w < c^* + d$. Then w is in C and $c^* < w$, which contradicts the fact that c^* is an upper bound of C. Hence we have shown that $b = c^*$ is in C, so φ is bounded in $[a,b]$.

Now we turn to the second part of the proof. We write this part out only for the case of the absolute maximum value. By what we have just proved, f is bounded on $[a,b]$, and so the collection of all numbers $f(x)$, for x in $[a,b]$, has an upper bound. Therefore, this collection has a least upper bound, which we denote by N. Thus $f(x) \leq N$ for any x in $[a,b]$. We are going to show that there is a number $\bar{c}$ in $[a,b]$ such that

$$f(\bar{c}) = N.$$

Suppose there is no such number. Then $N - f(x) > 0$ for each x in $[a,b]$. Consequently the function g, defined by

$$g(x) = \frac{1}{N - f(x)}$$

is defined for each x in $[a,b]$ and, since f is continuous, g is also continuous at each point of this interval. (Why?) But then we can apply the result proved above to the function g, and there is a number M such that $|g(x)| \leq M$ for each x in $[a,b]$. Note that $M > 0$. (Why?) But

$$|g(x)| = \left| \frac{1}{N - f(x)} \right| = \frac{1}{N - f(x)} \leq M,$$

and so

$$f(x) \leq N - \frac{1}{M}$$

for each x in $[a,b]$. But this is impossible, since $N - 1/M < N$, while N is the *least* upper bound of the numbers $f(x)$. Hence our supposition was incorrect, and there is a number $\bar{c}$ such that $f(\bar{c}) = N$. Finally, since N is an upper bound of the collection of numbers $f(x)$, for x in $[a,b]$, we have

$$f(\bar{c}) = N \geq f(x)$$

for any x in $[a,b]$, which means that $f(\bar{c})$ is an absolute maximum value for f in the interval.

Theorem 5.3 will now be used to prove another theorem which will bring us one step closer to our goal of proving Theorem 5.2.

Theorem 5.4: (*Rolle's Theorem.*) *If a function f has a derivative at each number in a closed interval $[a,b]$, and if $f(a) = f(b) = 0$, then there is a number c inside (a,b), i.e., $a < c < b$, such that $f'(c) = 0$.*

Proof: There are three cases to consider.
Case 1. $f(x) = 0$ for each x in $[a,b]$. In this case, by Theorem 4.2, $f'(x) = 0$ for each x, and hence for at least one x between a and b.
Case 2. $f(x) > 0$ for some x in $[a,b]$. Since f has a derivative at each point of $[a,b]$, it is continuous there. By Theorem 5.3, there is a number $\bar{c}$ in $[a,b]$ such that $f(\bar{c}) \geq f(x)$ for any x in $[a,b]$. Since $f(x) > 0$ for at least one x, and since $f(a) = f(b) = 0$, $\bar{c} \neq a$ and $\bar{c} \neq b$. Now, by Definition 5.3, $\bar{c}$ is an extreme point of f, and $a < \bar{c} < b$. Since f has a derivative at $\bar{c}$, Theorem 5.1 tells us that $f'(\bar{c}) = 0$.
Case 3. $f(x) < 0$ for some x in $[a,b]$. The proof for this case is similar to that for Case 2, with the minimum value of f over $[a,b]$ replacing the maximum value.

Exercise: Write out in detail the proof for Case 3.

The next theorem is the most useful and hence most important one of this section.

Theorem 5.5: (*Mean Value Theorem.*) *If f has a derivative at each number in the closed interval $[a,b]$, then there is a number c, with $a < c < b$, such that*

$$f(b) = f(a) + (b - a) \cdot f'(c).$$

Proof: Consider the function

$$g(x) - f(x) - f(a) - \frac{f(b) - f(a)}{b - a} \cdot (x - a).$$

We first note that $g(a) = 0$, and $g(b) = 0$. Furthermore, f is differentiable throughout $[a,b]$ and the other components of $g(x)$ are also differentiable so

$g(x)$ is differentiable throughout $[a,b]$. (Why?) Therefore we can apply Rolle's Theorem to $g(x)$. There is therefore a number c, with $a < c < b$, such that

$$g'(c) = 0.$$

But

$$g'(x) = f'(x) - \frac{f(b) - f(a)}{b - a}.$$

Now

$$g'(c) = f'(c) - \frac{f(b) - f(a)}{b - a} = 0.$$

Hence

$$f'(c) = \frac{f(b) - f(a)}{b - a}, \text{ or}$$

$$f(b) = f(a) + (b - a) \cdot f'(c).$$

Remark: This proof is not as artificial as it seems at first glance, and in particular an inspection of the graph of f suggests very naturally the function g defined above. See Problem 1 below.

Exercise: Show that the equation in the Mean Value Theorem can be written in the form

$$f(a + h) = f(a) + hf'(a + \theta h), 0 < \theta < 1.$$

As a first illustration of the use of this Mean Value Theorem, we prove Theorem 5.2.

Proof of Theorem 5.2: Suppose x is any point in the interval (a,c). Then f' is defined at each point in the interval $[x,c]$. Hence, by the Mean Value Theorem,

$$f(c) = f(x) + (c - x) \cdot f'(x_1), x < x_1 < c.$$

But $(c - x) > 0$ and $f'(x_1) > 0$, so $f(c) > f(x)$. If x is in the interval (c,b), then, by the same reasoning,

$$f(x) = f(c) + (x - c) \cdot f'(x_1), c < x_1 < x.$$

Now $(x - c) > 0$ and $f'(x_1) < 0$, so again $f(c) > f(x)$. But this means that $f(c)$ is a relative maximum.

The proof for the case of a relative minimum is similar, and so is the proof of the last part of Theorem 5.2.

PROBLEMS

1. Show that the function g defined in the proof of Theorem 5.5 has the following property: for each number x in $[a,b]$, $g(x)$ is the vertical distance over x from the straight line containing the points $(a,f(a))$ and $(b,f(b))$ to the graph of f.

2. The conclusion of Rolle's Theorem can be rephrased geometrically as asserting the existence of a tangent line to the graph of f which is horizontal. By considering the line joining the endpoints of the graph, give a geometric interpretation of the conclusion of the Mean Value Theorem.

3. Write out the proof of the part of Theorem 5.2 for the case where $f'(x) > 0$ for $a < x < c$ and $c < x < b$.

4. Prove the following theorem:

   Theorem: *If a function f has a derivative at each point of an open interval (a,b), and if f is continuous at a and at b, and if $f(a) = f(b) = 0$, then there is a point c, with $a < c < b$, such that $f'(c) = 0$.*

   Hint: Compare the hypotheses of this theorem with those of Rolle's Theorem and then observe where each of the hypotheses of Rolle's Theorem is used in its proof.

5. Prove the following theorem:

   Theorem: *If the function f has a derivative at each point of an open interval (a,b), and if f is continuous at a and at b, then there is a point c, with $a < c < b$, such that*

$$f(b) = f(a) + (b - a)f'(c).$$

6. Prove the following theorem:

   Theorem: *If f is a continuous function, c a point inside an interval belonging to the domain of definition of f such that $f'(c)$ does not exist, and if there is an interval (a,b) containing c such that $f'(x) > 0$ for $a < x < c$ and $f'(x) < 0$ for $c < x < b$, then $f(c)$ is a relative maximum value for f.*

7. State and prove a theorem concerning a relative minimum value similar to the theorem in Problem 6.

8. Find the critical points and extreme values of the following functions:

   a) $f(x) = x^{1/3}$.   Ans.   0 is a critical point, but $f(0)$ is not an extreme value.

   b) $f(x) = x^{2/3}$.   Ans.   0 is a critical point, and $f(0)$ is a relative minimum.

   c) $f(x) = (x - 1)^{1/5}$.

   d) $f(x) = |x|$.

   e) $f(x) = x(x + 1)^{2/3}$.   Ans.   Critical points at -1 and $-\frac{3}{5}$, $f(-1)$ a relative maximum, $f(-\frac{3}{5})$ a relative minimum.

   f) $f(x) = x(x + 1)^{1/3}$.   g) $f(x) = x^{1/3}(x + 1)^{2/3}$.

   h) $f(x) = x^{2/3}(x + 1)^{1/3}$.   i) $f(x) = x^{2/3}(x + 1)^{2/3}$.

   j) $f(x) = x^2(x + 1)^{2/3}$.

9. Let f be a function whose domain of definition is the closed interval $[a,b]$ and which is differentiable at each point of this interval. Show that if $f'(a) > 0$, then $f(a)$ is a relative minimum value for f.

10. Let f be a function whose domain of definition is the closed interval $[a,b]$, which is continuous at a and b, which is differentiable in the interval (a,b), and for which $f'(a) = 0$ or does not exist. Show that if there is a point c such that $f'(x) > 0$ for $a < x < c$, then $f(a)$ is a relative minimum value for f.

11. State and prove results similar to those in Problems 9 and 10 for relative maxima instead of minima and also for b instead of a.

12. Find the critical points and extreme values for the functions:

a) $f(x) = \sqrt{x}$.   Ans.   0 is a critical point, $f(0)$ is a relative minimum.

b) $f(x) = x^{3/2}$.

c) $f(x) = \sqrt{1 + x}$.

d) $f(x) = \sqrt{1 - x}$.

e) $f(x) = \sqrt{1 - x^2}$.

f) $f(x) = (1 - x^2)^{3/2}$.

g) $f(x) = (x^2 - 1)^{3/2}$.

3. SECOND DERIVATIVE TEST

In applying the test given by Theorem 5.2, we often run into the practical difficulty that we need to know how f' behaves at each point of an interval. If the expression for f' cannot be factored, this test usually becomes impractical. The theorem below will take care of some of these cases.

Theorem 5.6: *If f is defined throughout an interval (a,b), if f' is also defined throughout (a,b), if for some point c, with $a < c < b$, $f'(c) = 0$, and if $f''(c) < 0$, then $f(c)$ is a relative maximum value for f, and if $f''(c) > 0$, then $f(c)$ is a relative minimum value for f.*

Proof: Since

$$f''(c) = \lim_{x \to c} \frac{f'(x) - f'(c)}{x - c} < 0,$$

by Theorem 3.8b, we must have

$$\frac{f'(x) - f'(c)}{x - c} < 0$$

for x in some interval $(\bar{a}, \bar{b})$ containing c, and we may assume that $a < \bar{a} < c < \bar{b} < b$. Now $f'(c) = 0$, so

$$\frac{f'(x)}{x - c} < 0, \quad \bar{a} < x < \bar{b}, \quad x \neq c.$$

Now, if $\bar{a} < x < c$, then $(x - c) < 0$, so $f'(x) > 0$. If $c < x < \bar{x}$, then $(x - c) > 0$, so $f'(x) < 0$. Hence, by Theorem 5.2, $f(c)$ is a relative maximum value for f.

The proof for the case $f''(c) > 0$ is similar.

The examples of the functions $f(x) = x^3$ and $f(x) = x^4$ show that if $f'(c) = 0$ and $f''(c) = 0$, we can draw no conclusion. For f' and f'' are zero when $x = 0$ for both these functions, but the first has neither a relative maximum nor a relative minimum while the other does have a relative minimum at $x = 0$.

PROBLEMS

1. Using Theorem 5.6 to test the critical points, find the extreme values of the functions:

a) $f(x) = 8x^3 - 9x^2 + 1$.

b) $f(x) = 8x^3 - 75x^2 + 150x$.

c) $f(x) = x^4 - 6x^2 + 8x + 2$.

d) $f(x) = x^2 - \dfrac{2}{x}$.   Ans. $f(-1)$ is a relative minimum.

e) $f(x) = x^2 + \dfrac{1}{x^2}$.

f) $f(x) = x\sqrt{1 - x^2}$.

g) $f(x) = x\sqrt{x - x^2}$.

2. Given a function f which has a derivative at each point of an interval $[a,b]$, we have, by the Mean Value Theorem,

$$f(b) - f(a) = (b - a) \cdot f'(c),$$

where c is some point between a and b. Let us denote the quantity $f(b) - f(a)$ by Δf. (See Section 9 of Chapter 4.) Then

$$\Delta f = (b - a) \cdot f'(c).$$

There are some problems where we wish to know this quantity Δf, which is the amount the value of the function has changed in going from a to b. Since we know nothing about the number c, except that it is between a and b, the above formula is not very useful for calculating Δf. But if we are satisfied with an approximate answer, we can find a formula which is usually easy to use. Let us define the symbol df by the equation

$$df = (b - a) \cdot f'(a).$$

In the rest of this problem we will show how good an approximation df is to Δf.

a) Let the number R be defined by the equation $R = \Delta f - df$. Show that $R = (b - a)(f'(c) - f'(a))$, and $f(b) = f(a) + (b - a) \cdot f'(a) + R$.

b) Show that, if f'' is defined at each point of the interval $[a,b]$, there is a number d in this interval such that

$$R = (b - a)(c - a) \cdot f''(d).$$

Hint: Use the Mean Value Theorem for the function f' on the interval $[a,c]$.

c) Show that if M is a number such that $|f''(x)| \leq M$ for each x in $[a,b]$, then

$$|R| \leq M|b - a|^2.$$

d) Show that the above results still hold if $b < a$.

The inequality in c) tells us that if we take df to be an approximation to Δf, the maximum error we make is no more than $M|b - a|^2$. Note that the closer b is to a, the smaller this error term is.

3. In each of the following cases calculate the quantities $\Delta f = f(b) - f(a)$ and df, verify that $|f''(x)| \leq M$ for each point in the indicated interval, and compare $|\Delta f - df|$ with $M|b - a|^2$.

a) $f(x) = x^2$, $a = 2$, $b = 2.1$, $M = 2$.   Ans. $\Delta f = 0.41$, $df = 0.4$,
$|\Delta f - df| = 0.01 \leq 2 \cdot \frac{1}{100} = 0.02$.

b) $f(x) = x^2$, $a = 3$, $b = 3.1$, $M = 2$.

c) $f(x) = x^2$, $a = 2$, $b = 2.2$, $M = 2$.

d) $f(x) = x^2$, $a = 2$, $b = 1.9$, $M = 2$.   Ans. $\Delta f = -0.39$, $df = -0.4$,
$|\Delta f - df| = 0.01 \leq 0.02$.

e) $f(x) = x^2$, $a = -3$, $b = -2.8$, $M = 2$.

f) $f(x) = x^2$, $a = 2$, $b = 4$, $M = 2$.

g) $f(x) = x^3$, $a = 1$, $b = 1.01$, $M = 7$.   Ans. $\Delta f = 0.030301$, $df = 0.03$, $|\Delta f - df| = .000301 \leq 0.0042$.

h) $f(x) = x^3 + x^2 + x$, $a = 0$, $b = 0.1$, $M = 3$.

i) $f(x) = \dfrac{1}{x}$, $a = 3$, $b = 3.5$, $M = \frac{1}{3}$.

j) $f(x) = \dfrac{1}{x^2}$, $a = 10$, $b = 11$, $M = \frac{1}{100}$.

4. Find an approximate value for $\sqrt{101}$, and estimate how much this approximation differs from the correct value.

Solution: Let f be defined by the equation $f(x) = \sqrt{x}$. Let $a = 100$ and $b = 101$. Then $\sqrt{101} = f(b) = f(a) + (f(b) - f(a)) = f(a) + \Delta f$. Now $f(a)$ is easy to calculate: $f(a) = \sqrt{100} = 10$. Also, we can take df as an approximation to Δf, so $10 + df$ is an approximation to $\sqrt{101}$.

But $df = (b - a) \cdot f'(a) = 1 \cdot \dfrac{1}{2\sqrt{100}} = \dfrac{1}{20}$. Hence $\sqrt{101}$ is approximately 10.05.

Since $f''(x) = -1/4x^{3/2}$, $|f''(x)| \leq \frac{1}{4000}$ for x between 100 and 101. Hence our approximation differs from the correct value by no more than $M|b - a|^2 = \frac{1}{4000} = .00025$.

5. Find approximate values for each of the following numbers, and estimate how much they differ from the correct values:

   a) $\sqrt{99}$.   b) $\sqrt{65}$.

   c) $\sqrt[3]{1010}$.   d) $\frac{1}{11}$.   Ans.   0.09, .002.

REVIEW PROBLEMS

1. A function f, defined only on the interval $[a,b]$, has for its graph this
   figure:

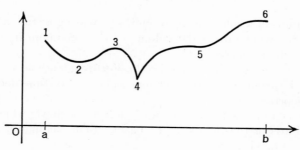

Fig. 5.4

a) Which of the six points is

    i) an absolute maximum?

    ii) an absolute minimum?

    iii) a relative maximum?

    iv) a relative minimum?

b) What can you say about the value of f' and f'' at each of these six
   points?

2. For which values of a and b will the function h have a horizontal tangent at $(1,5)$ if

$$h(t) = at^2 + b/t^3?$$

Does h have a relative maximum or minimum at $(1,5)$? What are the
critical points of h?   Ans. $a = 3, b = 2$. $f(1)$ is a relative minimum.

3. A function g is such that g'' is continuous on the interval $[a,b]$. The
   equation $g(x) = 0$ has three different solutions in the open interval
   (a,b). Show that the equation $g''(x) = 0$ has at least one solution
   in (a,b).

   Hint: Use Rolle's Theorem.

4. Show that $x^2 + x + 1$ is positive for all values of x.

5. Find the greatest and least values of the fraction whose denominator
   is 49 greater than the square of its numerator.   Ans. $-\frac{7}{98}$ least, $\frac{7}{98}$
   greatest.

6. What number exceeds its kth power by the greatest amount, k being a positive integer?

7. Find the maximum area of an isosceles triangle whose perimeter is 6 in.

8. In a triangle ABC the angle A is fixed while the side BC passes through a given point D lying within the angle A. Show that the area of the triangle is a minimum when D is the midpoint of BC.

9. Through the point (a,b) a line is drawn such that the part intercepted between the axes is a minimum. Prove that its length is

$$(a^{\frac{2}{3}} + b^{\frac{2}{3}})^{\frac{3}{2}}.$$

10. If the radius of a sphere is 12 in. and is increasing at the rate of $\frac{1}{12}$ in. per sec., at what rate is the volume of the maximum inscribed right circular cylinder increasing?

11. Water flows out of a hemispherical basin through a hole at the bottom so that the volume of the water remaining at any time decreases at a rate proportional to the square root of the depth of the water remaining. Prove that the level of the water falls most slowly when the depth is two-thirds of the radius of the basin. (The volume of a spherical segment of one base is

$$\frac{\pi}{3}(3Rh^2 - h^3),$$

where R is the radius of the sphere and h is the height of the segment.)

12. The segment of the graph of $y^2 = 2px$ bounded by the line $x = p/2$ is rotated about the x-axis forming a solid of revolution. Find the dimensions of the cylinder of maximum volume which can be inscribed in the solid.

13. A wall 27 ft. high is 8 ft. from a building. Find the length of the shortest ladder which will reach the building if one end rests on the ground outside of the wall.

14. A girder 27 ft. long is moved on rollers along a passageway and into a corridor 8 ft. wide at right angles to the passageway. Neglecting the horizontal width of the girder, find how wide the passageway must be in order that the girder may go around the corner.   Ans. $5\sqrt{5}$ ft.

15. Cylindrical cans, with top and bottom, are to be made. The top and bottom pieces are cut from square pieces of metal and the scraps left over from these squares are wasted. There is no other waste. Find the ratio of height to diameter of the least expensive can.

16. What is the largest parcel post package, rectangular with square ends, which will be accepted at the post office. (See Problem 7 in the review problems at the end of Chapter 3.)

17. Find the area of the largest rectangle with lower base on the x-axis and the upper vertices on the curve $y = 1 - x^2$.

18. A line segment has one end on the line whose equation is $y = -1$. It passes through the origin and is terminated at the point where it

meets the curve $y = x^2$ a second time. Find the slope of the shortest segment which can be drawn. Ans. $\pm 1/\sqrt{2}$.

19. Find the point on the graph of $y = \sqrt{x}$ which is nearest to

a) $(1,0)$.
b) $(\frac{1}{4},0)$.
c) $(-1,0)$.

20. At a point P in the first quadrant on the curve $y = 7 - x^2$ a tangent is drawn, meeting the coordinate axes at A and B. Find the position of P which makes AB a minimum.

21. Show that for fixed a, the function

$$y = (a - (1/a) - x) \cdot (4 - 3x^2)$$

has just one maximum and one minimum, and that the difference between them is

$$\left(\frac{4}{9}\right)\left(a + \frac{1}{a}\right)^3.$$

If a is allowed to vary, find the least value of this difference.

22. If f is a function which has a second derivative at each point of an interval $[a,b]$, show that there is a number d inside this interval such that

$$f(b) = f(a) + f'(a)(b - a) + \frac{f''(d)}{2}(b - a)^2.$$

Hint: Consider the function φ defined by

$$\varphi(x) = f(x) - f(a) - f'(a)(x - a) - k(x - a)^2,$$

where the number k is so chosen that $\varphi(b) = 0$.

23. If f and g are functions which are differentiable in an interval $[a,b]$, and if $g'(x) \neq 0$ for any x in $[a,b]$, show that there is a number c, with $a < c < b$, such that

$$\frac{f(b) - f(a)}{g(b) - g(a)} = \frac{f'(c)}{g'(c)}.$$

Hint: Consider the function φ defined by

$$\varphi(x) = \frac{f(b) - f(a)}{g(b) - g(a)}(g(x) - g(a)) - (f(x) - f(a)).$$

Analytic Geometry (Continued)

1. INTRODUCTION

In Chapter 1, we defined what is meant by the graph of an equation containing two unknowns. For the particular case of an equation of the first degree, we were able to get complete information about the graph, for, as we showed, the graph must be a straight line.

As we shall see in this chapter, we can also get complete information about the graph of a second-degree equation. For other equations, however, the best that we shall do in general is to discover the approximate shape and position of the graph.

2. INTERCEPTS, SYMMETRY, AND EXCLUDED REGIONS

There is a considerable amount of information concerning the graph of an equation which can be obtained by purely algebraic procedures.

Definition 6.1: *The **intercepts** of a curve are the points where the curve meets the axes.*

In order to find these points, it often suffices to solve ordinary equations in one unknown. At a point where the curve meets the x-axis, say, the y-coordinate is 0. Hence, if we set y equal to 0 in the equation of the curve, any solution of the resulting equation is the x-coordinate of a point where the curve crosses the x-axis.

Consider, for example, the equation

$$x^2 - y - 4 = 0.$$

Setting $y = 0$, we have

$$x^2 - 4 = 0.$$

The solutions of this equation are $x = \pm 2$.
Setting $x = 0$, we have

$$-y - 4 = 0.$$

130

The solution of this equation is $y = -4$. Hence the intercepts of the graph of this equation are $(2,0)$, $(-2,0)$, and $(0,-4)$.

Definition 6.2: *Two points, P and Q, are **symmetric with respect to a line,** L, if the line segment PQ is perpendicular to L and if its midpoint is on L. They are **symmetric with respect to a point,** R, if R is the midpoint of PQ.*

Definition 6.3: *A curve is **symmetric** with respect to a line, L, if whenever P is a point on the curve, then the point Q, symmetric to P with respect to L, is also on the curve.*

Exercise: Define symmetry of a curve with respect to a point.

Let us first consider the case where the line L is the x-axis. Now if the coordinates of P are (a,b), then the coordinates of the symmetric point Q are $(a,-b)$. (Why?) Thus, if the equation of the curve is such that whenever (a,b) satisfy the equation, so do $(a,-b)$, then the curve is symmetric with respect to the x-axis. Similarly, if $(-a,b)$ satisfy the equation whenever (a,b) do, then the curve is symmetric with respect to the y-axis, and if $(-a,-b)$ satisfy the equation whenever (a,b) do, then the curve is symmetric with respect to the origin.

Consider again the equation

$$x^2 - y - 4 = 0.$$

If the point (a,b) is on the curve, i.e., if $a^2 - b - 4 = 0$, then so is the point $(-a,b)$, since $(-a)^2 = a^2$, and hence $(-a)^2 - b - 4 = 0$. Hence the graph of this equation is symmetric with respect to the y-axis. However, the point $(a,-b)$ is in general not on the curve, since $a^2 - b - 4 = 0$ does not imply $a^2 - (-b) - 4 = 0$ unless $b = 0$. Hence the curve is not symmetric with respect to the x-axis. A similar consideration shows that it is not symmetric with respect to the origin.

Take the same equation again and solve for x:

$$x = \pm\sqrt{y + 4}.$$

Since the coordinates of a point in the plane must both be real numbers, and since the square root of a negative number is not a real number, there can be no point on the graph of our equation for which $y + 4 < 0$, for then the x-coordinate of such a point would not be a real number. Hence the graph of our equation cannot contain any points lying below the line $y = -4$. (Why?) We say that the part of the plane below the line $y = -4$ is an excluded region for this curve.

Let us now put together the information we have obtained about the graph of our equation. We first plot the intercepts. Next we draw the line $y = -4$ and remember that the graph cannot go below this line. The graph must be symmetric with respect to the y-axis. Hence the graph must look something like the curve in Figure 6.1.

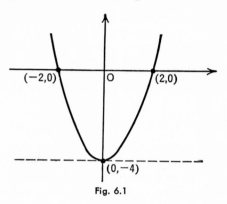

Fig. 6.1

Of course, any one of the graphs shown in Figure 6.2 also satisfies all of these conditions, but, while at first glance they all seem quite dissimilar, nevertheless a second glance shows that all five graphs have the same general shape and position.

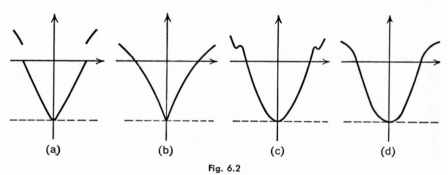

Fig. 6.2

In order to decide which of these figures is nearest to the actual graph of our equation, we shall resort to other techniques involving calculus. We discuss these in sections 4 and 5. We can, however, immediately rule out Figure 6.2a as a possible graph of our equation. The graph must be the graph of the function f, defined by $f(x) = x^2 - 4$ (Why?), and this function is continuous. Now the graph of a continuous function cannot have any jumps, such as Figure 6.2a has at -2 and at $+2$, because at a point where the graph makes a jump, the limit of the function does not exist. (Why?)

PROBLEMS

1. Discuss the intercepts, symmetry, and excluded regions for the graphs of the following equations, and sketch the graphs.

a) $x^2 + 4y^2 = 16$. Ans. Intercepts are $(\pm4,0)$ and $(0,\pm2)$. The curve is symmetric with respect to both axes and the origin. The parts of the plane for which $x > 4$, $x < -4$, $y > 2$, and $y < -2$ are excluded regions for this curve. The graph is shown in Figure 6.3.

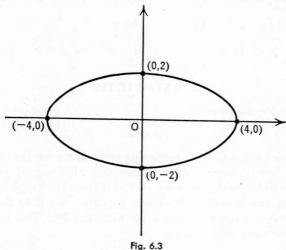

$(0,2)$

$(-4,0)$ O $(4,0)$

$(0,-2)$

Fig. 6.3

b) $4x^2 + y^2 = 4$.

c) $x^2 + 4y^2 = 1$.

d) $x^2 + 2y = 1$. Ans. Intercepts: $(\pm1,0)$, $(0,\frac{1}{2})$. Symmetry with respect to y-axis only. The part of the plane for which $y > \frac{1}{2}$ is excluded.

e) $x^2 + 1 = 2y$.   f) $y^2 + x + 1 = 0$.

g) $y^2 = 4 + 4x$.   h) $x^2 + y^3 = 1$.

i) $x^2y + 4y = 8$. Ans. Intercept: $(0,2)$. Symmetry about y-axis. Parts of the plane for which $y > 2$ and $y \le 0$ are excluded.

j) $xy = 1$.   k) $x^2y = 1$.

l) $xy = -2$.   m) $x = y - y^3$.

n) $x^2 = y - y^3$.

o) $x^2 - y^2 = 1$. Ans. Intercepts: $(\pm1,0)$. Symmetry with respect to both axes and origin. The part of the plane for which $-1 < x < 1$ is excluded.

p) $x^2 - 4y^2 = 4$.

q) $y^2 - 4x^2 = 16$.

r) $y^2 = x(x + 1)(x + 2)$. Ans. Intercepts: $(0,0)$, $(-1,0)$, $(-2,0)$. Symmetry with respect to x-axis. The parts of the plane for which $x < -2$ and $-1 < x < 0$ are excluded.

s) $y = x(x + 1)(x + 2)$.

t) $y^2 = x(x + 1)(x - 1)$.

u) $y^2 = x^2 + 3x - 4$.

2. What are the excluded regions for each of the following equations?

a) $4x^2 + 9y^2 = 36$.

b) $4x^2 - 9y^2 = 36$.

c) $4x^2 + 9y^2 = 1$.

d) $4x^2 + 9y^2 = 0$.

e) $4x^2 + 9y^2 = -1$.

f) $y = \sqrt{1 - \sqrt{1 - x}}$.

g) $y = \sqrt{2x - \sqrt{1 - 3x}}$.

h) $y = \dfrac{x - 2}{x}$.

i) $(x + 3)(y^2 - 1) = 3$.

j) $xy^2 + x^2 y = 8$.

3. ASYMPTOTES

Let us consider the equation

$$xy = 1.$$

Applying the analysis of the preceding section, we see that the graph of this equation has no intercepts, is symmetric with respect to the origin, and that only the x- and y-axes are excluded from the graph.

For this equation a new phenomenon appears. We note that when x is very close to zero, y must be very large numerically. This is more easily seen if we solve the equation for y:

$$y = \frac{1}{x}.$$

Now when x is just to the right of the origin, then $1/x$ is large and positive, and the closer x is to the origin, the larger $1/x$ is. When x is just to the left of the origin, then $1/x$ is numerically large but negative, and the closer x is to the origin, the larger $1/x$ is numerically. Hence the graph, for small values of x, must look like Figure 6.4. In this case we call the y-axis a **vertical asymptote** of our graph.

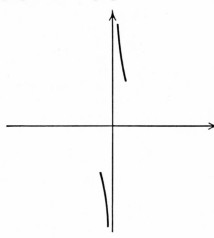

Fig. 6.4

Similarly, when y is very small numerically, x is very large. Hence the complete graph looks something like Figure 6.5. We call the x-axis a **horizontal asymptote** for this graph.

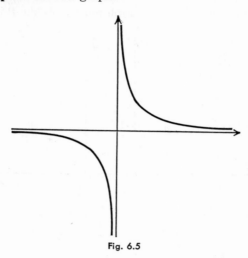

Fig. 6.5

In general, a vertical asymptote of a graph is a vertical line, $x = a$, such that as x gets close to a, y becomes numerically large without bound and the graph "goes off to infinity." A horizontal asymptote is described similarly. (How?)

One method for finding vertical asymptotes is to solve the given equation for y and find where the denominator of the resulting expression becomes zero. Thus, for the equation

$$x^2 y - y + 2 = 0,$$

we have

$$y = \frac{-2}{x^2 - 1}.$$

The denominator, $x^2 - 1$, is zero when $x = \pm 1$, and when x gets close to $+1$ or -1, the denominator becomes very small and y becomes very large. The lines $x = 1$ and $x = -1$ are vertical asymptotes.

Solving for x, we have

$$x = \pm \sqrt{\frac{y - 2}{y}}.$$

When y is close to zero, x is very large, so the line $y = 0$ is a horizontal asymptote.

To see what the graph of this equation is like, we note that the only intercept is $(0,2)$; the graph is symmetric with respect to the y-axis; and the graph does not enter the strip between the x-axis and the line

$y = 2$. If we take a value of x slightly larger than 1, we see that y is large and negative, while for x slightly to the left of 1, y is large and positive. For x very large, y is near 0 and negative.

Near these asymptotes then the graph must look like this:

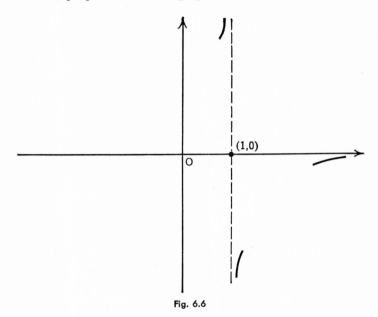

Fig. 6.6

Since there is no x-intercept, and since $f(x) = -2/(x^2 - 1)$ is continuous, the part of the graph in the fourth quadrant must look like this:

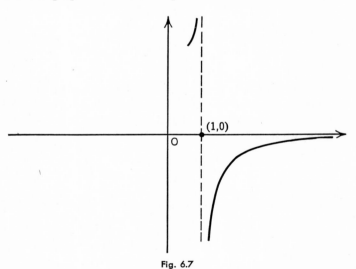

Fig. 6.7

Since (0,2) is on the graph, the part of the graph in the first quadrant must look like this:

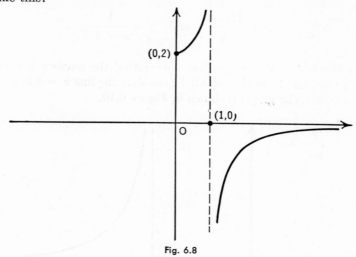

Fig. 6.8

Finally, since the graph is symmetric with respect to the y-axis, the complete graph must look like this:

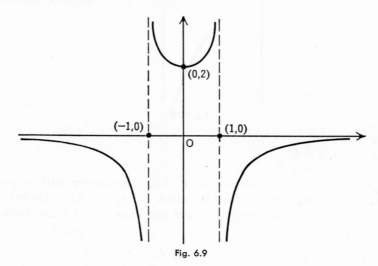

Fig. 6.9

PROBLEM

Find the intercepts, symmetry, excluded regions, and asymptotes of the graphs of the following equations, and sketch the graphs.

a) $xy - 4y = 4$. *Solution:* Using the methods of Section 2, we find the only intercept to be $(0,-1)$, no symmetry, and no excluded regions.

Next, solving first for x and then for y we have

$$x = \frac{4 + 4y}{y} \quad \text{and} \quad y = \frac{4}{x - 4}.$$

From the first of these equations we see that the x-axis is a horizontal asymptote, and from the second we see that the line $x = 4$ is a vertical asymptote.   The graph is shown in Figure 6.10.

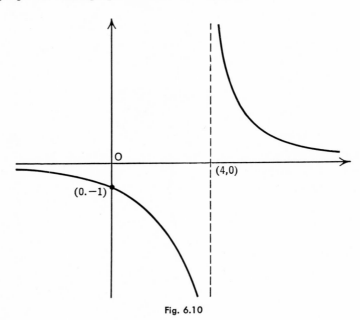

Fig. 6.10

b) $xy - 2y = 4.$
c) $xy - x + y = 2.$
d) $xy + 2x - 3y = 4.$
e) $xy^2 = x + 1.$ Ans.   Intercepts: $(-1,0)$.   Symmetry with respect to x-axis.   The part of the plane for which $-1 < x \le 0$ is excluded.   The y-axis is a vertical asymptote, and the lines $y = \pm 1$ are horizontal asymptotes.

f) $(x + 1)y^2 = x.$ g) $(x + 1)^2 y = 1.$
h) $(x + 1)^2 y = x.$ i) $(x^2 + 1)y = 1.$
j) $(x^2 + 1)y = x.$ k) $(x + 1)y^2 = 1.$
l) $(x + 1)y^2 = x.$

m) $y = \dfrac{6x - 10}{x^2 - 1}.$ Ans.   Intercepts: $(\tfrac{5}{3},0)$ and $(0,10)$.   No symmetry.   Excluded region: $1 < y < 9.$ Asymptotes: $x = 1$, $x = -1$, $y = 0.$

n) $y^2 = \dfrac{6x - 10}{x^2 - 1}.$

o) $x = \dfrac{y^2 + 1}{y + 1}.$

p) $xy = x^2 - 1.$

q) $xy = x^2 + 1.$

r) $x^2(y + 1) + 1 = 0.$

s) $xy = x^2 - x.$

4. INCREASING AND DECREASING FUNCTIONS

In order to gain more information about a graph we need now to appeal to calculus. Here we should recall (see Section 8 of Chapter 4) that an equation implicitly defines, in general, one or more functions. One thing that suggests itself immediately is to locate maximum and minimum points. Also, further useful information is gained by finding where the graph is going up and where it is going down.

Definition 6.4: *A function f is* **increasing** *in an interval* [a,b] *if whenever* $a \leq x_1 < x_2 \leq b$, *then* $f(x_1) < f(x_2)$.

Exercise: Write a similar definition for a function decreasing in an interval.

Theorem 6.1: *If f is a function such that* $f'(x)$ *exists for each x in a closed interval* [a,b], *and if* $f'(x) > 0$ *when* $a < x < b$, *then for any two numbers* $x_1 < x_2$ *in* [a,b], *we have*

$$f(x_1) < f(x_2),$$

i.e., f is increasing in [a,b].

Proof: Since $f'(x)$ exists at each point of [a,b], we can apply the Mean Value Theorem to f for the interval $[x_1,x_2]$. Then

$$f(x_2) = f(x_1) + f'(x_3)(x_2 - x_1), \; x_1 < x_3 < x_2.$$

Now $x_2 - x_1 > 0$ and $f'(x_3) > 0$ by hypothesis. Hence $f(x_2) - f(x_1) > 0$.

Exercise: State and prove a similar theorem about a function decreasing in an interval if $f'(x) < 0$ for each number x in the interval.

To see how we can use this information, let us consider again the example of Section 2:

$$x^2 - y - 4 = 0$$

or

$$y = x^2 - 4.$$

This equation defines the function f given by $f(x) = x^2 - 4$.

Since $f'(x) = 2x$, we see that the graph is always increasing when x is positive and always decreasing when x is negative. Also there is a minimum at $(0,-4)$. Hence Figure 6.2c is ruled out, for in that figure the graph is sometimes decreasing for positive values of x. Also Figure 6.2b is ruled out, for, by the above calculation, the graph has a tangent line at the point $(0,-4)$, namely the line $y = -4$.

In the next section we shall see why Figure 6.2d is also impossible.

PROBLEMS

1. Find the extreme values of the following functions. Find the intervals inside which the graph is increasing and those where the graph is decreasing for each of these functions, and use this information to make a sketch of the graph.

a) $f(x) = x - x^2$. *Solution:* Since $f'(x) = 1 - 2x$, $f'(x) > 0$ and f is increasing in the interval $(-\infty, \frac{1}{2}]$, while $f'(x) < 0$ and f is decreasing in the interval $[\frac{1}{2}, \infty)$. $f(\frac{1}{2})$ is a relative maximum value.

b) $f(x) = 4x^3 - 3x^2 - 6x + 1$. Ans. f is increasing in $(-\infty, -\frac{1}{2}]$ and in $[1, \infty)$, and is decreasing in $[-\frac{1}{2}, 1]$. $f(-\frac{1}{2})$ is a relative maximum and $f(1)$ a relative minimum.

c) $f(x) = x^3 + x^2 - x + 10$. d) $g(x) = x^3 - 2x^2 + x + 5$.

e) $h(x) = x^4 + 4x^3 + 3$. f) $\varphi(x) = x^4 + 3x^2 - 6$.

g) $\varphi(t) = t^3 + t^2 + 1$.

h) $f(y) = y^4 + 32y + 32$. Ans. f increasing in $[-2, \infty)$ and decreasing in $(-\infty, -2]$. $f(-2)$ is a relative minimum.

i) $f(x) = \dfrac{1}{x}$.

j) $f(x) = \dfrac{1}{x^2}$.

k) $f(x) = \dfrac{1}{x^3}$.

l) $f(x) = x + \dfrac{1}{x}$. Ans. f is increasing in $(-\infty, -1]$ and in $[1, \infty)$, decreasing in $[-1, 1]$. $f(-1)$ is a relative maximum, $f(1)$ a relative minimum.

m) $f(x) = \dfrac{x}{1 + x^2}$. n) $g(z) = z^2 + \dfrac{2}{z}$.

o) $\varphi(s) = \dfrac{1}{s} + \dfrac{1}{1 - s}$. p) $h(w) = \dfrac{w^2}{1 + w}$.

q) $g(t) = \dfrac{t^3}{1 + t}$.

r) $g(x) = \sqrt{1 - x^2}$. Ans. g increasing in $[-1, 0]$, decreasing in $[0, 1]$. $g(0)$ is a relative maximum, $g(-1)$ and $g(1)$ relative minima.

s) $h(x) = \sqrt{x^2 - 1}$.

t) $\varphi(z) = z\sqrt{1 - z}$.

u) $\varphi(s) = s\sqrt{1 - s^2}$.

2. For which values of b will the graph of

$$y = 2x^3 - 3x^2 + bx + 1$$

be always increasing?

3. Show that if $1 < a < b$, then $a + \dfrac{1}{a} < b + \dfrac{1}{b}$.

4. A merchant buys water pistols at 8 cents each. He finds that if he sells them at x cents each, he can sell $50(15 - x)^2$ a day. His overhead is $10 a day. At what price should he sell them to make the greatest profit?

Solution: His profit, at a selling price of x cents is $50(x(15 - x)^2 - 20 - 8(15 - x)^2)$. Since the smallest coin available in this country is a penny, his selling price must be a whole number. Therefore we want the maximum value of the function

$$f(x) = 50(x(15 - x)^2 - 20 - 8(15 - x)^2),$$

where the domain of definition consists of the integers 1, 2, $\cdots$, 14.

Now consider the function g which has the same rule as f but whose domain of definition is the collection of all numbers in the interval [1,14]. By the methods developed in the last chapter, we find that g has a maximum at $x = 10\frac{1}{3}$, which is not an integer. Now we find that g is increasing in the interval [1,10]. Therefore $g(x) < g(10) = f(10)$ for any number x, and in particular any integer, which is in [1,10). Also, g is decreasing in [11,14], so $f(11) = g(11) > g(x)$ for any integer x in (11,14]. By substitution we find $f(10) = g(10) = 1500 > 1450 = f(11) = g(11)$, so the merchant should put his selling price at 10 cents.

5. In Chapter 3, Section 5, Problem 17, find the maximum possible weekly profit. Ans. Maximum profit at a selling price of $105.

6. In the same problem, find the maximum profit if the production cost increases to $11 per set.

7. In Chapter 3, Section 5, Problem 18, find the maximum weekly profit,

    a) for production costs of $9 per set.
    b) for production costs of $11 per set.

8. In Chapter 3, Section 5, Problem 19, find the maximum weekly profit.

9. In Chapter 3, Section 5, Problem 20, what rate of excise tax will bring in the maximum revenue to the government?

5. INFLECTION POINTS

On the basis of what we have studied so far in this section, we are not yet able to decide between Figure 6.1 and Figure 6.2d as possible shapes for the graph of

$$x^2 - y - 4 = 0.$$

Notice that if we take any point on the graph in Figure 6.1, and draw the tangent to the graph at this point, then all the nearby points of the graph are above this tangent line. The same is true for Figure 6.2d for points whose x-coordinates are small, but as we move far out on the graph, we find points near which the graph is below the tangent.

Definition 6.5: *The graph of a function f is* **concave upward** *at a point $(c, f(c))$ if there is an interval (a,b) containing c such that over this interval the graph of f is above the tangent line to the graph at $(c, f(c))$.*

Exercise: Write a definition of concave downward.

To discover where the graph is concave upward and where it is concave downward, we resort to the second derivative.

Theorem 6.2: *If f is a function such that $f''(x)$ exists and is positive for each point of an interval (a,b), then the graph of f is concave upward at each point of this interval.*

Proof: Let c be any point of the interval, so that $a < c < b$. The equation of the tangent line at $(c, f(c))$ is

$$y = f(c) = f'(c)(x - c).$$

Hence, if d is any point between a and b, the vertical distance at d to the tangent line is

$$f(c) + f'(c)(d - c).$$

The vertical distance to the graph of f is $f(d)$. By the Mean Value Theorem, this distance is

$$f(d) = f(c) + f'(e)(d - c), \quad d < e < c \quad \text{or} \quad c < e < d.$$

Hence the vertical distance from the tangent line to the graph of f is

$$(f(c) + f'(e)(d - c)) - (f(c) + f'(c)(d - c)) = (f'(e) - f'(c))(d - c).$$

By Theorem 6.1, applied to the function f', f' is increasing through the interval (a,b). Hence if $c < d$, $f'(e) > f'(c)$ and $(d - c) > 0$, so $(f'(e) - f'(c)) \cdot (d - c) > 0$. If $d < c$, then $f'(e) < f'(c)$ and $(d - c) < 0$, so again $(f'(e) - f'(c))(d - c) > 0$. Thus in each case the vertical distance from the tangent line to the graph of f is positive, i.e., the graph is above the tangent and the graph is concave upward at c.

Exercise: State and prove a similar theorem for the case $f''(x)$ negative.

Applying this theorem to our example of $y = x^2 - 4$, we see that the graph is concave upward at every point, since $y'' = 2 > 0$. Hence Figure 6.2d must be ruled out.

In actual practice in sketching graphs, it is usually sufficient to find those points which separate the concave upward parts of the graph from the concave downward parts.

Definition 6.6: *A point $(c, f(c))$ on the graph of a function f is an* **inflection point** *of the graph if there is an interval (a,b) containing c such that at each point in (a,c) the graph is concave upward and at each point in (c,b) it is concave downward, or vice versa.*

In view of Theorem 6.2, a point $(c, f(c))$ for which $f''(c) = 0$ is an inflection point if f'' is positive on one side of c and negative on the other.

PROBLEMS

1. Find the extreme values, the intervals where the graph is increasing, the intervals where it is decreasing, and the inflection points of the following, and sketch their graphs:

a) $f(x) = 3x^3 + 5x^2 + x + 1$.   *Solution:* We have $f'(x) = 9x^2 + 10x + 1$ and $f''(x) = 18x + 10$. $f'(x) > 0$ and f is increasing if x is in $(-\infty, -1]$ or $\left[\frac{-1}{9}, \infty\right)$, and f is decreasing in $\left[-1, \frac{-1}{9}\right]$. $f(-1)$ is a relative maximum and $f\left(\frac{-1}{9}\right)$ a relative minimum.   There is an inflection point at $\left(\frac{-5}{9}, f\left(\frac{-5}{9}\right)\right)$.

b) $f(x) = x^2 - x^3$.   Ans. f is increasing in $[0, \frac{2}{3}]$, otherwise decreasing. $f(0)$ is a relative minimum, $f(\frac{2}{3})$ a relative maximum, and $(\frac{1}{3}, f(\frac{1}{3}))$ an inflection point.

c) $g(x) = x^5 - 20x^2$.

d) $h(t) = t^3 - 12t + 2$.

e) $\varphi(w) = 2w^3 - 3w^2 + 6$.

f) $h(x) = x^4$.   Ans. h is increasing in $[0, \infty)$, decreasing in $(-\infty, 0]$. $f(0)$ is a relative minimum.   There is no inflection point.

g) $f(x) = x^4 + 4x^3 + 6x^2 + 10$.   h) $\varphi(x) = x^4 + 4x^3 + 10$.

i) $f(y) = (y^2 - 1)(y^2 + 1)$.   j) $g(s) = (s - 1)^2(s^2 + 1)$.

k) $\varphi(s) = (s - 1)(s + 1)^2$.

l) $f(x) = \dfrac{x}{x^2 + 1}$.   Ans. f is increasing in $[-1, 1]$, otherwise decreasing. $f(-1)$ is a relative minimum, $f(1)$ a relative maximum.   There are inflection points at $x = -\sqrt{3}$, $x = 0$, and $x = \sqrt{3}$.

m) $f(x) = \dfrac{x}{x^2 - 1}$.

n) $g(t) = \dfrac{1}{t^3 + 1}$.

o) $h(s) = s^2 + \dfrac{1}{s}$.   Ans. h is increasing in $[\sqrt[3]{\frac{1}{2}}, \infty)$, otherwise decreasing. $f(\sqrt[3]{\tfrac{1}{2}})$ is a relative minimum. $(-1,0)$ is an inflection point.

p) $f(y) = y^2 + \dfrac{1}{y^2}$.

q) $g(x) = x\sqrt{1 + x}$.

2. Where is the graph of $x^2/a^2 + y^2/b^2 = 1$ concave up and where is it concave down?

Hint: This equation defines two functions. Discuss each one separately.

6. LOCUS PROBLEMS

So far in this chapter we have been working from algebra to geometry. We have started with an equation, an algebraic entity, and have found out something about its graph, which is a geometric entity. As a preparation for our study of the second-degree equation in the following sections, we now consider problems of the opposite type: to find an equation for a given graph or locus.

There is no one procedure which can be used for all such problems. The problems below illustrate some of the more useful procedures.

PROBLEMS

1. A curve consists of all points P in the plane for which the slope of the line joining P to the origin is greater by 2 than the slope of the line joining P to the point (1,0). Find an equation of this curve.

Solution: If (a,b) is any point in the plane, the slope of the line joining it to the origin is
$$b/a.$$

The slope of the line joining it to the point (1,0) is
$$b/(a - 1).$$

Hence if this point is to lie on our curve, we must have
$$\frac{b}{a} - 2 = \frac{b}{a - 1},$$
or
$$2a^2 - 2a + b = 0.$$

Therefore, any point on our curve has coordinates satisfying the equation
$$2x^2 - 2x + y = 0.$$

We have not yet shown that this is an equation of our curve. To finish the argument, we must show (see again Definition 2.11) that a point not on the curve has coordinates not satisfying the equation. This is the same as showing that if the coordinates (a,b) satisfy the equation, then the point (a,b) is on the curve. But if

$$2a^2 - 2a + b = 0,$$

then, retracing our steps, we find

$$\frac{b}{a} - 2 = \frac{b}{a-1},$$

which means that (a,b) is on our curve.

Remark 1: There are two exceptions to the last sentence above. If $a = 0$ or $a = 1$, we cannot proceed from

$$2a^2 - 2a + b = 0$$

to

$$\frac{b}{a} - 2 = \frac{b}{a-1},$$

for in either case we would be dividing by zero. This means that the points $(0,0)$ and $(1,0)$ do not belong to our locus, which is correct, since, in the definition of the locus, if we take P at either of these points, the slope is not defined. The locus looks like Figure 6.11 with the two intercepts deleted. However, it is a standard convention to add these two points to the locus to make a more natural looking graph. We shall do this in general without bothering to make explicit mention of the fact each time.

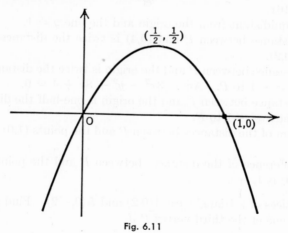

Fig. 6.11

Remark 2: Another way of stating this problem is: Find an equation of the locus of a point P such that the slope of the line joining P to the origin is greater by 2 than the slope of the line joining P to the point $(1,0)$.

Remark 3: It is hard to see, merely looking at its definition, what the shape of the curve is. But, after finding an equation for the curve, we can apply the methods developed in the first part of the chapter to make a sketch of the graph of this equation, and this graph is our curve. We find that the curve looks like Figure 6.11.

2. From the point (1,0) on the circle $x^2 + y^2 = 1$ chords are drawn to the other points of the circle. Find an equation of the locus of the mid-points of these chords.

Solution: Let $P(a,b)$ be the midpoint of one such chord. Then the coordinates of the other end of the chord are $(2a - 1, 2b)$. (Why?) This last point is on the circle, so its coordinates satisfy its equation, and so

$$(2a - 1)^2 + (2b)^2 = 1,$$

or

$$a^2 + b^2 - a = 0.$$

Hence the coordinates of P satisfy the equation

$$x^2 + y^2 - x = 0.$$

As in the previous problem, we can retrace our steps to show that any point whose coordinates satisfy this equation is indeed on our locus, and hence that $x^2 + y^2 - x = 0$ is an equation of this curve.

3. Find an equation for the locus of a point P such that

a) P is equidistant from (1,2) and (−2,3). Ans. $3x - y + 4 = 0$.
b) P is equidistant from the point (4,0) and the line $x = -4$. Ans. $y^2 = 16x$.
c) P is equidistant from the origin and the line $y = 1$.
d) the distance between P and (0,4) is twice the distance between P and (0,2).
e) the distance between P and the origin is twice the distance from the line $x = -1$ to P. Ans. $3x^2 - y^2 + 8x + 4 = 0$.
f) the distance between P and the origin is one-half the distance from the line $x = -1$ to P.
g) the sum of the distances between P and the points (1,0) and (−1,0) is 5.
h) the difference of the distances between P and the points (1,0) and (−1,0) is 1.

4. Two vertices of a triangle are $A(0,2)$ and $B(0,-2)$. Find an equation for the locus of the third vertex P if

a) AP and BP are perpendicular. Ans. $x^2 + y^2 = 4$.
b) the angle at P is 45°.
c) the sum of the slopes of AP and BP is 10.
d) the product of the slopes of AP and BP is 10. Ans. $10x^2 - y^2 + 4 = 0$.
e) the slope of AP is twice that of BP.

5. From the point $(0,2)$ on the graph of the equation $4x^2 + y^2 = 4$ chords are drawn to the other points of the graph. Each of these chords is extended beyond the graph to a segment twice the length of the chord. Find an equation for the locus of the end points of these segments.

6. A segment of length 12 has one end on the x-axis and the other end on the y-axis. Find an equation for the locus of its midpoint. Ans. $x^2 + y^2 = 36$.

7. Find an equation for the locus of a point P such that the distance between P and $(1,1)$ is equal to the slope of the line joining P to this point.

8. Find an equation for the locus of a point such that the sum of the squares of its distances from the points $(0,1)$, $(1,0)$, $(0,-1)$, and $(-1,0)$ is 5.

9. Find an equation for the locus of a point such that the product of its distances from two given points is a constant.

   Hint: Choose a convenient coordinate system.

10. Find an equation for the locus of a point such that its distance from one given point is equal to the slope of the line joining it to another given point.

7. SECOND-DEGREE EQUATIONS. THE PARABOLA

The general equation of the second degree has the form

$$Ax^2 + Bxy + Cy^2 + Dx + Ey + F = 0.$$

In certain special cases, the graph of such an equation can be a pair of straight lines, or a single straight line, or a single point, or may contain no points at all. But in general the graph is a curve of one of three types: parabola, ellipse, hyperbola. The circle is a special case of the ellipse.

It is convenient to study these curves individually and to define each one in geometric terms.

Definition 6.7: *A **parabola** is the locus of a point which is equidistant from a fixed line, the **directrix**, and a fixed point, the **focus**, not on the directrix.*

We shall use the letter p to denote one-half of the distance between the focus and the directrix. Thus, in all that follows, p always stands for a positive number.

As we shall see later, any parabola has an equation of the second degree. Now, however, we shall consider only parabolas so located in the plane that they have rather simple equations.

We say that a parabola is in *standard position* when its directrix is either horizontal or vertical, its focus is on a coordinate axis, and the origin is midway between the focus and the directrix.

Let us consider first the case where the directrix is vertical and to the left of the y-axis. Then the focus is on the x-axis to the right of the origin. Since the distance between the focus and directrix is $2p$, and since the origin is midway between them, the coordinates of the focus are $(p,0)$, and the equation of the directrix is $x = -p$.

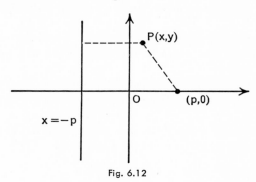

Fig. 6.12

For a point (x,y) to be on the parabola, the distance between this point and the directrix must be equal to the distance between this point and the focus. The first of these distances is $x + p$. (Why?) The other distance is $\sqrt{(x - p)^2 + y^2}$. (Why?) Hence if (x,y) is on the parabola, $x + p = \sqrt{(x - p)^2 + y^2}$, or, squaring and collecting terms,

$$y^2 = 4px.$$

Thus the coordinates of any point on the parabola satisfy this equation. Conversely, if the coordinates of a point satisfy this equation, we can retrace our steps and see that the point is on the parabola. Hence this is an equation of this parabola. We have proved the following theorem.

Theorem 6.3: *An equation for the parabola whose directrix is* $x = -p$ *and whose focus is* $(p,0)$ *is*

$$y^2 = 4px.$$

Exercise: Show that equations for the parabola in the other three standard positions are

$$y^2 = -4px, \quad x^2 = 4py, \quad x^2 = -4py.$$

We can apply the material in the early part of this chapter to find the shape and position of the parabola. The only intercept of the equation $y^2 = 4px$ is at the origin. The graph is symmetric to the x-axis but not the y-axis. (Why?) No part of the graph lies to the left of the y-axis. (Why?) The equation defines two functions: $f_1(x) = \sqrt{4px}$ and $f_2(x) = -\sqrt{4px}$. The graph of the first is increasing and of the second decreasing. Thus the parabola looks like this:

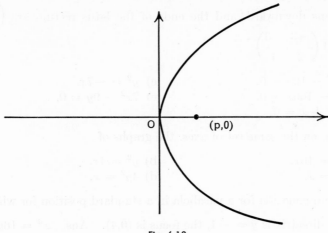

Fig. 6.13

Definition 6.8: *The line through the focus perpendicular to the directrix is the* **axis** *of the parabola.   The point where the parabola meets the axis is the* **vertex** *of the parabola.   The segment cut off by the parabola from the line through the focus and perpendicular to the axis is the* **latus rectum** *of the parabola.*

Exercise: Show that the length of the latus rectum of the parabola whose equation is $y^2 = 4px$ is $4p$.

PROBLEMS

1. Find the focus, directrix, and ends of the latus rectum, and sketch the graph of the parabola whose equation is

   a) $y^2 = 4x$.   *Solution:* Comparing this equation with our standard equation, we see that $p = 1$, the focus is at $(1,0)$ and the directrix is the line $x = -1$.   In view of the exercise immediately above, the ends of the latus rectum are $(1,2)$ and $(1,-2)$.   It has the shape and position shown in Figure 6.13.

   b) $x^2 = 8y$.   Ans. $p = 2$, the focus is at $(0,2)$, and the graph opens upward.   The ends of the latus rectum are $(4,2)$ and $(-4,2)$.

   c) $x^2 = -4y$.

   d) $4x^2 + y = 0$.

   e) $y^2 - 12x = 0$.

   f) $y^2 + 2x = 0$.   Ans. $p = \frac{1}{2}$, focus at $(-\frac{1}{2},0)$, graph opens out to the left, ends of the latus rectum are $(-\frac{1}{2},1)$ and $(-\frac{1}{2},-1)$.

2. Sketch the graphs of

   a) $x^2 + 3y = 0$.   Ans. $p = \frac{3}{4}$, the focus is at $\left(0,\frac{-3}{4}\right)$, the graph opens downward, and the ends of the latus rectum are $\left(\dfrac{3}{2}, \dfrac{-3}{4}\right)$

and $\left(\dfrac{-3}{2}, \dfrac{-3}{4}\right)$.

b) $3x^2 - 10y = 0$.   c) $y^2 = -7x$.

d) $y^2 - 100x = 0$.   e) $7x^2 - 9y = 0$.

f) $5y^2 + x = 0$.

3. Sketch, on the same set of axes, the graphs of

     a) $y^2 = 16x$.   b) $y^2 = 4x$.

     c) $y^2 = x$.   d) $4y^2 = x$.

4. Write an equation for a parabola in a standard position for which

     a) the directrix is $y = -4$, the focus is $(0,4)$.   Ans. $x^2 = 16y$.

     b) the directrix is $x = 2$, the focus is $(-2,0)$.

     c) the vertex is $(0,0)$, and the length of the latus rectum is 4.

     d) the axis is the x-axis, and the curve passes through the point $(1,1)$.

5. (In this problem, the parabolas are not necessarily in a standard position.)

     a) The directrix of a parabola is $3x + 4y + 5 = 0$. Its vertex is at the origin. Find the focus and the ends of the latus rectum, and sketch the parabola.

     b) The axis of a parabola is the line $y = 2$, one end of the latus rectum is $(4,3)$, and no part of the curve lies to the left of the y-axis. Find the vertex and the directrix, and sketch the parabola.

     c) The focus of a parabola is at the origin and the directrix is the line $x + y + 1 = 0$. Derive an equation for this parabola, and sketch it.

6. Show that the tangents to a parabola at the ends of the latus rectum are perpendicular and meet on the directrix.

7. An equilateral triangle is inscribed in the parabola $x^2 = 4py$ with one vertex at the origin. Find the length of a side of the triangle. Ans. $8\sqrt{3}\ p$.

8. Find an equation for the locus of a point whose distance from the point $(3,0)$ is two units less than its distance from the line $x = -5$.

9. In the parabola $x^2 = 8y$, chords are drawn from the vertex to each point. Find an equation for the locus of the midpoints of the chords.

10. From a point on a parabola, a perpendicular is dropped to its axis. Show that the length of this segment is a mean proportional between the length of the latus rectum and the distance between the vertex and the foot of the perpendicular.

11. In this figure, a perpendicular to the x-axis is erected at C. A circle with center at $F(p,0)$ and radius equal to the distance between D and

C cuts this line at points A and B. Show that these points are on the parabola whose directrix is $x = -p$ and whose focus is $F(p,0)$.

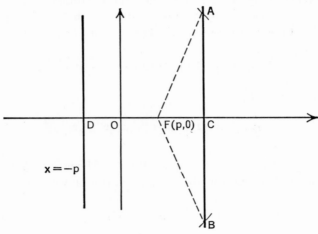

Fig. 6.14

12. A mirror has the form of the surface obtained by rotating a piece of the parabola $y^2 = 4px$ around the x-axis. A ray of light is emitted from the focus. Show that it is reflected from the mirror along a line parallel to the x-axis.

   Hint: The angle of incidence and the angle of reflection are equal.

8. THE ELLIPSE

Definition 6.9: *An **ellipse** is the locus of a point such that the sum of the distances between it and two fixed points, the **foci**, is constant.*

We shall use the letter c to denote one-half the distance between the foci, so that c always stands for a positive number in what follows.

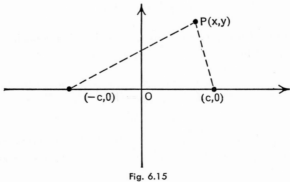

Fig. 6.15

An ellipse is in *standard position* if its foci are both on a coordinate axis with the origin midway between them. Let us consider first the case where the foci are on the x-axis. Then the coordinates of the foci are $(c,0)$ and $(-c,0)$. Denote by $2a$ the constant of the definition, so that a stands always for a positive number. Then a point (x,y) is on the ellipse if

$$\sqrt{(x+c)^2 + y^2} + \sqrt{(x-c)^2 + y^2} = 2a.$$

This can be simplified to

$$(a^2 - c^2)x^2 + a^2 y^2 = a^2(a^2 - c^2).$$

Note that a^2 must be larger than c^2. (Why?) Hence $b = \sqrt{a^2 - c^2}$ is a positive real number, and the above equation can be written

$$b^2 x^2 + a^2 y^2 = a^2 b^2,$$

or

$$\frac{x^2}{a^2} + \frac{y^2}{b^2} = 1.$$

Thus the coordinates of any point on the ellipse satisfy this last equation. Conversely, if the coordinates of a point satisfy the equation, we can, by retracing our steps, see that the point is on the ellipse. Therefore, this is an equation of our ellipse. We have proved the following theorem.

Theorem 6.4: *An equation for the ellipse whose foci are at $(c,0)$ and $(-c,0)$ and for which the sum of the distances between the foci and any point of the ellipse is $2a$, is*

$$\frac{x^2}{a^2} + \frac{y^2}{b^2} = 1,$$

where

$$b = \sqrt{a^2 - c^2}.$$

Exercise: Show that if the foci are on the y-axis, with coordinates $(0,c)$ and $(0,-c)$, then an equation for the ellipse is

$$\frac{y^2}{a^2} + \frac{x^2}{b^2} = 1.$$

Having an equation for an ellipse, we can now find intercepts, symmetry, etc., and sketch its graph. For the case $x^2/a^2 + y^2/b^2 = 1$, the graph looks like this:

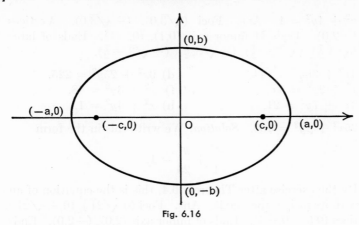

Fig. 6.16

Definition 6.10: *The line containing the foci of an ellipse is its **principal axis**. The points where the ellipse meets its principal axis are its **vertices**. The segment cut off on the principal axis by the vertices is its **major axis**. The midpoint between the foci is the **center**. The segment cut off by the ellipse on the line through the center and perpendicular to the principal axis is the **minor axis**. The segments cut off by the ellipse on the lines through the foci and perpendicular to the principal axis are the **latera recta**.*

Exercise: For the ellipse whose equation is $x^2/a^2 + y^2/b^2 = 1$, show that:

   i) the vertices are $(a,0)$ and $(-a,0)$.

  ii) the length of the major axis is $2a$ and of the minor axis is $2b$.

 iii) the center is at the origin.

 iv) the length of each latus rectum is $2b^2/a$.

PROBLEMS

1. Find the foci, vertices, ends of the minor axis, and ends of the latera recta of each of the following ellipses, and sketch the graphs:

a) $4x^2 + 9y^2 = 36$. *Solution:* We rewrite this equation as

$$\frac{x^2}{9} + \frac{y^2}{4} = 1.$$

Comparing this with the equation in Theorem 6.4, we see that $a = 3$, $b = 2$, and $c = \sqrt{5}$. Therefore the foci are at $(\sqrt{5},0)$ and $(-\sqrt{5},0)$. The vertices are at $(3,0)$ and $(-3,0)$. The ends of the minor axis are $(0,2)$ and $(0,-2)$. The ends of the latera recta, by iv) of the exercise above, are $(\sqrt{5},\frac{4}{3})$, $(\sqrt{5},-\frac{4}{3})$, $(-\sqrt{5},\frac{4}{3})$, and $(-\sqrt{5},-\frac{4}{3})$.

b) $x^2 + 4y^2 = 4$.   Ans. Foci $(\sqrt{3},0)$, $(-\sqrt{3},0)$.   Vertices $(2,0)$, $(-2,0)$.   Ends of minor axis $(0,1)$, $(0,-1)$.   Ends of latera recta $(\sqrt{3},\frac{1}{2})$, $(\sqrt{3},-\frac{1}{2})$, $(-\sqrt{3},\frac{1}{2})$, $(-\sqrt{3},-\frac{1}{2})$.

c) $4x^2 + 36y^2 = 144$.   d) $9x^2 + 25y^2 = 225$.
e) $x^2 + 2y^2 = 50$.   f) $x^2 + 3y^2 = 48$.
g) $3x^2 + 7y^2 = 21$.   h) $x^2 + 4y^2 = 1$.

i) $25x^2 + 4y^2 = 100$.   *Solution:* We write this in the form

$$\frac{x^2}{4} + \frac{y^2}{25} = 1.$$

By the exercise after Theorem 6.4, this is the equation of an ellipse with its foci on the y-axis. Ans. Foci $(0,\sqrt{21}\,)$, $(0,-\sqrt{21}\,)$. Vertices $(0,5)$, $(0,-5)$. Ends of minor axis $(2,0)$, $(-2,0)$. Ends of latera recta $(\frac{4}{5},\sqrt{21})$, $(-\frac{4}{5},\sqrt{21})$, $(\frac{4}{5},-\sqrt{21})$, $(-\frac{4}{5},-\sqrt{21})$.
j) $2x^2 + y^2 = 72$.
k) $5x^2 + y^2 = 45$.
l) $9x^2 + y^2 = 9$.
m) $4x^2 + 3y^2 = 12$. Ans. Foci $(0,1)$, $(0,-1)$. Vertices $(0,2)$, $(0,-2)$. Ends of minor axis $(\sqrt{3},0)$, $(-\sqrt{3},0)$. Ends of latera recta $(\frac{3}{2},1)$, $(-\frac{3}{2},1)$, $(\frac{3}{2},-1)$, $(-\frac{3}{2},-1)$.
n) $9x^2 + 2y^2 = 32$.
o) $9x^2 + 4y^2 = 1$.

2. Find an equation for and sketch the graph of the ellipse such that

a) the center is at the origin, the principal axis is the x-axis, and one end of a latus rectum is $(12,7)$.   Ans. $\dfrac{x^2}{256} + \dfrac{y^2}{112} = 1.$

b) the center is at the origin, the principal axis is the y-axis, the point $(3,4)$ is on the ellipse, and the minor axis is 8 units long.

3. (In this problem, the ellipses are not necessarily in a standard position.)

a) The center of an ellipse is at the origin and one focus is at $(1,1)$. The minor axis is 2 units long. Find the coordinates of the vertices and sketch the ellipse.

b) The vertices of an ellipse are $(1,3)$ and $(4,-1)$. The length of a latus rectum is 2. Find the coordinates of the foci and sketch the ellipse.

c) Find an equation for the ellipse whose center is at the vertex of the parabola $x^2 = 16y$, one of whose foci is at the focus of this parabola, and such that its latera recta have the same length as the latus rectum of the parabola. Sketch the ellipse.

4. Find an equation for the locus of a point whose distance from the point $(0,2)$ is half its distance from the line $y = 8$. Ans. $4x^2 + 3y^2 = 48$.

5. Is there any point on the ellipse $16x^2 + 25y^2 = 400$ such that the lines from the foci to this point make an angle of $45°$?

6. Show that half the length of the minor axis of an ellipse is a mean proportional between the two segments into which a focus divides the major axis.

7. A straight line through the center of an ellipse meets it at points R and S. If F is a focus, show that the sum of the distances between R and F and S and F is equal to the length of the major axis.

8. Two concentric circles have their common center at the origin 0. For any point A on the larger circle, let the radius to A meet the smaller circle at B. Let the horizontal line through B meet the vertical line through A at a point P. Find an equation for the locus of P.

9. A mirror has the form of the surface obtained by rotating the ellipse $x^2/a^2 + y^2/b^2 = 1$ around the x-axis. Show that a ray of light emitted from one focus will pass through the other focus.

10. Sketch, using the same set of axes, the graphs of

a) $4x^2 + y^2 = 4$.
c) $4x^2 + y^2 = \frac{1}{4}$.
e) $4x^2 + y^2 = -1$.

b) $4x^2 + y^2 = 1$.
d) $4x^2 + y^2 = 0$.

9. THE HYPERBOLA

Definition 6.11: *A **hyperbola** is the locus of a point such that the absolute value of the difference between the distances between it and two fixed points, the **foci**, is constant.*

As in the case of the ellipse, we shall use the letter c to denote half the distance between the foci, so that c always stands for a positive number in what follows.

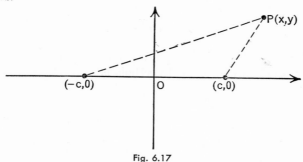

Fig. 6.17

A hyperbola is in *standard position* if its foci are both on a coordinate axis with the origin midway between them. Taking the case where the foci are on the x-axis, the coordinates of the foci are $(c,0)$ and $(-c,0)$. Let the constant of the definition be $2a$, so that a always stands for a positive number. Then a point (x,y) is on the hyperbola if

$$\left| \sqrt{(x+c)^2 + y^2} - \sqrt{(x-c)^2 + y^2} \right| = 2a,$$

or

$$\sqrt{(x+c)^2 + y^2} - \sqrt{(x-c)^2 + y^2} = \pm 2a.$$

This can be simplified to

$$(c^2 - a^2)x^2 - a^2 y^2 = a^2(c^2 - a^2).$$

Note that c^2 must be larger than a^2. (Why?) Hence $b = \sqrt{c^2 - a^2}$ is a real positive number, and the above equation can be written

$$b^2 x^2 - a^2 y^2 = a^2 b^2,$$

or

$$\frac{x^2}{a^2} - \frac{y^2}{b^2} = 1.$$

Thus the coordinates of any point on the hyperbola satisfy this last equation. Conversely, if the coordinates of a point satisfy this equation, we can, by retracing our steps, see that the point is on the hyperbola, so this is an equation of the hyperbola. We have proved the following theorem.

Theorem 6.5: *An equation of the hyperbola whose foci are at $(c,0)$ and $(-c,0)$ and for which the absolute value of the difference of the distances between the foci and any point of the hyperbola is $2a$ is*

$$\frac{x^2}{a^2} - \frac{y^2}{b^2} = 1,$$

where

$$b = \sqrt{c^2 - a^2}.$$

Exercise: Show that if the foci are on the y-axis, with coordinates $(0,c)$ and $(0,-c)$, then an equation for the hyperbola is

$$\frac{y^2}{a^2} - \frac{x^2}{b^2} = 1.$$

Having an equation for a hyperbola, we can now find intercepts, symmetry, etc., and sketch its graph. For the case

$$\frac{x^2}{a^2} - \frac{y^2}{b^2} = 1,$$

the graph looks like this:

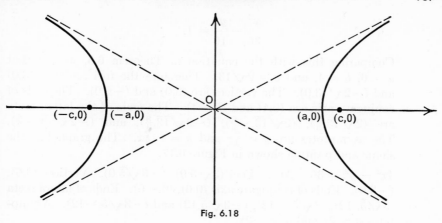

Fig. 6.18

Remark: The dotted lines in this figure are the graphs of the equations $y = (b/a)x$ and $y = -(b/a)x$. They are asymptotes for the hyperbola in the sense that as a point moves along the hyperbola, the farther it gets from the origin, the closer it gets to one of these lines. See v) of the exercise below.

Definition 6.12: *The line containing the foci of a hyperbola is its* **principal axis.** *The points where the hyperbola meets its principal axis are its* **vertices.** *The segment cut off on the principal axis by the vertices is its* **transverse axis.** *The midpoint between the vertices is the* **center.** *The segment on the line through the center and perpendicular to the principal axis of length 2b, where* $b^2 = c^2 - a^2$, *with midpoint at the center is its* **conjugate axis.** *The segments cut off by the hyperbola on the lines through the foci perpendicular to the principal axis are the* **latera recta.**

Exercise: For the hyperbola whose equation is $x^2/a^2 - y^2/b^2 = 1$, show that:

   i) the vertices are $(a,0)$ and $(-a,0)$.

  ii) the length of the transverse axis is $2a$.

 iii) the center is at the origin.

 iv) the length of each latus rectum is $2b^2/a$.

  v) the distance between the points P on the hyperbola and Q on the line $y = \dfrac{b}{a}x$ over the point $(x,0)$ becomes small as x becomes large.

PROBLEMS

1. Find the foci, vertices, ends of the conjugate axis, ends of the latera recta, and the asymptotes of each of the following hyperbolas, and sketch the graphs.

  a) $4x^2 - 9y^2 = 144$. *Solution:* We rewrite this in the form

$$\frac{x^2}{36} - \frac{y^2}{16} = 1.$$

Comparing this with the equation in Theorem 6.5, we see that $a = 6$, $b = 4$, and $c = 2\sqrt{13}$. Therefore the foci are $(2\sqrt{13},0)$ and $(-2\sqrt{13},0)$. The vertices are $(6,0)$ and $(-6,0)$. The ends of conjugate axis are $(0,4)$ and $(0,-4)$. The ends of the latera recta are $(2\sqrt{13},\frac{8}{3})$, $(2\sqrt{13},-\frac{8}{3})$, $(-2\sqrt{13},\frac{8}{3})$, and $(-2\sqrt{13},-\frac{8}{3})$. The asymptotes are $y = \frac{2}{3}x$ and $y = -\frac{2}{3}x$. The graph has the shape and position shown in Figure 6.17.

b) $4x^2 - y^2 = 36$. Ans. Foci $(3\sqrt{5},0)$, $(-3\sqrt{5},0)$. Vertices $(3,0)$, $(-3,0)$. Ends of conjugate axis $(0,6)$, $(0,-6)$. Ends of latera recta $(3\sqrt{5}, 12)$, $(3\sqrt{5},-12)$, $(-3\sqrt{5},12)$ and $(-3\sqrt{5},-12)$. Asymptotes $y = 2x$ and $y = -2x$.

c) $x^2 - y^2 = 25$.

d) $3x^2 - 4y^2 = 48$.

e) $16x^2 - 9y^2 = 144$.

f) $9y^2 - 4x^2 = 36$. *Solution:* We rewrite this equation in the form

$$\frac{y^2}{4} - \frac{x^2}{9} = 1.$$

Comparing this with the equation in the exercise after Theorem 6.5, we see that the foci are on the y-axis, $a = 2$, $b = 3$, and $c = \sqrt{13}$. The foci are $(0,\sqrt{13}\,)$ and $(0,-\sqrt{13}\,)$. The vertices are $(0,2)$ and $(0,-2)$. The ends of the conjugate axis are $(3,0)$ and $(-3,0)$. The ends of the latera recta are $(\frac{9}{2},\sqrt{13})$, $(-\frac{9}{2},\sqrt{13})$, $(\frac{9}{2},-\sqrt{13})$, and $(-\frac{9}{2},-\sqrt{13})$. The asymptotes are $y = \frac{2}{3}x$ and $y = -\frac{2}{3}x$.

g) $4y^2 - 5x^2 = 80$. Ans. Foci $(0,6)$, $(0,-6)$. Vertices $(0,2\sqrt{5}\,)$, $(0,-2\sqrt{5}\,)$. Ends of conjugate axis $(4,0)$, $(-4,0)$. Ends of latera recta $\left(\frac{8\sqrt{5}}{5},6\right)$, $\left(\frac{8\sqrt{5}}{5},-6\right)$, $\left(\frac{-8\sqrt{5}}{5},6\right)$, and $\left(\frac{-8\sqrt{5}}{5},-6\right)$.

Asymptotes $y = \frac{\sqrt{5}}{2}x$ and $y = \frac{-\sqrt{5}}{2}x$.

h) $3y^2 - x^2 = 27$.

i) $2y^2 - 3x^2 = 72$.

j) $25y^2 - 9x^2 = 225$.

k) $25y^2 - 16x^2 + 400 = 0$. Ans. Foci $(\sqrt{41},0)$, $(-\sqrt{41},0)$. Vertices $(5,0)$, $(-5,0)$. Ends of conjugate axis $(0,4)$, $(0,-4)$. Ends of latera recta $(\sqrt{41},\frac{16}{5})$, $(\sqrt{41},-\frac{16}{5})$, $(-\sqrt{41},\frac{16}{5})$, $(-\sqrt{41},-\frac{16}{5})$. Asymptotes $y = \frac{4}{5}x$ and $y = -\frac{4}{5}x$.

l) $x^2 - 2y^2 + 18 = 0$.

m) $9y^2 - x^2 + 36 = 0$.

n) $y^2 - 3x^2 + 48 = 0$.

o) $4x^2 - 5y^2 = 100$.

p) $x^2 - 4y^2 + 1 = 0$.

2. Find equations for hyperbolas which are in a standard position and for which

    a) one focus is (0,4) and one asymptote has slope 2. Ans. $5y^2 - 20x^2 = 64$.

    b) one vertex is (3,0) and the length of a latus rectum is 3.

    c) one vertex is (10,0) and the point $(20,\sqrt{12})$ is on the hyperbola.

3. (In this problem the hyperbolas are not necessarily in a standard position.)

    a) The center of a hyperbola is at the origin and one focus is at the point (1,1). The x- and y-axes are the asymptotes. Find the coordinates of the vertices, and sketch the hyperbola.

    b) The center of a hyperbola is at the point (2,4), one focus is at the point (7,4), and one vertex at the point (6,4). Find the equations of the asymptotes, and sketch the hyperbola.

4. Show that the length of the conjugate axis of a hyperbola is the mean proportional between the lengths of the transverse axis and a latus rectum.

5. Find an equation for the locus of a point whose distance from the line $x = 1$ is one-half the distance between the point and (4,0).

6. Find a point on the hyperbola $5y^2 - 3x^2 = 75$ for which the lines joining the point to the two foci are perpendicular. Ans. $(\pm\sqrt{\frac{125}{8}}, \pm\sqrt{\frac{195}{8}})$.

7. A hyperbola is in standard position with its foci on the x-axis. The point $(\sqrt{28},6)$ is on the curve and the lines joining it to the two foci are perpendicular. Find an equation for the hyperbola.

8. Show that any line parallel to an asymptote of a hyperbola meets it at only one point.

9. The sound of a bursting shell is heard at one listening post 3 sec. after it is heard at another post. What is the locus of the possible locations of the bursting shell?

10. Sketch, using the same set of axes, the graphs of

    a) $x^2 - y^2 = 4$.   b) $x^2 - y^2 = 1$.

    c) $x^2 - y^2 = \frac{1}{4}$.   d) $x^2 - y^2 = 0$.

    e) $x^2 - y^2 = -1$.

10. TRANSLATIONS

So far we have found equations for the parabola, ellipse, and hyperbola only when they are in a standard position. However, any one of these curves, no matter where it is located in the plane, is in standard position with respect to some coordinate system. (Why?) Hence we would like to have a method for passing from one coordinate system to another.

Suppose then that we have two coordinate systems in the plane. In the first, which we call the xy-system, the coordinates of a point are denoted by (x,y). In the other, which we call the XY-system, the coordinates of a point are denoted by (X,Y). Suppose further that the x-axis and the X-axis are parallel. We say in this case that the XY-system is obtained from the xy-system by a *translation*.

Each point in the plane now has two pairs of coordinates, (x,y) and (X,Y). In particular, the origin of the XY-system has coordinates (h,k) in the xy-system. The two pairs of coordinates are related by the equations:

$$x = X + h \qquad X = x - h$$
$$\text{or}$$
$$y = Y + k \qquad Y = y - k$$

Now if we have a curve in the plane and an equation for it in the xy-system, say $f(x,y) = 0$, we can obtain an equation for this curve in the

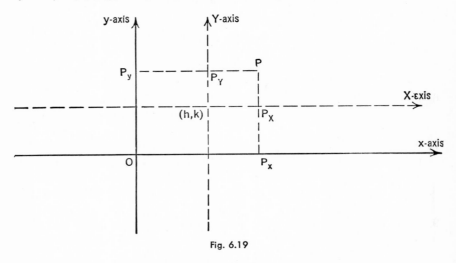

Fig. 6.19

XY-system merely by substituting $X + h$ for x and $Y + k$ for y, the result being $f(X + h, Y + k) = 0$.

For example, suppose we are given the equation

$$y^2 - 4x - 8y + 8 = 0.$$

Suppose the coordinates, in the xy-system, of the origin of the XY-system are $(-2,4)$. Then the equation

$$(Y + 4)^2 - 4(X - 2) - 8(Y + 4) + 8 = 0$$

and the original equation have the same graph. But note that this second equation, when simplified, becomes

$$Y^2 = 4X,$$

which we recognize as a parabola in standard position with respect to the XY-system. We can now sketch its graph, and thus have a sketch of the graph of the original.

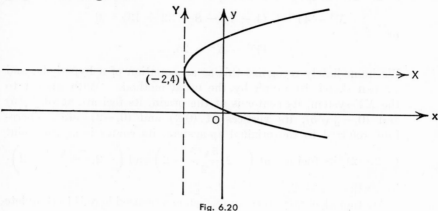

Fig. 6.20

The example above suggests that in some cases it may be possible, given an equation in x and y, to choose an XY-system in which the graph of the original equation has a simpler form. As we shall see in the problems below, whenever we have a second-degree equation of the form

$$Ax^2 + Cy^2 + Dx + Ey + F = 0,$$

we can translate to a new coordinate system in which the graph of this equation has an equation which has fewer first-degree terms, and in fact is one which we can recognize.

PROBLEMS

1. Name and sketch the graphs of

    a) $x^2 - 4y^2 + 4x - 16y + 13 = 0$. *Solution:* Let (h,k) be the coordinates in the xy-system of the origin of an XY-system. Then the graph of the original equation has, in the XY-system, the equation

$$(X + h)^2 - 4(Y + k)^2 + 4(X + h) - 16(Y + k) + 13 = 0.$$

    Squaring and collecting terms, we have

$$X^2 - 4Y^2 + (2h + 4)X + (-8k - 16)Y$$
$$+ (h^2 - 4k^2 + 4h - 16k + 13) = 0.$$

    Since we wish to be rid of first degree terms, we set the coefficients of these terms equal to zero:

$$2h + 4 = 0 \quad \text{and} \quad -8k - 16 = 0.$$

The solutions of these equations are $h = -2$ and $k = -2$. Therefore, if we translate to the XY-system whose origin is at the point $(-2,-2)$, our graph has the equation

$$X^2 - 4Y^2 + (4 - 16 - 8 + 32 + 13) = 0$$

or

$$4Y^2 - X^2 = 25.$$

We immediately recognize this as an equation of a hyperbola, and we can sketch its graph by the usual methods. With respect to the XY-system, its center is at the origin, its foci are at $(0,\frac{5}{2}\sqrt{5})$ and $(0,-\frac{5}{2}\sqrt{5})$, its vertices at $(0,\frac{5}{2})$ and $(0,-\frac{5}{2})$, etc. Therefore, referred to the original xy-system, its center is at the point $(-2,-2)$, its foci are at $\left(-2, \frac{5\sqrt{5}}{2} - 2\right)$ and $\left(-2, \frac{-5\sqrt{5}}{2} - 2\right)$, its vertices at $(-2,\frac{1}{2})$ and $(-2,-\frac{9}{2})$.

Another algebraic procedure which can be used here is to complete the square in x and y, as follows:

$$x^2 - 4y^2 + 4x - 16y + 13 = 0$$

$$x^2 + 4x \qquad - 4(y^2 + 4y \quad) = -13$$

$$x^2 + 4x + 4 - 4(y^2 + 4y + 4) = -13 + 4 - 16$$

$$(x + 2)^2 \quad - 4(y + 2)^2 = -25$$

$$4(y + 2)^2 \quad - (x + 2)^2 = 25.$$

Now we see that if we set $x + 2 = X$ and $y + 2 = Y$, so that $h = -2$ and $k = -2$, we obtain the equation

$$4Y^2 - X^2 = 25$$

as above.

b) $x^2 - 4x + 2y + 10 = 0$. *Solution:* Let (h,k) be the coordinates in the xy-system of the origin of an XY-system. Then the graph of our equation has, in the XY-system, the equation

$$(X + h)^2 - 4(X + h) + 2(Y + k) + 10 = 0.$$

Squaring and collecting terms, we have

$$X^2 + (2h - 4)X + 2Y + (h^2 - 4h + 2k + 10) = 0.$$

This time we can eliminate the first-degree term in X by setting $2h - 4 = 0$ or $h = 2$. Then the equation becomes

$$X^2 + 2Y + (2k + 6) = 0.$$

We can now eliminate the constant term by setting $2k + 6 = 0$ or $k = -3$. Thus, translating to the XY-system whose origin is at

$(2,-3)$, we obtain the equation

$$X^2 = -2Y.$$

We recognize this as an equation for a parabola, opening downward, with $p = \frac{1}{2}$, vertex at the origin of the XY-system, focus at $(0, -\frac{1}{2})$, etc. Therefore, referred to the original xy-system, the vertex is at the point $(2, -3)$, the focus is at the point $\left(2, \frac{-7}{2}\right)$, etc.

We can also apply the method of completing the square:

$$x^2 - 4x + 2y + 10 = 0$$

$$x^2 - 4x \qquad\qquad = -2y - 10$$

$$x^2 - 4x + 4 \qquad\quad = -2y - 10 + 4$$

$$(x - 2)^2 \qquad\qquad = -2(y + 3).$$

Now we see that if we set $x - 2 = X$ and $y + 3 = Y$, we obtain

$$X^2 = -2Y,$$

as above.

c) $4x^2 + 9y^2 + 8x - 36y + 4 = 0$.   Ans. $4X^2 + 9Y^2 = 36$, center at $(-1,2)$. See Problem 1a of Section 8.

d) $x^2 - 2y^2 + 4x - 4y = 62$.

e) $x^2 - 2y^2 + 10x + 20y = 61$.

f) $9x^2 - 4y^2 - 54x + 45 = 0$.   Ans. $9X^2 - 4Y^2 = 36$, center at $(3,0)$. See Problem 1f of Section 9.

g) $y^2 + 8x - 6y + 33 = 0$.

h) $x^2 - 20x - 8y + 92 = 0$.   Ans. $X^2 = 8Y$, center at $(10, -1)$. See Problem 1b of Section 7.

i) $y^2 - 4x + 2y + 5 = 0$.

j) $4y^2 - 5x^2 - 50x - 8y - 201 = 0$.   Ans. $4Y^2 - 5X^2 = 80$, center at $(-5,1)$. See Problem 1g of Section 9.

k) $9x^2 - y^2 - 72x + 80 = 0$.

l) $3x^2 - y^2 + 20y = 148$.

m) $4x^2 + 3y^2 + 4x - 11 = 0$.   Ans. $4X^2 + 3Y^2 = 12$, center at $(-\frac{1}{2},0)$. See Problem 1m of Section 8.

n) $x^2 + 4y^2 - 2x - 16y = 83$.

o) $9x^2 + 5y^2 - 54x + 30y = 54$.

p) $4x^2 + 8y^2 - 12x + 8y = 89$.

q) $x^2 - 2x + 3y = 0$.   Ans. $X^2 + 3Y = 0$, center at $(1,\frac{1}{3})$. See Problem 2a of Section 7.

r) $x^2 - 8x + 6y + 16 = 0$.

s) $y^2 + 10x + 9 = 0$.

2. Find an equation for a parabola for which

a) the vertex is the point $(-1,4)$ and the directrix is the line $y = 6$.
Solution: Since the vertex of a parabola is halfway between the focus
and the directrix, the focus must be at $(-1,2)$. The vertex, for a

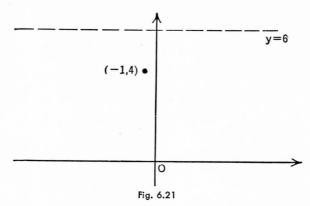

$y=6$

$(-1,4)$ •

O

Fig. 6.21

parabola in standard position, is at the origin. Let us therefore take
an XY-system with its origin at $(-1,4)$ so that

$$X = x + 1 \quad \text{and} \quad Y = y - 4$$

Referred to the XY-system, our parabola has the equation

$$X^2 = -8Y,$$

and hence, referred to the xy-system, the equation

$$(x + 1)^2 = -8(y - 4),$$

or

$$x^2 + 2x + 8y - 31 = 0.$$

b) the focus is the point $(2,-1)$ and the vertex is the point $(2,7)$.
c) the directrix is the y-axis and the point $(4,5)$ is one end of the latus
rectum.

3. Find an equation for an ellipse for which

a) the center is $(2,-2)$, one vertex is $(2,4)$ and one focus is $(2,2)$.
b) the foci are $(2,-1)$ and $(8,-1)$ and the length of the minor axis is 8.
c) one vertex is $(-3,1)$, the center is $(0,1)$ and the length of a latus
rectum is $10/3$.

4. Find an equation for a hyperbola for which

a) the center is $(2,-1)$, a vertex is $(4,-1)$ and a focus is $(5,-1)$.
b) the lines $x - 2y + 4 = 0$ and $x + 2y = 0$ are the asymptotes, and
the length of the major axis is 12.
c) a vertex is $(3,1)$, a focus is $(3,3)$ and the asymptotesar eperpendicular.

5. Using the same set of axes, sketch the graphs of

a) $x^2 + 4x + 3 = 4y$ b) $x^2 + 4x + 3 = y$
c) $x^2 + 4x + 3 = y/4$ d) $x^2 + 4x + 3 = y/16$
e) $x^2 + 4x + 3 = 0$.

11. ROTATIONS

With the methods developed in the preceding sections, we can identify the graph of any equation of the form

$$Ax^2 + Cy^2 + Dx + Ey + F = 0.$$

To handle cases in which the equation contains an xy term, we need to consider what happens when we rotate a coordinate system.

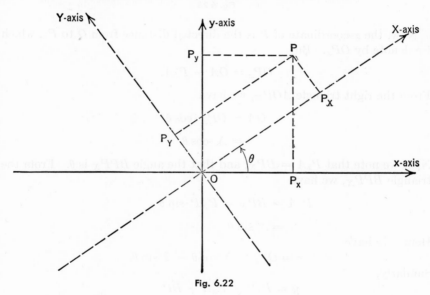

Fig. 6.22

Let us start with an xy-system. Consider the XY-system obtained by rotating the axes through an angle θ.

A point in the plane now has two pairs of coordinates, (x,y) and (X,Y). These pairs of coordinates are related by the formulas

$$x = X \cos \theta - Y \sin \theta$$

$$y = X \sin \theta + Y \cos \theta.$$

To see that this is so, drop a perpendicular from P_X to the x-axis, meeting the latter at A. Draw a line parallel to the x-axis, meeting the line P_xP at B.

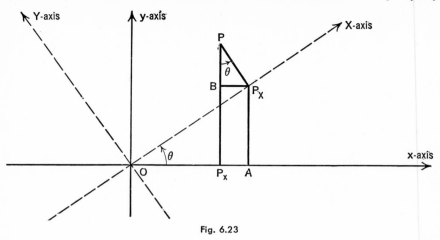

Fig. 6.23

Now, the x-coordinate of P is the directed distance from O to P_x, which we denote by OP_x. But

$$OP_x = OA - P_xA.$$

From the right triangle AOP_X, we have

$$OA = OP_X \cdot \cos \theta$$

$$= X \cdot \cos \theta.$$

Next we note that $P_xA = BP_X$, and that the angle BPP_X is θ. From the triangle BPP_X, we have

$$P_xA = BP_X = P_XP \cdot \sin \theta$$

$$= Y \sin \theta.$$

Hence we have

$$x = OP_x = X \cos \theta - Y \sin \theta.$$

Similarly,

$$y = P_xP = P_xB + BP$$

$$= AP_X + BP$$

$$= OP_X \cdot \sin \theta + P_XP \cos \theta$$

$$= X \sin \theta + Y \cos \theta.$$

If we have now a curve in the plane and an equation for it in the xy-system, say $f(x,y) = 0$, we can obtain an equation for this curve in the XY-system by substituting $X \cos \theta - Y \sin \theta$ for x and $X \sin \theta + Y \cos \theta$ for y, obtaining $f(X \cos \theta - Y \sin \theta, X \sin \theta + Y \cos \theta) = 0$.

For example, suppose we start with the equation

$$xy - 1 = 0,$$

and suppose that the XY-system is obtained from the xy-system by rotating through 45°. Then the equation

$$(X \cos 45° - Y \sin 45°)(X \sin 45° + Y \cos 45°) - 1 = 0$$

and the original equation have the same graph.

Note now that this equation in X and Y, after multiplying out, reduces to

$$\frac{X^2}{2} - \frac{Y^2}{2} = 1,$$

which we recognize as an equation of a hyperbola in standard position with respect to the XY-system. We can now sketch its graph, and thus have a graph of the original equation.

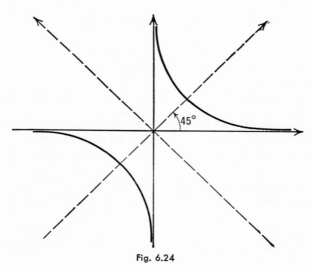

Fig. 6.24

This example suggests that if we start with a second-degree equation containing an xy term, we may be able to rotate through such an angle θ that, referred to the resulting XY-system, the graph has an equation without an XY term. It is indeed the case that this is always possible.

Theorem 6.6: *Given any equation of the form*

$$Ax^2 + Bxy + Cy^2 + Dx + Ey + F = 0,$$

there is an angle θ such that the graph of this equation, when referred to the XY-system obtained by rotating the axes through the angle θ, has an equation without a cross product term.

Proof: Starting with the equation

$$Ax^2 + Bxy + Cy^2 + Dx + Ey + F = 0,$$

substitute $X \cos \theta - Y \sin \theta$ for x, and $X \sin \theta + Y \cos \theta$ for y.   After collecting terms, we have

$$X^2[A \cos^2 \theta + B \cos \theta \sin \theta + C \sin^2 \theta]$$

$$+ XY[-2A \cos \theta \sin \theta + B(\cos^2 \theta - \sin^2 \theta) + 2C \cos \theta \sin \theta]$$

$$+ Y^2[A \sin^2 \theta + B \cos \theta \sin \theta + C \cos^2 \theta]$$

$$+ X[D \cos \theta + E \sin \theta] + Y[E \cos \theta - D \sin \theta] + F = 0.$$

We wish the XY term to drop out.   This will happen if

$$-2A \cos \theta \sin \theta + B(\cos^2 \theta - \sin^2 \theta) + 2C \cos \theta \sin \theta = 0.$$

But this can be written:

$$(A - C) \sin 2\theta = B \cos 2\theta,$$

or

$$\tan 2\theta = \frac{B}{A - C}.$$

This can always be solved for 2θ and hence for θ.   (If $A - C = 0, 2\theta = 90°$.)

We have seen in the previous sections that a second-degree equation without a cross product term can have for its graph a parabola, an ellipse or circle, or a hyperbola.   In addition, there are certain "degenerate" cases.   The graph can consist of a pair of intersecting lines (Problem 10d of Section 9), a pair of parallel lines (Problem 5e of Section 10), a single line ($y^2 = 0$), a single point (Problem 10d of Section 8), or may contain no points at all (Problem 10e of Section 8).

By virtue of Theorem 6.6, any second-degree equation has for its graph a parabola, an ellipse or circle, a hyperbola, or one of these degenerate cases.

PROBLEMS

1. Name and sketch the graph of

   a) $16x^2 + 24xy + 9y^2 + 15x - 20y = 0$.   *Solution:* Since $A = 16$, $B = 24$, and $C = 9$, $\tan 2\theta = \frac{24}{7}$.   By constructing a right triangle with sides 24 and 7 and noting that the hypotenuse is 25, we see that $\cos 2\theta = \frac{7}{25}$.   Using the formulas $\sin \theta = \sqrt{\dfrac{1 - \cos 2\theta}{2}}$ and $\cos \theta = \sqrt{\dfrac{1 + \cos 2\theta}{2}}$, we find that $\sin \theta = \frac{3}{5}$ and $\cos \theta = \frac{4}{5}$.   Substituting $x = \frac{4}{5}X - \frac{3}{5}Y$ and $y = \frac{3}{5}X + \frac{4}{5}Y$, our equation becomes

   $$X^2 = -2Y.$$

We recognize this as a parabola in standard position with respect to the XY-system, and we can sketch its graph by the methods of Section 7.

b) $8x^2 - 12xy + 17y^2 = 20$.   Ans. $\sin\theta = \dfrac{1}{\sqrt{5}}$, $X^2 + 4Y^2 = 4$.

c) $x^2 - 14xy + y^2 - 10\sqrt{2}\,x + 22\sqrt{2}\,y + 122 = 0$.   Ans. $\sin\theta = \dfrac{1}{\sqrt{2}}$, $3X^2 - 4Y^2 - 6X - 16Y = 61$.

d) $16x^2 - 24xy + 9y^2 + 150x - 50y + 275 = 0$.

e) $17x^2 - 12xy + 22y^2 - 8\sqrt{13}\,x + 12\sqrt{13}\,y = 0$.

f) $27x^2 + 78xy - 77y^2 + 360 = 0$.

2. Show that the graph of

$$Ax^2 + Bxy + Cy^2 + Dx + Ey + F = 0,$$

if not degenerate, is an ellipse or circle, parabola, or hyperbola according as $B^2 - 4AC$ is negative, zero, or positive.

12. CONIC SECTIONS

The three curves, parabola, ellipse or circle, and hyperbola are related by the fact that they all have second-degree equations and by the fact that any second-degree equation has for its graph either one of these curves or a degenerate case. However, there are other relations between these curves.

Any one of these curves can be obtained by slicing with a plane a cone. For this reason these curves are often called conic sections, or simply conics.

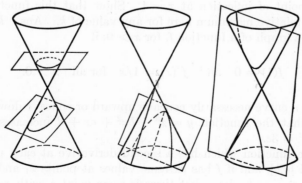

Fig. 6.25

Another way of seeing that these curves all belong to one family appears in the following theorem.

Theorem 6.7: *The locus of a point such that its distance from a fixed point has a constant ratio to its distance from a fixed line is a conic section with the fixed point as a focus.*

Exercise: Let the fixed line in this theorem be the y-axis and the fixed point be $(p,0)$. Let the constant ratio be denoted by e. Derive an equation for the locus and show that if $e < 1$, the locus is an ellipse, if $e = 1$, it is a parabola, and if $e > 1$, it is a hyperbola.

PROBLEMS

1. The number e in the exercise above is called the **eccentricity** of the conic. For the ellipse and hyperbola, find a formula for the eccentricity in terms of a, b, and c.
2. To each point (α,β) in a plane there corresponds a conic, the graph of $\alpha x^2 + \beta y^2 = 1$. For which parts of the plane are the corresponding conics ellipses with horizontal axis? with vertical axis? hyperbolas with horizontal axis? with vertical axis?

REVIEW PROBLEMS

1. The graph of $y = \dfrac{x + a}{x^2 + a^2}$ has three inflection points. Show that they lie on a straight line.
2. Find a constant k such that the function f, defined by the equation

$$f(x) = x^2 + k/x,$$

has a point of inflection at $x = 1$. Show that this function cannot have a relative maximum here for any value of k. Ans. $k = -1$.
3. Sketch a graph of a function f, for $x > 0$, if

$$f(1) = 0 \quad \text{and} \quad f'(x) = 1/x \quad \text{for all} \quad x > 0.$$

Is such a curve necessarily concave upward or concave downward?
4. Show that the function $y = x^3 + bx^2 + cx + d$ increases for all x, when $b^2 = 3c$.
5. If f is a function which has a second derivative at each point of an interval $[a,b]$, and if f has extreme values at points x_1 and x_2, where $a < x_1 < x_2 < b$, show that there is some point c, with $x_1 < c < x_2$, such that $(c,f(c))$ is an inflection point for f. Is this result still true if we merely require $a \le x_1 < x_2 \le b$?
6. Sketch the graph of each of the following equations:

a) $y^2 = \dfrac{x^2}{(x-1)(x-2)}$.

b) $x^3 + xy^2 + 4y^2 - 4x^2 = 0$.

c) $y^2 = x^2(x-1)(2-x)$.

d) $\dfrac{1}{y} = 3x^2 - x^6$.

e) $y = \dfrac{x^2}{x^2+3}$.

7. Through the point $(2,0)$ a line is drawn which meets the lines $y = x$ and $y = 3x$ in the points R and S; find an equation for the locus of the midpoint of RS.   Ans. $3x^2 - 4xy + y^2 - 6x + 4y = 0$.

8. The three points O, M, N are collinear. Find an equation for the locus of a point P such that angle OPM equals angle MPN.

9. Find an equation for the locus of the midpoint of a line which is always 2 units long and which has its two ends always on the parabola $2y = x^2$.

10. The ends A and B of a rod of length a slide on the axes of x and y. If AP and BP are perpendicular to the axes, find an equation for the locus of P.   Ans. $x^2 + y^2 = a^2$.

11. Two parabolas have a common focus and axis, but open in opposite directions. Show that they meet at right angles.

12. PQ is a focal chord of a parabola; the tangents at P, Q meet at T and the normals at R. Show that $PTQR$ is a rectangle.

13. Given the three points $(-1,2)$, $(1,-1)$ and $(2,1)$:

     a) Find a parabola passing through the given points and having its axis parallel to the x-axis.

     b) Find a parabola passing through the given points and having its axis parallel to the y-axis.

14. Show that if tangents are drawn to the ellipse $x^2/a^2 + y^2/b^2 = 1$ and to the circle $x^2 + y^2 = a^2$ at points having the same abscissa, these tangents intersect on the x-axis.

15. Show that the segment of any normal, not the x- or y-axis, to the ellipse $x^2 + 2y^2 = a^2$, between the point of intersection and the y-axis, is bisected by the x-axis.

16. Find the maximum length of the straight line drawn from the end of the minor axis of an ellipse to meet the curve.

17. A chord of a hyperbola meets an asymptote at M. R is the midpoint of the chord and C is the center of the hyperbola. Prove $CR = RM$.

18. Let the line $y = mx + k$ intersect the hyperbola $b^2x^2 - a^2y^2 = a^2b^2$ at A, A^*, and its asymptotes at B, B^*. Show that the line segments AA^* and BB^* have the same midpoint.

19. Show that the equation $x^2 + y^2 = r^2$ becomes $X^2 + Y^2 = r^2$ for every choice of the angle θ in the equations for rotation of axes.

Definite Integrals

1. INTRODUCTION

We have been studying the derivative and its applications. We now turn to the other half of calculus, *integration*.

In discussing integration we shall have to consider numerous sums, and it will be helpful to have a convenient notation for these sums. We shall use the Greek letter Σ to indicate a sum. The following equations illustrate how we use this symbol to abbreviate sums. In each case, the left-hand side is an abbreviation for the right-hand side.

$$\sum_{i=1}^{i=4} x_i = x_1 + x_2 + x_3 + x_4.$$

$$\sum_{j=7}^{j=9} w^j = w^7 + w^8 + w^9.$$

$$\sum_{s=3}^{s=8} (2 + s) = (2 + 3) + (2 + 4) + (2 + 5) + (2 + 6) + (2 + 7) + (2 + 8).$$

$$\sum_{i=1}^{i=5} i^2 = 1^2 + 2^2 + 3^2 + 4^2 + 5^2.$$

$$\sum_{i=1}^{i=n} i^2 = 1^2 + 2^2 + \cdots + n^2.$$

$$\sum_{j=0}^{j=n} j^2 = 0^2 + 1^2 + 2^2 + \cdots + n^2.$$

$$\sum_{i=2}^{i=n-1} (1 - \sqrt{i}) = (1 - \sqrt{2}) + (1 - \sqrt{3}) + \cdots + (1 - \sqrt{n-1}).$$

$$\sum_{i=0}^{i=k} x_i = x_0 + x_1 + \cdots + x_k.$$

$$\sum_{k=1}^{k=5} x_k(2 - x_k)^k = x_1(2 - x_1) + x_2(2 - x_2)^2 + x_3(2 - x_3)^3 + x_4(2 - x_4)^4 + x_5(2 - x_5)^5.$$

$$\sum_{i=1}^{i=n} x_{i-1} \cdot x_{i+1} = x_0 \cdot x_2 + x_1 \cdot x_3 + x_2 \cdot x_4 + \cdots + x_{n-1} \cdot x_{n+1}.$$

$$\sum_{i=1}^{i=n} f(c_i)(x_i - x_{i-1}) = f(c_1)(x_1 - x_0) + f(c_2)(x_2 - x_1) + \cdots \cdots + f(c_n)(x_n - x_{n-1}).$$

PROBLEMS

1. By writing each side of the following equations in unabbreviated form, show that the equations are correct:

a) $\displaystyle\sum_{i=1}^{i=n} k \cdot x_i = k \cdot \sum_{i=1}^{i=n} x_i.$

b) $\displaystyle\sum_{j=1}^{j=t} (x_j + y_j) = \sum_{j=1}^{j=t} x_j + \sum_{j=1}^{j=t} y_j.$

c) $\displaystyle\sum_{i=1}^{i=n} x_i = \sum_{k=1}^{k=n} x_k.$

d) $\displaystyle\sum_{t=1}^{t=u} (1 + 2t) = u + 2 \sum_{t=1}^{t=u} t.$

e) $\displaystyle\sum_{i=1}^{i=5} i = \sum_{i=6}^{i=10} (11 - i).$

f) $\displaystyle\sum_{k=1}^{k=n} z_k = \sum_{p=t+1}^{p=t+n} z_{p-t}.$

2. Verify each of the following identities for the cases $n = 3$ and $n = 5$:

a) $\displaystyle\sum_{i=1}^{i=n} i = \frac{n(n + 1)}{2}.$

b) $\displaystyle\sum_{i=1}^{i=n} i^2 = \frac{n(n + 1)(2n + 1)}{6}.$

c) $\displaystyle\sum_{i=1}^{i=n} i^3 = \frac{n^2(n + 1)^2}{4}.$

2. TWO PROBLEMS

As an introduction to integration, we first discuss two specific problems.

We meet with the concept of work in physics. The amount of work done when a constant force moves a body a certain distance (e.g., when a weight is pulled up against the force of gravity) is defined as the product of the magnitude of the force by the distance moved.

But suppose we have a case where the force is not constant. What then is the amount of work done? To be specific, let us consider a spring which satisfies Hooke's Law. This law says that the force, which we shall measure in pounds, necessary to hold the spring when it has been stretched x feet beyond its natural length is proportional to x. Let us denote by F the function which expresses this relationship between amount of stretching and force, i.e., F assigns to each non-negative number x the numerical value of the force exerted by the spring when it has been stretched x feet. If Hooke's Law is satisfied, then $F(x) = kx$. In order to keep the numerical calculations which follow as simple as possible, let us suppose that we are dealing with a spring whose natural length is 10 ft. and for which the constant k is 1, so that $F(x) = x$.

Now we may ask how much work is done when we pull out the spring from its original length of 10 ft. to a total length of 15 ft. Note that as we start to pull out the spring, x, the amount of stretching, is small and hence the force we are applying is also small. But as we pull out the spring further, x increases and so does $F(x)$. The force is not constant. Therefore, we cannot use the old definition of work, force times distance, to find out how much work is done in this case.

After some reflection, we see that the real problem here is to decide precisely what we mean by the term "work" when we have a case, such as this, where the force is not constant. Since this is a physical problem, we may have an intuitive idea of what "work" should mean in this case. But whatever we mean by "work," we agree that the "work" done in stretching this spring from 10 ft. to 15 ft. is no more than $5 \cdot 5 = 25$ ft.-lbs., for the total distance involved is 5 ft., and the maximum force involved is 5 lbs., which is reached at the end of the stretching.

Also, the "work" done is certainly no less than $5 \cdot 0 = 0$ ft.-lbs., for the minimum force involved, which comes at the beginning of the stretching, is 0 lbs. Therefore, denoting by W the amount of "work" done, we agree that

$$0 \leq W \leq 25.$$

Now suppose that we consider that the stretching is done in two steps. We first pull out the spring half way, $2\frac{1}{2}$ ft., and then pull it out the rest of the way, another $2\frac{1}{2}$ ft. In the first step, the amount of "work" done, call it W_1, is certainly no greater than $2\frac{1}{2} \cdot 2\frac{1}{2} = 6\frac{1}{4}$ and no less than $2\frac{1}{2} \cdot 0 = 0$,

$$0 \leq W_1 \leq 6\frac{1}{4}.$$

In the second step, the amount of "work" done—call it W_2—is no greater than $2\frac{1}{2} \cdot 5 = 12\frac{1}{2}$ since the distance is $2\frac{1}{2}$ ft. and the maximum force, reached at the end, is 5 lbs. Also, W_2 is no less than $2\frac{1}{2} \cdot 2\frac{1}{2} = 6\frac{1}{4}$, since the distance is again $2\frac{1}{2}$ ft. but the minimum force, which occurs at the beginning of this step, is $2\frac{1}{2}$ lbs. Then

$$6\frac{1}{4} \leq W_2 \leq 12\frac{1}{2}.$$

Now the total amount of "work" done, W, is given by

$$W = W_1 + W_2.$$

But, from the inequalities above, we have

$$0 + 6\frac{1}{4} \leq W_1 + W_2 \leq 6\frac{1}{4} + 12\frac{1}{2}$$

or

$$6\frac{1}{4} \leq W \leq 18\frac{3}{4}.$$

By considering the stretching process as done in two steps rather than one, we have found a larger lower bound for W, $6\frac{1}{4}$ as against 0, and a smaller upper bound, $18\frac{3}{4}$ as against 25. Suppose we now consider the stretching process as done in five equal steps. Then we find that

$$10 \leq W \leq 15.$$

Exercise: Carry out this calculation.

Thus we see that by taking more and smaller steps, we pin W down into a smaller range, since we find a larger lower bound and a smaller upper bound for the "work" done.

In general, we could take any finite sequence of points, starting at 0 and ending at 5, say $x_0 = 0 < x_1 < x_2 < \cdots < x_n = 5$, and consider the first step as stretching from x_0 to x_1, etc., and the last as stretching from x_{n-1} to x_n. During any step, say the kth step, the distance stretched is $x_k - x_{k-1}$. The minimum force involved in this step, which occurs at the beginning of the step, is equal to x_{k-1} and the maximum to x_k. Therefore, the "work" done in this step is no less than $x_{k-1}(x_k - x_{k-1})$ and no greater than $x_k(x_k - x_{k-1})$:

$$x_{k-1}(x_k - x_{k-1}) \leq W_k \leq x_k(x_k - x_{k-1}).$$

Adding these inequalities, we have

$$x_0(x_1 - x_0) + x_1(x_2 - x_1) + \cdots + x_{n-1}(x_n - x_{n-1}) \leq W$$

and

$$W \leq x_1(x_1 - x_0) + x_2(x_2 - x_1) + \cdots + x_n(x_n - x_{n-1}),$$

or

$$\sum_{i=1}^{i=n} x_{i-1}(x_i - x_{i-1}) \leq W \leq \sum_{i=1}^{i=n} x_i(x_i - x_{i-1}).$$

These inequalities hold no matter what sequence $x_0 < x_1 < \cdots < x_n$ we choose. The left-hand side of the double inequality above says that W is an upper bound for the collection of all numbers of the form

$$\sum_{i=1}^{i=n} x_{i-1}(x_i - x_{i-1}),$$

obtained by taking all possible sequences. Therefore W is at no smaller than the *least* upper bound of this collection:

$$LUB\left(\sum_{i=1}^{i=n} x_{i-1}(x_i - x_{i-1})\right) \leq W.$$

Similarly,

$$W \leq GLB\left(\sum_{i=1}^{i=n} x_i(x_i - x_{i-1})\right).$$

In our calculations above we saw that by doing the stretching in one step, the distance between our calculated lower and upper bounds was 25, for two steps it was $12\frac{1}{2}$, and for five steps it was 5. This would seem to indicate that by taking enough steps, the distance between these bounds becomes as small as we please, i.e., that the least upper bound and the greatest lower bound above are actually equal.

If this should turn out to be the case, it would then be reasonable to define the amount of work done in stretching our spring to be

$$W = LUB \left(\sum_{i=1}^{i=n} x_{i-1}(x_i - x_{i-1}) \right) = GLB \left(\sum_{i=1}^{i=n} x_i(x_i - x_{i-1}) \right).$$

We shall see later in this chapter that for this particular problem the greatest lower bound and least upper bound are indeed equal, (their common value, incidentally, is $12\frac{1}{2}$), so for this problem we do have a plausible definition of what we mean by the "work" done.

Before going on to our next problem, let us rewrite our final result above in a slightly different form. Given a sequence, $x_0 = 0 < x_1 < \cdots < x_n = 5$, let us denote by $F(\underline{x}_i)$ the minimum value, in the interval $[x_{i-1}, x_i]$, of the function F which expresses the relationship between the amount of stretching and the force exerted by the spring. In this problem $F(x) = x$, so $F(\underline{x}_i) = x_{i-1}$. Similarly, let us denote by $F(\bar{x}_i)$ the maximum value, in this interval, of the function F. Then $F(\bar{x}_i) = x_i$.

With this notation, we can write our last two inequalities above as

$$LUB \left(\sum_{i=1}^{i=n} F(\underline{x}_i)(x_i - x_{i-1}) \right) \leq W \leq GLB \left(\sum_{i=1}^{i=n} F(\bar{x}_i)(x_i - x_{i-1}) \right).$$

Let us now consider our second problem, that of finding the area of a figure in the plane. Suppose the figure is bounded below by the x-axis, to the right and left by vertical lines, $x = a$ and $x = b$, and above by the

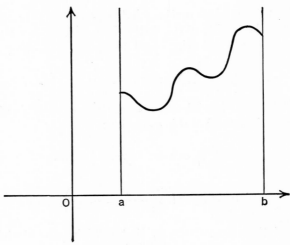

Fig. 7.1

graph of some continuous function, f. How can we find the area of this figure?

We know, of course, how to find the area of some simple figures. For example, the area of a rectangle is defined to be the product of the base by the altitude. In the usual first course in geometry, it is shown how the areas of triangles, parallelograms, etc., can be obtained by comparing them

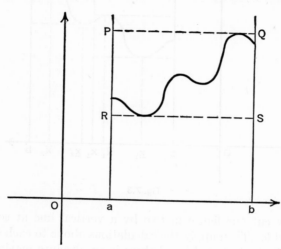

Fig. 7.2

with rectangles. The area of a circle is obtained by a limiting process from the areas of sums of triangles.

Returning now to our figure, after some consideration we see that the basic problem is to decide what we mean by its "area." We all have an intuitive idea of what we should mean by the "area" of this figure, and we certainly would agree that, whatever this meaning is to be, the "area" of the figure is no greater than the area of the rectangle $abQP$ whose top touches the highest point of the graph. We recall (Theorem 5.3) that there is some point $\bar{x}$ in the interval $[a,b]$ such that $f(\bar{x})$ is an absolute maximum of the function in this interval. The area of the rectangle is then $f(\bar{x})(b - a)$. If we denote the "area" of the figure by A, we have then

$$A \leq f(\bar{x})(b - a).$$

Similarly, we would agree that the "area" of the figure should be no less than the area of the rectangle $abSR$, whose top side passes through the lowest point of the graph. By Theorem 5.3 again, there is a point $\underline{x}$ in $[a,b]$ such that $f(\underline{x})$ is an absolute minimum for f in the interval $[a,b]$. Then the area of this rectangle is $f(\underline{x})(b - a)$, so we have

$$f(\underline{x})(b - a) \leq A \leq f(\bar{x})(b - a).$$

Now, no matter what we mean by the "area" of the figure, we have at least pinned it down between two bounds.

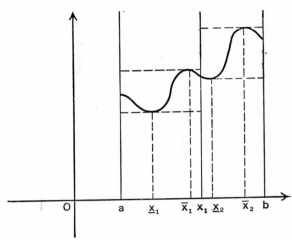

Fig. 7.3

Let us now cut our figure in two by a vertical line at some point x_1 between a and b. Then apply the calculations above to each of the resulting figures. In the interval $[a,x_1]$ there is an absolute maximum at, say, $\bar{x}_1$, and an absolute minimum at, say, $\underline{x}_1$. Then

$$f(\underline{x}_1)(x_1 - a) \leq A_1 \leq f(\bar{x}_1)(x_1 - a).$$

Similarly,

$$f(\underline{x}_2)(b - x_1) \leq A_2 \leq f(\bar{x}_2)(b - x_1).$$

Now, since $A = A_1 + A_2$, we have

$$f(\underline{x}_1)(x_1 - a) + f(\underline{x}_2)(b - x_1) \leq A \leq f(\bar{x}_1)(x_1 - a) + f(\bar{x}_2)(b - x_1).$$

It is easy to see that

$$f(\underline{x})(b - a) \leq f(\underline{x}_1)(x_1 - a) + f(\underline{x}_2)(b - x_1)$$

and

$$f(\bar{x}_1)(x_1 - a) + f(\bar{x}_2)(b - x_1) \leq f(\bar{x})(b - a),$$

so we have pinned A down between closer bounds.

Exercise: Show that these last two inequalities are correct.

In general, if we divide the interval from a to b into a number of smaller intervals by means of a sequence of points, $x_0 = a < x_1 < x_2 < \cdots < x_{n-1} < x_n = b$, and divide the figure into smaller figures by the vertical lines through these points, then the total area of our figure should be no less than the sum of the areas of the inside rectangles, and no greater than the sum of the areas of the outside rectangles. In any interval, say the

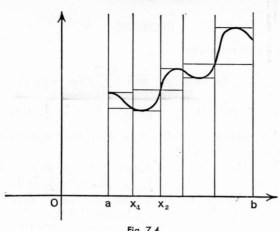

Fig. 7.4

kth, $[x_{k-1},x_k]$, f has an absolute maximum at some point $\bar{x}_k$ and an absolute minimum at some point $\underline{x}_k$. The areas of the outside and inside rectangles are then $f(\bar{x}_k)(x_k - x_{k-1})$ and $f(\underline{x}_k)(x_k - x_{k-1})$. Hence we have

$$f(\underline{x}_1)(x_1 - x_0) + f(\underline{x}_2)(x_2 - x_1) + \cdots + f(\underline{x}_n)(x_n - x_{n-1}) \leq A$$

and

$$A \leq f(\bar{x}_1)(x_1 - x_0) + f(\bar{x}_2)(x_2 - x_1) + \cdots + f(\bar{x}_n)(x_n - x_{n-1}),$$

or

$$\sum_{i=1}^{i=n} f(\underline{x}_i)(x_i - x_{i-1}) \leq A \leq \sum_{i=1}^{=n} f(\bar{x}_i)(x_i - x_{i-1}).$$

These inequalities hold no matter which sequence $x_0, x_1, \cdots, x_n$ we use, so, from the first of these,

$$LUB\left(\sum_{i=1}^{i=n} f(\underline{x}_i)(x_i - x_{i-1})\right) \leq A.$$

Similarly,

$$A \leq GLB\left(\sum_{i=1}^{i=n} f(\bar{x}_i)(x_i - x_{i-1})\right).$$

From the figures we have drawn, it seems plausible that we can, by choosing the sequence $x_0, x_1, \cdots, x_n$ properly, have the difference between the lower and upper bounds as small as we please. This means that the least upper bound and greatest lower bound above are equal. If so, then it would be reasonable to define the "area" of our figure to be the common value of the least upper bound and greatest lower bound.

We shall see later in this chapter that as long as f is continuous, the least upper bound and greatest lower bound are indeed equal.

PROBLEMS

1. Compute the two numbers

$$\sum_{i=1}^{i=10} x_{i-1}(x_i - x_{i-1}) \quad \text{and} \quad \sum_{i=1}^{i=10} x_i(x_i - x_{i-1})$$

for the sequence $x_0 = 0$, $x_1 = \frac{1}{2}$, $x_2 = \frac{2}{2}$, $x_3 = \frac{3}{2}$, $\cdots$, $x_i = \frac{i}{2}$, $\cdots$,

$x_{10} = \frac{10}{2} = 5$. What does this tell us about the "work" done in pulling out the spring discussed above?

2. Suppose a spring has a natural length of 6 ft. and that for it $F(x) = 4x$. Use the sequence $x_0 = 1$, $x_1 = \frac{3}{2}$, $x_2 = 2$, $x_3 = \frac{5}{2}$, and $x_4 = 3$ to find lower and upper bounds for the amount of "work" done in stretching the spring from a length of 7 ft. to a length of 9 ft.

3. Suppose that for a certain spring $F(x) = \sqrt{x}$. Find lower and upper bounds for the amount of "work" done in stretching it 16 ft. beyond its natural length by using first the sequence $x_0 = 0$, $x_1 = 8$, $x_2 = 16$ and then the sequence $x_0 = 0$, $x_1 = 4$, $x_2 = 9$, $x_3 = 16$.

4. a) Draw the figure in the plane bounded below by the x-axis, to the right by the line $x = 1$, and above by the graph of the function f, where $f(x) = 2x$.

b) Compute the numbers

$$\sum_{i=1}^{i=4} f(\underline{x}_i)(x_i - x_{i-1}) \quad \text{and} \quad \sum_{i=1}^{i=4} f(\bar{x}_i)(x_i - x_{i-1})$$

for the sequence $x_0 = 0$, $x_1 = \frac{1}{4}$, $x_2 = \frac{1}{2}$, $x_3 = \frac{3}{4}$, $x_4 = 1$.

c) Do the same for the sequence

$x_0 = 0$, $x_1 = \frac{1}{10}$, $x_2 = \frac{3}{10}$, $x_3 = \frac{4}{10}$, $x_4 = \frac{7}{10}$, $x_5 = \frac{8}{10}$, $x_6 = 1$.

d) What do the numbers obtained in *b*) and *c*) tell us about the "area" of this figure?

e) Observe that this figure is a triangle and compute its area. Compare with your answer to *d*).

5. Carry out the program of Problem 4 for the figure bounded below by the x-axis, on the left by the y-axis, and above by the graph of g where $g(x) = 3 - 3x$.

6. Consider the figure bounded below by the x-axis, on the right by the line $x = 2$, and above by the graph of h, where $h(x) = x^3$. Find upper and lower bounds for the "area" of this figure by using first the sequence $x_0 = 0$, $x_1 = 1$, $x_2 = 2$ and then the sequence $x_0 = 1$, $x_1 = \frac{1}{2}$, $x_2 = \frac{3}{2}$, $x_3 = 2$.

7. Consider the figure bounded below by the x-axis, on the left and right by the lines $x = -2$ and $x = 2$, and above by the graph of φ, where $\varphi(x) = 1 + x^2$. Find upper and lower bounds for the "area" of this figure by using first the sequence $x_0 = -2$, $x_1 = 0$, $x_2 = 2$, next the sequence $x_0 = -2$, $x_1 = -1$, $x_2 = 0$, $x_3 = 1$, $x_4 = 2$, and finally the sequence $x_0 = -2$, $x_1 = -1$, $x_2 = 0$, $x_3 = 1$, $x_4 = \frac{3}{2}$, $x_5 = 2$.

3. DEFINITION AND PROPERTIES OF UPPER AND LOWER DEFINITE INTEGRALS

In both of the problems examined in the previous section, we went through the same kind of process. We now wish to study this process by itself, abstractly. Later we will return to these problems and apply the results of our study to them, but we shall also find many other applications.

Definition 7.1: *Let f be a function which is continuous on an interval $[a,b]$. To each sequence $x_0 = a < x_1 < \cdots < x_n = b$ we associate the number*

$$\sum_{i=1}^{i=n} f(\bar{x}_i)(x_i - x_{i-1}),$$

*where $\bar{x}_i$ is a point in the interval $[x_{i-1}, x_i]$ at which f has an absolute maximum value for this interval. The **upper definite integral** of f over this interval, denoted by*

$$\overline{\int_a^b} f,$$

is the number which is the greatest lower bound, for all possible sequences, of these numbers:

$$\overline{\int_a^b} f = GLB\left(\sum_{i=1}^{i=n} f(\bar{x}_i)(x_i - x_{i-1}) \right).$$

Definition 7.2: *Let f be a function which is continuous on an interval $[a,b]$. To each sequence $x_0 = a < x_1 < \cdots < x_n = b$ we associate the number*

$$\sum_{i=1}^{i=n} f(\underline{x}_i)(x_i - x_{i-1}),$$

*where $\underline{x}_i$ is a point in the interval $[x_{i-1}, x_i]$ at which f has an absolute minimum value for this interval. The **lower definite integral** of f over this interval, denoted by*

$$\underline{\int_a^b} f,$$

is the number which is the least upper bound, for all possible sequences, of these numbers:

$$\underline{\int_a^b} f = LUB\left(\sum_{i=1}^{i=n} f(\underline{x}_i)(x_i - x_{i-1}) \right).$$

It is necessary to observe that the upper and lower definite integrals always exist. For the lower definite integral, consider any sequence $x_0 = a < x_1 < \cdots < x_n = b$. Since f is continuous, it has an absolute maximum in $[a,b]$ at some point $\bar{x}$. (Why?) This means that for any x in $[a,b]$,

$$f(x) \leq f(\bar{x}).$$

In particular, for each i,

$$f(\underline{x}_i) \leq f(\bar{x}).$$

Then

$$\sum_{i=1}^{i=n} f(\underline{x}_i)(x_i - x_{i-1}) \leq \sum_{i=1}^{i=n} f(\bar{x})(x_i - x_{i-1})$$

$$= f(\bar{x}) \sum_{i=1}^{i=n} (x_i - x_{i-1})$$

$$= f(\bar{x})(b - a).$$

Thus we see that the number $f(\bar{x})(b - a)$ is an upper bound for the collection of numbers $\sum_{i=1}^{i=n} f(\underline{x}_i)(x_i - x_{i-1})$. Therefore, by the least upper bound axiom, this collection does have a least upper bound.

Exercise: Show that the upper definite integral always exists.

Definition 7.3: *If* $\int_{\underline{a}}^{b} f = \int_{a}^{\overline{b}} f$, *this number, the common value of the upper and lower integrals, is called the* **definite integral** *of f over the interval* $[a,b]$.

We denote the definite integral of f over $[a,b]$ by

$$\int_{a}^{b} f.$$

The problems which we analyzed in Section 2 lead us to hope that for most functions the lower and upper definite integrals will be equal. Fortunately this turns out to be the case for every function which is continuous. We state this theorem here, but postpone its proof to the next section.

Theorem 7.1: *If f is a function which is continuous on an interval* $[a,b]$, *then*

$$\int_{\underline{a}}^{b} f = \int_{a}^{\overline{b}} f,$$

i.e., $\int_{a}^{b} f$ *exists.*

For the proof of this theorem we need a number of preliminary results, to which the rest of this section is devoted. In order to simplify writing out the details of the proofs which follow, it is convenient to introduce the following notation which will be used only in this section. Let f be a function which is continuous on an interval $[a,b]$ and let σ denote a sequence $x_0 = a < x_1 < \cdots < x_n = b$ from a to b. We now define the symbols $\underline{S}_a^b(\sigma)$ and $\overline{S}_a^b(\sigma)$ by the equations

$$\underline{S}_a^b(\sigma) = \sum_{i=1}^{i=n} f(\underline{x}_i)(x_i - x_{i-1})$$

$$\overline{S}_a^b(\sigma) = \sum_{i=1}^{i=n} f(\bar{x}_i)(x_i - x_{i-1}).$$

In this notation, $\displaystyle\underline{\int_a^b} f = LUB(\underline{S}_a^b(\sigma))$ for all sequences σ from a to b, and

similarly $\displaystyle\overline{\int_a^b} f = GLB(\overline{S}_a^b(\sigma))$.

Theorem 7.2: *Let f be a function which is continuous on an interval $[a,b]$. Let $x_0 = a < x_1 < \cdots < x_n = b$ and $z_0 = a < z_1 < \cdots < z_m = b$ be two sequences. If each point of the first sequence is also a point of the second sequence, then*

$$\sum_{i=1}^{i=m} f(\underline{z}_i)(z_i - z_{i-1}) \geq \sum_{i=1}^{i=n} f(\underline{x}_i)(x_i - x_{i-1})$$

and

$$\sum_{i=1}^{=m} f(\bar{z}_i)(z_i - z_{i-1}) \leq \sum_{i=1}^{i=n} f(\bar{x}_i)(x_i - x_{i-1}).$$

Proof: In terms of the notation explained above, we are to show that if σ_1 and σ_2 are two sequences from a to b and if each point of σ_1 is also a point of σ_2, then

$$\underline{S}_a^b(\sigma_1) \leq \underline{S}_a^b(\sigma_2) \quad \text{and} \quad \overline{S}_a^b(\sigma_1) \geq \overline{S}_a^b(\sigma_2).$$

We shall prove only the first of these inequalities, leaving the proof of the second as an exercise. Let us take one of the points of σ_2 which is not already in σ_1 and add it to σ_1 to obtain a new sequence σ^*. Suppose the new point lies between x_{i-1} and x_i. Denote it by y_i, so we have $x_{i-1} < y_i < x_i$. Now one term in $\underline{S}_a^b(\sigma_1)$ is $f(\underline{x}_i)(x_i - x_{i-1})$, where $f(\underline{x}_i)$ is the minimum value of f in $[x_{i-1},x_i]$. Two terms of $\underline{S}_a^b(\sigma^*)$ are $f(\underline{s}_i)(y_i - x_{i-1}) + f(\underline{t}_i)(x_i - y_i)$, where $f(\underline{s}_i)$ is the minimum value of f in $[x_{i-1},y_i]$ and $f(\underline{t}_i)$ is the minimum value of f in $[y_i,x_i]$. Also, all the other terms of $\underline{S}_a^b(\sigma_1)$ and $\underline{S}_a^b(\sigma^*)$ are the same, since σ^* differs from σ_1 only in containing the point y_i.

Since $\underline{s}_i$ and $\underline{t}_i$ are both in the interval $[x_{i-1},x_i]$, $f(\underline{x}_i) \leq f(\underline{s}_i)$ and $f(\underline{x}_i) \leq f(\underline{t}_i)$. Therefore $f(\underline{s}_i)(y_i - x_{i-1}) + f(\underline{t}_i)(x_i - y_i) \geq f(\underline{x}_i)(y_i - x_{i-1}) + f(\underline{x}_i)(x_i - y_i) = f(\underline{x}_i)(x_i - x_{i-1})$. Hence

$$\underline{S}_a^b(\sigma_1) \leq \underline{S}_a^b(\sigma^*).$$

Next we take another point of σ_2 which is not in σ^* and add it to σ^* to obtain a sequence σ^{**}. By exactly the same argument, we have

$$\underline{S}_a^b(\sigma^*) \leq \underline{S}_a^b(\sigma^{**}),$$

and so

$$\underline{S}_a^b(\sigma_1) \leq \underline{S}_a^b(\sigma^{**}).$$

But we can repeat this process, each time adding a new point of σ_2, until, after a finite number of steps, we arrive at σ_2 itself. Combining the inequalities, one for each step, we have

$$\underline{S}_a^b(\sigma_1) \leq \underline{S}_a^b(\sigma_2).$$

Exercise: Rewrite this proof without using the $\underline{S}_a^b(\sigma)$ notation.

Exercise: Prove the other inequality in Theorem 7.2.

In defining the upper definite integral, we took the maximum value of f on each interval considered, while for the lower definite integral we took the minimum value of f. One would guess, therefore, that we always have

$$\int_{\underline{a}}^b f \leq \overline{\int_a^b} f.$$

This guess is indeed correct, but the proof is not trivial.

Theorem 7.3: *If f is a function which is continuous on an interval $[a,b]$, then*

$$\int_{\underline{a}}^b f \leq \overline{\int_a^b} f.$$

Proof: We first show that if σ_1 and σ_2 are any two sequences from a to b, then

$$\underline{S}_a^b(\sigma_1) \leq \overline{S}_a^b(\sigma_2).$$

Let σ_3 be the sequence from a to b obtained by lumping together all the points of both σ_1 and σ_2. Then every point of σ_1 is also a point of σ_3, so by Theorem 7.2 we have

$$\underline{S}_a^b(\sigma_1) \leq \underline{S}_a^b(\sigma_3).$$

Similarly, we have

$$\overline{S}_a^b(\sigma_2) \geq \overline{S}_a^b(\sigma_3).$$

Now, if σ_3 is the sequence $x_0 = a < x_1 < \cdots < x_n = b$, then $f(\underline{x}_i)$ is the absolute minimum value of f in the interval $[x_{i-1}, x_i]$ and $f(\bar{x}_i)$ is the absolute maximum, and so $f(\underline{x}_i) \leq f(\bar{x}_i)$. Therefore

$$\underline{S}_a^b(\sigma_3) \leq \overline{S}_a^b(\sigma_3). \quad \text{(Why?)}$$

This inequality, together with the two above, gives

$$\underline{S}_a^b(\sigma_1) \leq \overline{S}_a^b(\sigma_2).$$

This inequality holds for any two sequences σ_1 and σ_2, and so for any particular sequence σ_1, the number $\underline{S}_a^b(\sigma_1)$ is a lower bound for the collection of numbers $\overline{S}_a^b(\sigma_2)$ for all sequences σ_2. Therefore

$$\underline{S}_a^b(\sigma_1) \leq \overline{\int_a^b} f. \quad \text{(Why?)}$$

But this inequality tells us that the number $\overline{\int_a^b} f$ is an upper bound of

the collection of numbers $\underline{S}_a^b(\sigma_1)$ for all sequences σ_1, and so

$$\underline{\int_a^b} f \leq \overline{\int_a^b} f. \quad \text{(Why?)}$$

Theorem 7.4: *If f is a function which is continuous on an interval $[a,b]$, and if M and m are numbers such that*

$$m \leq f(x) \leq M$$

for all x in $[a,b]$, then

$$m(b - a) \leq \underline{\int_a^b} f \quad and \quad \overline{\int_a^b} f \leq M(b - a).$$

Proof: We prove only the second of these inequalities. By Definition 7.1, $\overline{\int_a^b} f$ is the greatest lower bound of the collection of numbers of the form

$$\sum_{i=1}^{i=n} f(\bar{x}_i)(x_i - x_{i-1})$$

for all sequences $x_0 = a < x_1 < \cdots < x_n = b$. A particular sequence is the one consisting of just the two points $x_0 = a$ and $x_1 = b$. The number corresponding to this sequence is

$$\sum_{i=1}^{i=1} f(\bar{x}_i)(x_i - x_{i-1}) = f(\bar{x}_1)(x_1 - x_0) = f(\bar{x}_1)(b - a).$$

This number is then in our collection and consequently is greater than or equal to the greatest lower bound of the collection:

$$\overline{\int_a^b} f \leq f(\bar{x}_1)(b - a).$$

But, by hypothesis,

$$f(\bar{x}_1) \leq M.$$

Therefore

$$\overline{\int_a^b} f \le M(b - a).$$

Exercise: Prove that $m(b - a) \le \underline{\int_a^b} f.$

Theorem 7.5: *If f is a function which is continuous on an interval $[a,b]$, and if c is a number such that $a < c < b$, then*

$$\underline{\int_a^c} f + \underline{\int_c^b} f = \underline{\int_a^b} f \quad and \quad \overline{\int_a^c} f + \overline{\int_c^b} f = \overline{\int_a^b} f.$$

Proof: We prove only the first of these equalities, leaving the proof of the second as an exercise. Let σ_1 be a sequence from a to c and σ_2 a sequence from c to b. These two sequences together form a sequence σ_3 from a to b and

$$\underline{S}_a^c(\sigma_1) + \underline{S}_c^b(\sigma_2) = \underline{S}_a^b(\sigma_3). \quad \text{(Why?)}$$

But this equation tells us that

$$\underline{S}_a^c(\sigma_1) + \underline{S}_c^b(\sigma_2) \le \underline{\int_a^b} f, \quad \text{(Why?)}$$

or

$$\underline{S}_a^c(\sigma_1) \le \underline{\int_a^b} f - \underline{S}_c^b(\sigma_2).$$

This inequality holds for any pair of sequences σ_1 and σ_2, and so for any particular sequence σ_2 we have

$$\underline{\int_a^c} f \le \underline{\int_a^b} f - \underline{S}_c^b(\sigma_2), \quad \text{(Why?)}$$

or

$$\underline{S}_c^b(\sigma_2) \le \underline{\int_a^b} f - \underline{\int_a^c} f.$$

This inequality holds for any sequence σ_2, so

$$\underline{\int_c^b} f \le \underline{\int_a^b} f - \underline{\int_a^c} f,$$

or

$$\underline{\int_a^c} f + \underline{\int_c^b} f \le \underline{\int_a^b} f,$$

and the first half of the proof is finished.

Next let σ be any sequence from a to b, and let σ^* be the sequence from a to b obtained by adding to σ the point c. (If c is already in σ, then $\sigma^* = \sigma$.) Denote by σ_1 the points of σ^* in $[a,c]$ and by σ_2 the points of σ^* in $[c,b]$. Then σ_1 is a sequence from a to c and σ_2 is a sequence from c to b, and

$$\underline{S}_a^c(\sigma_1) + \underline{S}_c^b(\sigma_2) = \underline{S}_a^b(\sigma^*).$$

Now

$$\underline{S}_a^c(\sigma_1) \le \underline{\int_a^c} f \quad \text{and} \quad \underline{S}_c^b(\sigma_2) \le \underline{\int_c^b} f, \quad \text{(Why?)}$$

so

$$\underline{\int_a^c} f + \underline{\int_c^b} f \ge \underline{S}_a^b(\sigma^*).$$

But, by Theorem 7.2, $\underline{S}_a^b(\sigma^*) \ge \underline{S}_a^b(\sigma)$, so

$$\underline{\int_a^c} f + \underline{\int_c^b} f \ge \underline{S}_a^b(\sigma).$$

Now this inequality holds for any sequence σ from a to b, so we have

$$\underline{\int_a^c} f + \underline{\int_c^b} f \ge \underline{\int_a^b} f. \quad \text{(Why?)}$$

Combining this with the inequality obtained above, we have

$$\underline{\int_a^c} f + \underline{\int_c^b} f = \underline{\int_a^b} f.$$

Exercise: Carry out the proof of the other equation of Theorem 7.5.

In the definition of the upper and lower definite integrals, we took $a < b$ and our sequences ran from a to b. If we were to proceed in the opposite direction, then for each term $f(\bar{x}_i)(x_i - x_{i-1})$ we would now have the term $f(\bar{x}_i)(x_{i-1} - x_i)$ and for $f(\underline{x}_i)(x_i - x_{i-1})$ we would have $f(\underline{x}_i)(x_{i-1} - x_i)$. But

$$f(\bar{x}_i)(x_{i-1} - x_i) = -f(\bar{x}_i)(x_i - x_{i-1}),$$

and

$$f(\underline{x}_i)(x_{i-1} - x_i) = -f(\underline{x}_i)(x_i - x_{i-1}).$$

This makes reasonable the following definition:

Definition 7.4: *If f is a function which is continuous on an interval $[a,b]$, then*

$$\underline{\int_b^a} f = -\underline{\int_a^b} f \quad \text{and} \quad \overline{\int_b^a} f = -\overline{\int_a^b} f.$$

The next definition is also a reasonable one.

Definition 7.5: *If f is a function which is defined at a number a, then*

$$\int_{\underline{a}}^a f = 0 = \int_a^{\overline{a}} f.$$

The symbols $\int_{\underline{a}}^b f$ and $\int_a^{\overline{b}} f$ are now defined no matter what the relative positions of a and b, provided only that f is continuous on the interval defined by these two numbers.

Theorem 7.6: *If f is a function which is continuous on an interval I, and if a, b, and c are three numbers in the interval I, then*

$$\int_{\underline{a}}^c f + \int_{\underline{c}}^b f = \int_{\underline{a}}^b f \quad and \quad \int_a^{\overline{c}} f + \int_c^{\overline{b}} f = \int_a^{\overline{b}} f.$$

Exercise: Prove this theorem.

Hint: The case $a < c < b$ is given by Theorem 7.5.   Consider each of the other cases, $a < b < c$, $a < c = b$, etc., separately and use Definitions 7.4 and 7.5.

PROBLEMS

1. For each of the problems discussed in Section 2, write the final result as a definite integral.
2. Consider the function defined by the equation $f(x) = x$.

   a) Take the sequence $x_0 = 0 < x_1 < \cdots < x_4 = 1$ which divides the interval from 0 to 1 into four equal parts.   For this sequence, compute

   $$\sum_{i=1}^{i=4} f(\underline{x}_i)(x_i - x_{i-1}) \quad and \quad \sum_{i=1}^{i=4} f(\bar{x}_i)(x_i - x_{i-1}).$$

   b) Take the sequence $x_0 = 0 < x_1 < \cdots < x_{10} = 1$ which divides the interval from 0 to 1 into 10 equal parts and compute

   $$\sum_{i=1}^{i=10} f(\underline{x}_i)(x_i - x_{i-1}) \quad and \quad \sum_{i=1}^{i=10} f(\bar{x}_i)(x_i - x_{i-1}).$$

   c) Take the sequence $x_0 = 0 < x_1 < \cdots < x_n = 1$ which divides the interval from 0 to 1 into n equal parts and show that

   $$\sum_{i=1}^{i=n} f(\underline{x}_i)(x_i - x_{i-1}) = \frac{1}{2} - \frac{1}{2n}$$

   and

   $$\sum_{i=1}^{i=n} f(\bar{x}_i)(x_i - x_{i-1}) = \frac{1}{2} + \frac{1}{2n}.$$

$$\left(\text{Use the algebraic identity } \sum_{i=1}^{i=n} i = \frac{n(n+1)}{2}.\right)$$

d) Show that the least upper bound of the collection of numbers of the form $\dfrac{1}{2} - \dfrac{1}{2n}$, n an integer, is the number $\frac{1}{2}$.

e) Use c) and d) to show that

$$\underline{\int_0^1} f \geq \tfrac{1}{2}.$$

$\left(\textit{Hint: In c) we have calculated } \sum_{i=1}^{i=n} f(x_i)(x_i - x_{i-1}) \text{ only for those sequences which divide } [0,1] \text{ into equal parts.}\right)$

f) Show that $\overline{\int_0^1} f \leq \tfrac{1}{2}$.

g) Using e), f) and Theorem 7.3, show that

$$\int_0^1 f = \tfrac{1}{2}.$$

3. Follow the procedure of Problem 2 to show that

$$\int_0^1 g = \tfrac{1}{3}$$

where g is defined by the equation $g(x) = x^2$. $\left(\text{Use the algebraic identity: } \sum_{i=1}^{i=n} i^2 = \frac{n(n+1)(2n+1)}{6}.\right)$

4. Follow the procedure of Problem 2 to show that

$$\int_0^1 h = 1,$$

where h is defined by the equation $h(x) = 2(1 - x)$.

5. Use the procedure of Problem 2 to calculate the amount of work done in pulling a spring 1 ft. if $F(x) = 5x$.

6. Show that if the function f is continuous on the interval $[a,b]$, then

$$\underline{\int_a^b} f = -\overline{\int_a^b}(-f).$$

Hint: Show that on any interval $[x_{i-1}, x_i]$, the minimum value of f is the maximum value of $(-f)$. Then recall Problem 7 of Section 5 of Chapter 1.

7. Use the result of Problem 6 to prove the second equation of Theorem 7.5.

4. EXISTENCE AND EVALUATION OF DEFINITE INTEGRALS

We saw in Section 2 of this chapter that certain kinds of problems lead to upper and lower definite integrals, and we saw that these problems have reasonable solutions if the lower and upper definite integrals are equal, i.e., if the definite integrals exist. In Section 3 we discussed at some length the properties of lower and upper definite integrals. The time and trouble invested in this discussion will not be justified until we have a proof of Theorem 7.1 and know that the definite integral of any continuous function does exist.

We shall give in this section a proof of Theorem 7.1. Then, however, we shall be faced with one more (but fortunately the last) difficulty in connection with definite integrals. Any particular definite integral is, by definition, a number. But the definition does not tell us which number. We need, then, a method for discovering, given a definite integral, which number it is, or, as we usually say, a method for *evaluating* the definite integral. Fortunately there is such a method which works in many, though not all, cases.

A clue to this method is furnished by the following problem: Suppose we have a particle moving on a straight line and suppose we know its velocity at any instant. To be specific, let us consider the case where

$$v(t) = t^3.$$

Suppose the particle is at the origin when $t = 0$. Then we can ask where the particle is at the end of, say, 2 sec.

We recall (Definition 4.5) that if the position at any time t of a particle is given by the value $s(t)$ of a function s, then its velocity at any time t is defined to be $s'(t)$. In this case we are given the velocity, t^3, and would like to know the function s.

Now we can express the distance moved by our particle in these two seconds as a definite integral. For any interval of time $[t_{i-1}, t_i]$, the distance moved is $s_i = s(t_i) - s(t_{i-1})$. By the Mean Value Theorem,

$$s(t_i) = s(t_{i-1}) + s'(t_i^*)(t_i - t_{i-1}), \quad t_{i-1} < t_i^* < t_i,$$

and so

$$s_i = s(t_i) - s(t_{i-1}) = v(t_i^*)(t_i - t_{i-1}).$$

Now the minimum value of the velocity for this interval of time is t_{i-1}^3 and the maximum is t_i^3, so $t_{i-1}^3 \leq v(t_i^*) \leq t_i^3$ and we have

$$t_{i-1}^3(t_i - t_{i-1}) \leq s_i \leq t_i^3(t_i - t_{i-1})$$

and

$$\sum_{i=1}^{i=n} t_{i-1}^3(t_i - t_{i-1}) \leq \sum_{i=1}^{i=n} s_i \leq \sum_{i=1}^{i=n} t_i^3(t_i - t_{i-1}).$$

But $\sum_{i=1}^{i=n} s_i$ is the total distance which the particle travels during the 2 sec.

and, since it starts at the origin, this is the same as $s(2)$. Thus we have

$$\underline{\int_0^2} v \leq s(2) \leq \overline{\int_0^2} v,$$

where $v(t) = t^3$. Assuming the correctness of Theorem 7.1, we have $s(2)$ $= \int_0^2 v$, where $v(t) = t^3$.

On the other hand, we can see by inspection that the function q defined by $q(t) = t^4/4$ is a function whose derivative is t^3. Furthermore, when $t = 0$, $q(t) = 0$.   Thus the function q behaves very much like the function s that we are looking for, and we might suspect that actually q is the same as s. If so, if $q = s$, then the position of the particle is given on the one hand by the value of q when $t = 2$ and on the other hand by the definite integral of v from 0 to 2:

$$\int_0^2 v = q(2) = 2^4/4 = 4.$$

We can guess, then, that it may be possible to evaluate a definite integral by means of a function whose derivative is the function we start with. This guess is indeed correct. Furthermore, in the course of showing that it is correct we prove two theorems which turn out to be just what we need for the proof of Theorem 7.1.

Theorem 7.7: *Let f be a function which is continuous on an interval I, and let a be a number in I.   Let $\overline{F}$ be the function defined by the equation*

$$\overline{F}(x) = \overline{\int_a^x} f,$$

and $\underline{F}$ the function defined by the equation

$$\underline{F}(x) = \underline{\int_a^x} f.$$

Then

$$\overline{F}' = f = \underline{F}'.$$

Proof: We prove only the first of these two equations. We are to show that, for any number c in the domain of definition of $\overline{F}$,

$$\lim_{x \to c} \frac{\overline{F}(x) - \overline{F}(c)}{x - c} = f(c).$$

To show this, we must show that for any number $e > 0$ there is a number $d > 0$ such that when

$$0 < |x - c| < d,$$

then
$$\left| \frac{\bar{F}(x) - \bar{F}(c)}{x - c} - f(c) \right| < e.$$

Now
$$\bar{F}(x) - \bar{F}(c) = \overline{\int_a^x} f - \overline{\int_a^c} f = \overline{\int_c^x} f. \quad \text{(Why?)}$$

We now use the hypothesis that f is continuous. For the number $e^* = e/2$ there is then a number $d > 0$ such that when
$$|x - c| < d,$$

then
$$|f(x) - f(c)| < e^*,$$

or
$$f(c) - e^* < f(x) < f(c) + e^*.$$

Consider first the case where $c < x$ and $|x - c| < d$. By Theorem 7.4, we can conclude from the inequality above that
$$(f(c) - e^*)(x - c) \le \overline{\int_c^x} f \le (f(c) + e^*)(x - c),$$

and hence
$$f(c) - e^* \le \frac{\overline{\int_c^x} f}{x - c} \le f(c) + e^*.$$

If $x < c$, then $\overline{\int_c^x} f = -\overline{\int_x^c} f$, and we have
$$(f(c) - e^*)(c - x) \le \overline{\int_x^c} f \le (f(c) + e^*)(c - x),$$

and hence, since $(c - x) > 0$,
$$f(c) - e^* \le \frac{\overline{\int_x^c} f}{c - x} = \frac{\overline{\int_c^x} f}{x - c} \le f(c) + e^*.$$

But, as we saw above, $\bar{F}(x) - \bar{F}(c) = \overline{\int_c^x} f$, so we have shown that whenever
$$0 < |x - c| < d,$$

then
$$f(c) - e^* \le \frac{\bar{F}(x) - \bar{F}(c)}{x - c} \le f(c) + e^*.$$

This, however, can be written

$$\left| \frac{\overline{F}(x) - \overline{F}(c)}{x - c} - f(c) \right| \leq e^* = e/2 < e,$$

which completes the proof that $\overline{F}' = f$.

Exercise: Carry out the proof that $\underline{F}' = f$.

Now if we are asked to find the value of $\int_a^b f$ for some particular function f, one method would be to find the function $\overline{F}$, defined by the equation $\overline{F}(x) = \int_a^x f$, for then $\int_a^b f$ is the value of $\overline{F}$ at b. Theorem 7.7 tells us that $\overline{F}' = f$. But this, of course, does not specify $\overline{F}$. For example, if f is defined by the equation $f(x) = 2x$, then $F(x) = x^2$, $G(x) = x^2 + 2$, $H(x) = x^2 - 1$, $\varphi(x) = x^2 + k$ are all functions which have f for derivative. Our next theorem will show that nothing worse than this can happen.

Theorem 7.8: *If G and H are functions such that $G' = H'$ in an interval $[a,b]$, then there is a number k such that for any x in this interval*

$$G(x) = H(x) + k.$$

Proof: Let $\varphi = \{G - H\}$. Then φ has a derivative at each point of $[a,b]$; in fact the value of φ' is zero at every point of this interval. (Why?) Let x be any point in $[a,b]$. By the Mean Value Theorem,

$$\varphi(x) = \varphi(a) + \varphi'(c)(x - a),$$

where

$$a < c < x.$$

But $\varphi'(c) = 0$, so

$$\varphi(x) = \varphi(a).$$

Denote the number $\varphi(a)$ by k. Then

$$k = \varphi(x) = \{G - H\}(x) = G(x) - H(x),$$

so

$$G(x) = H(x) + k$$

for every x in $[a,b]$.

Having these two theorems, we can now finish our discussion of definite integrals. We first prove Theorem 7.1.

Proof of Theorem 7.1: Let $\overline{F}$ and $\underline{F}$ be the functions defined by the equations

$$\overline{F}(x) = \int_a^x f, \quad \underline{F}(x) = \int_{\underline{a}}^x f.$$

By Theorem 7.7,

$$\overline{F}' = \underline{F}'.$$

Therefore, by Theorem 7.8, there is a number k such that

$$\overline{F}(x) = \underline{F}(x) + k$$

for each x in $[a,b]$.

But for the particular case $x = a$,

$$\overline{F}(a) = \overline{\int_a^a} f = 0 \quad \text{and} \quad \underline{F}(a) = \underline{\int_a^a} f = 0.$$

Therefore, since

$$\overline{F}(a) = \underline{F}(a) + k$$

we have

$$0 = 0 + k,$$

or

$$k = 0.$$

Consequently

$$\overline{F}(x) = \underline{F}(x)$$

for any x in $[a,b]$. Therefore, for the particular case $x = b$,

$$\overline{F}(b) = \underline{F}(b),$$

or

$$\overline{\int_a^b} f = \underline{\int_a^b} f.$$

The next theorem gives us a method for evaluating definite integrals.

Theorem 7.9: (*The **Fundamental Theorem** of integral calculus.*)   *Let f be a function which is continouus on an interval $[a,b]$, and let G be any function such that*

$$G' = f.$$

Then

$$\int_a^b f = G(b) - G(a).$$

Proof: For each x in $[a,b]$, the function F defined by $F(x) = \int_a^x f$ is such that $F' = f$, by Theorems 7.7 and 7.1.

Also

$$F(b) - F(a) = \int_a^b f - \int_a^a f = \int_a^b f. \quad \text{(Why?)}$$

Let G be any other function such that $G' = f$. Then $G' = F'$, so by Theorem 7.8,

$$G = F + k$$

for some number k. Then

$$G(b) - G(a) = (F(b) + k) - (F(a) + k)$$
$$= F(b) - F(a)$$
$$= \int_a^b f.$$

Now, to evaluate a definite integral, $\int_a^b f$, it is only necessary to find one function, G, such that $G' = f$.

The next theorem is often useful in working with definite integrals.

Theorem 7.10: *Let f and g be functions which are continuous on an interval $[a,b]$, and let k be a number.   Then*

$$\int_a^b \{f + g\} = \int_a^b f + \int_a^b g,$$

and

$$\int_a^b \{kf\} = k \int_a^b f.$$

Proof: We prove only the first of these equations.   Let F be the function defined by the equation

$$F(x) = \int_a^x f.$$

Then $F' = f$.   (Why?)   Similarly, let G be defined by the equation

$$G(x) = \int_a^x g.$$

Then $G' = g$.   Let $H = \{F + G\}$.   Then $H' = \{f + g\}$, so $\int_a^b \{f + g\} = H(b) - H(a)$.   (Why?)   But $H(b) - H(a) = (F(b) + G(b)) - (F(a) + G(a)) = F(b) - F(a) + G(b) - G(a) = \int_a^b f + \int_a^b g$.   (Why?)

Exercise: Prove the other equation of this theorem.

The following theorem, which is called the Mean Value Theorem for Integrals, has a number of applications, though its chief use for us will be in the proof of a later theorem.

Theorem 7.11: *Let f be a function which is continuous on an interval $[a,b]$. Then there is a number c in $[a,b]$ such that*

$$\int_a^b f = f(c)(b - a).$$

Proof: Let $f(\underline{x})$ be the absolute minimum value of f in the interval $[a,b]$, and $f(\bar{x})$ the absolute maximum value. Then

$$f(\underline{x})(b-a) \le \int_a^b f \le f(\bar{x})(b-a). \text{(Why?)}$$

Hence

$$f(\underline{x}) \le \frac{\int_a^b f}{(b-a)} \le f(\bar{x}).$$

Now f is continuous, so, by Theorem 3.11, there is a number c between $\underline{x}$ and $\bar{x}$ such that

$$f(c) = \frac{\int_a^b f}{b-a},$$

or

$$\int_a^b f = f(c)(b-a).$$

Remark: As we shall see in Section 6, if we are given a figure in the plane bounded below by the x-axis, laterally by the lines $x = a$ and $x = b$, and above by the graph of a continuous function f, then the only reasonable definition of the "area," A, of this figure is

$$A = \int_a^b f.$$

A geometric interpretation of the theorem above is that there is a point c in $[a,b]$ such that the rectangle whose base is $[a,b]$ and whose top side passes through the point $(c,f(c))$ has the same area as the figure.

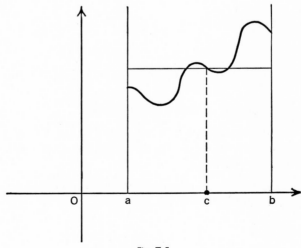

Fig. 7.5

PROBLEMS

1. Evaluate the following definite integrals:

a) $\int_1^3 f$ if $f(x) = 5x$. *Solution:* One function G, such that $G' = f$, is defined by the equation $G(x) = 5x^2/2$. Therefore $\int_1^3 f = G(3) - G(1)$
$= \frac{45}{2} - \frac{5}{2} = 20$.

b) $\int_1^2 f$ if $f(x) = 2x + 3$. *Solution:* One function G, such that $G' = f$, is defined by the equation $G(x) = x^2 + 3x$. Therefore $\int_1^2 f = G(2) - G(1) = 10 - 4 = 6$.

c) $\int_2^{10} f$ if $f(x) = x(x + 1)$. *Hint:* $x(x + 1) = x^2 + x$.

d) $\int_0^1 f$, if $f(x) = x^3$. Ans. $\frac{1}{4}$.

e) $\int_1^2 f$, if $f(x) = x^3$.

f) $\int_9^{10} f$, if $f(x) = x^3$.

g) $\int_0^1 f$, if $f(x) = 10x^3$. Ans. $\frac{5}{2}$.

h) $\int_{-1}^0 f$ if $f(x) = x^3$. Ans. $-\frac{1}{4}$.

i) $\int_{-1}^1 f$ if $f(x) = x^3$.

j) $\int_1^3 g$ if $g(x) = 1 - x + x^2$.

k) $\int_0^5 g$ if $g(x) = x^{10}$.

l) $\int_0^4 g$ if $g(x) = \sqrt{x}$. Ans. $\frac{16}{3}$.

m) $\int_1^2 h$ if $h(x) = \dfrac{1}{\sqrt{x}}$.

n) $\int_1^2 \varphi$ if $\varphi(x) = \dfrac{1}{x^2}$.

o) $\displaystyle\int_{10}^{11} \varphi$ if $\varphi(x) = \dfrac{1}{x^2}$.

p) $\displaystyle\int_{\frac{1}{2}}^{\frac{3}{2}} f$ if $f(y) = y^3 + y^{-3}$.

2. A particle moves on a line in such a way that its velocity, at any time t, is $6t + 1$. It is at the origin when $t = 2$. Find its position at any time.

Solution: Let s be the function whose value, at any instant t, is the distance from the origin to the particle. Then, by Definition 3.5, $s' = v$ where $v(t) = 6t + 1$.

Now, we observe that the function g, given by $g(t) = 3t^2 + t$, is such that $g' = v$. By Theorem 7.8 we must have

$$s = g + k,$$

or

$$s(t) = 3t^2 + t + k.$$

But we are told that $s(2) = 0$. Hence

$$3 \cdot 4 + 2 + k = 0,$$

or

$$k = -14.$$

Thus

$$s(t) = 3t^2 + t - 14.$$

3. A particle moves on a line in such a way that its velocity, at any time t, is $t^2 - t$. It is 3 units to the right of the origin when $t = 0$. Where is it when $t = 1$?

4. A particle moves on a line in such a way that its velocity, at any time t, is $2t - 3$. If $s(0) = 0$, when is it 4 units to the right of the origin?

5. For a particle moving down a rough inclined plane we find that $v(t) = \sqrt{t}$. Where is the particle at the end of 2 sec.?

6. The acceleration of a particle moving on a line is given by

$$a(t) = 2t + 1.$$

If it starts from the origin with an initial velocity of 3 ft. per sec., where is it at the end of 1 sec.?

Solution: Since $a(t) = v'(t) = 2t + 1$, we have $v(t) = t^2 + t + k$. But $v(0) = 3$, so $k = 3$ and $v(t) = t^2 + t + 3$. Next, $s'(t) = v(t) = t^2 + t + 3$, so $s(t) = t^3/3 + t^2/2 + 3t + k^*$. But $s(0) = 0$, so $k^* = 0$ and $s(t) = t^3/3 + t^2/2 + 3t$ and $s(1) = 23/6$.

7. Find the location of a particle at the end of 2 sec. if

a) $a(t) = 6t$, $s(0) = 0$, $v(0) = 0$.   Ans. $s(2) = 8$.

b) $a(t) = 6t$, $s(0) = 1$, $v(0) = 0$.

c) $a(t) = 6t$, $s(0) = 0$, $v(0) = 1$.

d) $a(t) = 6t$, $s(1) = 1$, $v(1) = 1$.

e) $a(t) = 6t + 12t^2$, $s(0) = 10$, $v(2) = 70$.   Ans. $s(2) = 86$.

f) $a(t) = 6t + 12t^2$, $s(1) = 5$, $v(1) = 10$.

8. At any point (x,y) on the graph of a function f the slope of the tangent line is $2x + 2$. Find an equation which defines f if the graph passes through the origin.

Solution: By Definition 4.2, $f'(x) = 2x + 2$. Therefore $f(x) = x^2 + 2x + k$ for some number k. (Why?) But $f(0) = 0$, so $k = 0$ and $f(x) = x^2 + 2x$.

9. Find an equation defining f if the tangent line to the graph of f at any point (x,y) has the indicated slope and if the graph passes through the indicated point:

a) $2x + 2$, $(1,1)$.   Ans. $f(x) = x^2 + 2x - 2$.

b) $2x + 2$, $(1,10)$.

c) $2 - 2x$, $(1,0)$.

d) $\dfrac{1}{x^2}$, $(1,-1)$.   Ans. $f(x) = -1/x$.

e) $x - \dfrac{1}{x^2}$, $(1,4)$.

f) $\sqrt{x}$, $(0,0)$.

5. WORK

We now illustrate how the theory we have developed concerning definite integrals can be applied to various kinds of problems. We start with problems involving work. In Section 2, we considered the case of a spring for which the force exerted by the spring when stretched x ft. beyond its natural length was $F(x)$ lbs., where $F(x) = x$. We saw that for any reasonable definition of the "work" done in stretching the spring a total of 5 ft., we should have

$$LUB \left(\sum_{i=1}^{i=n} F(\underline{x}_i)(x_i - x_{i-1}) \right) \le W \le GLB \left(\sum_{i=1}^{i=n} F(\bar{x}_i)(x_i - x_{i-1}) \right).$$

By Definitions 7.1 and 7.2, we can write this as

$$\int_0^5 F \le W \le \overline{\int}_0^5 F.$$

But F is continuous on $[0,5]$, so from Theorem 7.1 we have

$$\int_0^5 F = \overline{\int}_0^5 F.$$

Hence we conclude that the only reasonable definition of the "work" done in stretching the spring is

$$W = \int_0^5 F, \text{ where } F(x) = x.$$

To evaluate this definite integral, we note that G, defined by $G(x) = x^2/2$, is such that $G' = F$. Therefore, by Theorem 7.9

$$\int_0^5 F = G(5) - G(0) = \tfrac{25}{2} - 0 = 12\tfrac{1}{2}.$$

Thus the work done in stretching the spring is $12\tfrac{1}{2}$ ft.-lbs.

Further illustrations are in the problems below.

PROBLEMS

1. The radius of the base of a cylindrical tank is 5 ft. and the height of the tank is 10 ft. The tank is full of a liquid weighing 100 lbs. per cu. ft. How much work is done in pumping out the tank?

   Solution: As in the spring problem analyzed in the second section of this chapter, the main problem here is to decide what we mean by the "work" done, for while the force involved here is constant, various

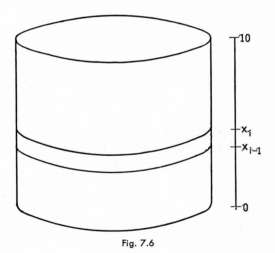

Fig. 7.6

parts of the liquid move different distances. But consider the vertical segment [0,10] and choose a sequence $x_0 = 0 < x_1 < \cdots < x_n = 10$. Consider that part of the liquid which is between the horizontal plane x_{i-1} ft. above the base and the one x_i ft. up. The volume occupied by this part of the liquid is $25\pi(x_i - x_{i-1})$ cu. ft. (Why?) Hence the weight of this part of the liquid is $2500\pi(x_i - x_{i-1})$.

When the tank is pumped out, all the liquid must be moved to the top of the tank. The maximum distance which any of the liquid in this slice is moved is then $10 - x_{i-1}$ and the minimum distance is $10 - x_i$. (Why?) The amount of "work," W_i, done on this part of the liquid is certainly no more than the product of the force, which is $2500\pi(x_i - x_{i-1})$ and the maximum distance, $10 - x_{i-1}$:

$$W_i \leq 2500\pi(10 - x_{i-1})(x_i - x_{i-1}).$$

Similarly,

$$2500\pi(10 - x_i)(x_i - x_{i-1}) \leq W_i.$$

Hence, as lower and upper bounds for the total amount of "work" done, we have

$$\sum_{i=1}^{i=n} 2500\pi(10 - x_i)(x_i - x_{i-1}) \leq W \leq \sum_{i=1}^{i=n} 2500\pi(10 - x_{i-1})(x_i - x_{i-1}).$$

Such inequalities hold no matter which sequence $x_0 = 0 < x_1 < \cdots < x_n = 10$ we choose, so

$$LUB\left(\sum_{i=1}^{i=n} 2500\pi(10 - x_i)(x_i - x_{i-1})\right) \leq W$$

$$\leq GLB\left(\sum_{i=1}^{i=n} 2500\pi(10 - x_{i-1})(x_i - x_{i-1})\right)$$

Now we recognize that

$$LUB\left(\sum_{i=1}^{i=n} 2500\pi(10 - x_i)(x_i - x_{i-1})\right) = \underline{\int_0^{10}} f$$

where

$$f(x) = 2500\pi(10 - x). \quad \text{(Why?)}$$

Similarly

$$GLB\left(\sum_{i=1}^{i=n} 2500\pi(10 - x_{i-1})(x_i - x_{i-1})\right) = \overline{\int_0^{10}} f,$$

so we have

$$\underline{\int_0^{10}} f \leq W \leq \overline{\int_0^{10}} f.$$

Now, by Theorem 7.1,

$$\underline{\int_0^{10}} f = \overline{\int_0^{10}} f = \int_0^{10} f,$$

so it is reasonable to define the amount of "work" done in pumping out this tank as:

$$W = \int_0^{10} f.$$

Now, to finish this problem, we must evaluate $\int_0^{10} f.$ But

$$f(x) = 2500\pi(10 - x) = 25{,}000\pi - 2500\pi x,$$

and we see that the function G, given by $G(x) = 25{,}000\pi x - 1250\pi x^2$ is such that $G' = f$. Hence, by Theorem 7.9, we have

$$\int_0^{10} f = G(10) - G(0)$$

$$= (250{,}000\pi - 125{,}000\pi) - 0$$

$$= 125{,}000\pi.$$

Thus the amount of work done is $125{,}000\pi$ ft.-lbs.

2. When a certain spring has been stretched 1 ft., a force of 6 lbs. is needed to hold it. How much work was done in stretching it this amount?

Hint: We assume that Hooke's Law is satisfied, so $F(x) = kx$. But $F(1) = 6$, so $k = 6$. Now follow the analysis of the spring problem in Section 2 to show that

$$W = \int_0^1 f,$$

where
$$f(x) = 6x. \hspace{3cm} \text{Ans. 3 ft. lbs.}$$

3. How much work is done if the spring in Problem 2 is stretched another foot?

4. A spring is found to be stretched from its natural length of 12 in. to 15 in. by a weight of 18 lbs. How much work is done in stretching the spring

a) from 12 to 15 in.?
b) from 13 to 16 in.?
c) from 14 to 17 in.?

5. To compress a spring from its natural length of 6 ft. to a length of 5 ft., 25 ft.-lbs. of work are needed. How much work is needed to compress it another foot? Ans. 75 ft.-lbs.

6. A piece of wire, hanging down from a windlass, weighs 8 oz. per ft. and is 200 ft. long. How much work does it take to wind it up? Ans. 10,000 ft.-lbs.

7. How much work is done in winding up the first half of the wire of Problem 6?

8. To the end of the wire of Problem 6 there is attached a bucket, weighing 10 lbs., containing 90 lbs. of water. How much work is done in winding it up to the windlass?

9. In Problem 8, suppose the wire is wound up at the rate of 50 ft. per min. and suppose the water leaks out at the rate of 2 lbs. per min. How much work is done in winding the bucket up to the windlass?

10. In Problem 9, suppose the wire is wound up at the rate of 5 ft. per min. How much work is done in this case?

11. The force due to gravity acting on a particle of mass m at a distance r from the center of the earth is

$$F = \frac{mgR^2}{r^2},$$

where $g = 32$ (approximately) and R is the radius of the earth. How much work is done in raising a particle from the surface of the earth to a point 100 mi. up? (Take $R = 4000$.) How much work does it take to raise it another 100 mi.?

12. If the temperature of a gas remains constant, then its pressure and volume are connected by the equation

$$PV = k.$$

Suppose the volume of a cylinder is 100 cu. ft., the area of the piston is 10 sq. ft., and the pressure is 1 lb. per sq. ft. How much work is done in compressing the gas to 25 cu. ft.? Can you evaluate the resulting definite integral?

13. If the pressure and volume of the gas of the previous problem are connected by the formula

$$PV^{3/2} = k,$$

find the work done.

14. Returning to Problem 1, suppose the liquid is pumped to a level 20 ft. above the top of the tank. How much work is done? Ans. $625,000\pi$ ft.-lbs.

15. Suppose the tank of Problem 1 were only half full to start with. How much work would be needed to pump it out?

16. A cylindrical tank is 10 ft. high. Its base is an equilateral triangle with each side 2 ft. long. It is filled with a liquid weighing 75 lbs. per cu. ft. How much work can be done by allowing the liquid to run out through a hole in the bottom of the tank? Ans. $3750\sqrt{3}$ ft.-lbs.

17. A cubical tank, whose volume is 1000 cu. ft., is placed with its top 15 ft. below the base of another cubical tank of the same dimensions. The lower tank is full of water. How much work does it take to pump the water into the upper tank if the connecting pipe runs to the top of the upper tank?

18. How much work is done if, in Problem 17, the connecting pipe runs to the base of the upper tank?

6. AREAS

In Section 1, we discussed a figure in the plane bounded below by the x-axis, laterally by the vertical lines $x = a$ and $x = b$, and above by the

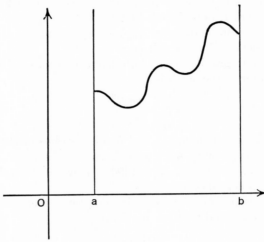

Fig. 7.7

graph of a continuous function, f. We saw there that for any reasonable definition of the "area" of the figure we should have

$$LUB\left(\sum_{i=1}^{i=n} f(\underline{x}_i)(x_i - x_{i-1})\right) \le A \le GLB\left(\sum_{i=1}^{i=n} f(\bar{x}_i)(x_i - x_{i-1})\right).$$

Using Definition 7.1, we can write this as

$$\underline{\int_a^b} f \le A \le \overline{\int_a^b} f.$$

Now by Theorem 7.1,

$$\underline{\int_a^b} f = \overline{\int_a^b} f = \int_a^b f,$$

so it is reasonable to define the "area" of our figure to be the number

$$\int_a^b f.$$

When we have a figure in the plane which is not of this particular type, we can often compare it with other figures which are. See in particular problem 2 below.

PROBLEMS

1. Find the areas of the figures bounded below by the x-axis and laterally and above by the given lines and the graphs of the given functions:

   a) $x = 1$, $x = 3$; $f(x) = x^3$. Ans. 20.
   b) $x = 2$, $x = 4$; $f(x) = x^3$. Ans. 60.
   c) $x = 0$, $x = 2$; $f(x) = x^3$.
   d) $x = a$, $x = b$; $f(x) = x^3$.
   e) $x = 1$, $x = 10$; $f(x) = x^4 + x^2$. Ans. 20,332.8.
   f) $x = 1$, $x = 2$; $f(x) = 5x^2$.
   g) $x = 0$, $x = 1$; $f(x) = 10x^9$.
   h) $x = 0$, $x = 1$; $f(x) = 1 + x + x^2 + x^3 + x^4$.

   i) $x = 5$, $x = 10$; $f(x) = \sqrt{x}$. Ans. $\dfrac{20\sqrt{10}}{3} - \dfrac{10\sqrt{5}}{3}$.
   j) $x = 1$, $x = 2$; $f(x) = x^4 - \sqrt[4]{x}$.
   k) $x = 1$, $x = 2$; $f(x) = 1/x^2$.
   l) $x = 2$, $x = 3$; $f(x) = 3x^3 - 3/x^3$.

2. Find the area of the figure bounded above by the parabola $x^2 = 3 - y$ and below by the parabola $x^2 = y - 1$.

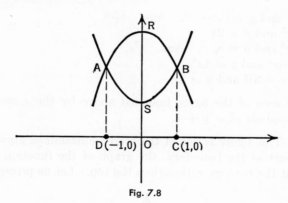

Fig. 7.8

Solution: These parabolas meet at the points $A(-1,2)$ and $B(1,2)$. We take the area of the figure $ARBSA$ to be the area of the figure $DARBCD$ minus the area of the figure $DASBCD$.

Now the figure $DARBCD$ is just the kind we have already considered. The equation of the parabola can be written $y = 3 - x^2$, so this figure is bounded above by the graph of the function f, where $f(x) = 3 - x^2$, and so the area of $DARBCD$ is

$$\int_{-1}^{1} f.$$

Since G, given by $G(x) = 3x - x^3/3$ is such that $G' = f$, we have area

$$DARBCD = \int_{-1}^{1} f = G(1) - G(-1) = \tfrac{16}{3}.$$

Similarly, the figure $DASBCD$ is bounded above by the graph of the function g given by $g(x) = 1 + x^2$, so the area of this figure is

$$\int_{-1}^{1} g = \tfrac{8}{3}.$$

Thus the area of the figure $ARBSA$ is $\tfrac{16}{3} - \tfrac{8}{3} = \tfrac{8}{3}$.

Remark: In this case, the area of our figure could be written as

$$\int_{-1}^{1} f - \int_{-1}^{1} g.$$

By Theorem 7.10, this can be written as

$$\int_{-1}^{1} h$$

where $h = \{f - g\}$ or $h(x) = 2 - 2x^2$.

3. Find the areas of the figures bounded by the following pairs of curves:

    a) $y = x$ and $y = 6x - x^2$. Ans. $\tfrac{125}{6}$.
    b) $y = x^3$ and $y = 2x$.
    c) $y = x^4$ and $y = \sqrt{x}$. Ans. $\tfrac{7}{15}$.
    d) $y = 16x^2$ and $y = 4x^4$.
    e) $y = (x - 3)^2$ and $y = 2x$.

4. Find the area of the figure bounded above by the x-axis and below by the parabola $x^2 = y + 1$.

Solution: This figure is not of the kind we examined above, since the curved part of the boundary, the graph of the function $f\colon f(x) = x^2 - 1$, is at the bottom, rather than the top. Let us proceed as we did

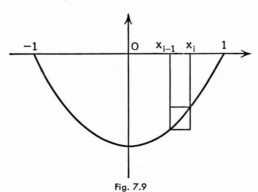

Fig. 7.9

in Section 2, and choose a sequence $x_0 = -1 < x_1 < \cdots < x_n = 1$. For any interval $[x_{i-1}, x_i]$, we have two rectangles. The base of each rectangle is $(x_i - x_{i-1})$. But the altitude of the larger rectangle is $-f(x_{i-1})$ and the altitude of the smaller is $-f(x_i)$. Therefore we take the area of this figure to be:

$$A = \int_{-1}^{1} (-f).$$

Remark: Another way to work this problem is to make a translation of the coordinate axes, taking the new origin to be at the point $(0, -1)$. Then $x = X$ and $y = Y - 1$. Referred to the XY-axes, our figure is now of the type con-

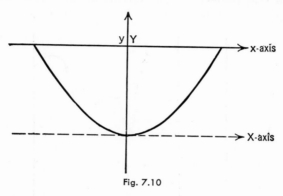

Fig. 7.10

sidered in Problem 2. It is bounded above by the graph of $Y = 1$ and below by the graph of $X^2 = Y$. Note that both methods of working this problem give the same result.

5. Find the areas of the figures bounded above by the x-axis and laterally and below by the graphs of the given equations:

   a) $x = 0$, $x = 1$; $y = -x^4$. Ans. $\frac{1}{5}$.
   b) $x = 1$, $x = 4$; $y = -\sqrt{x}$.
   c) $x = 0$, $x = 1$; $y = x^2 - 2x$.
   d) $x = 0$, $x = 1$; $y = x^3 - x$. Ans. $\frac{1}{4}$.

6. Find the areas of the figures lying between the x-axis and the graphs of

   a) $y = x^3 - x$.
   b) $y = (x + 2)(x + 1)(x - 1)(x - 2)$.

7. Find the area of the figure bounded by the graphs of $y + 2x = 1$ and $x^2 = 1 - y$. *Hint:* See the remark at the end of Problem 4.

8. Find the areas of the figures bounded by the following pairs of curves.

   a) $x^2 = y + 1$ and $x^2 = 1 - y$. Ans. $\frac{8}{3}$.
   b) $y = 4 - x^2$ and $x + y + 2 = 0$. Ans. $\frac{125}{6}$.

     c) $y = x - x^2$ and $y = x - 1$.

     d) $y = x^2 - 4$ and $2x - y = 1$.

     e) $y = x^3$ and $y = x$.

9. Find the areas of the figures bounded by the following pairs of curves.

     a) $y^2 = 1 - x$ and $x = 0$.   Ans. $\frac{4}{3}$.

     b) $y^2 = x + 2$ and $y = x$.

     c) $y^2 = 2x$ and $2x + y = 2$.

10. In discussing the area of a figure, such as that shown in Figure 7.8, we took any sequence $x_0 = a < x_1 < \cdots < x_n = b$ and, for each i, we considered that part of the figure lying in the vertical strip over the interval $[x_{i-1}, x_i]$. From Figure 7.11 it would seem that the area of

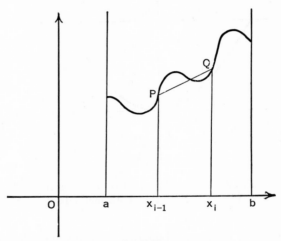

Fig. 7.11

the trapezoid x_{i-1}, x_i, Q, P might be a reasonable approximation to the area of that part of the figure lying in this vertical strip. Note that the area of this trapezoid is $\frac{1}{2}(f(x_{i-1}) + f(x_i))(x_i - x_{i-1})$. (Why?) Consequently the number

$$T_n = \sum_{i=1}^{i=n} \tfrac{1}{2}(f(x_{i-1}) + f(x_i))(x_i - x_{i-1})$$

might be a reasonable approximation to the area of the whole figure. But we also saw in Section 2 that the only reasonable definition of this area is the number

$$\int_a^b f.$$

Hence the sum above might be a reasonable approximation to this definite integral.

In the rest of this problem we assume that f'' is defined at each point of $[a,b]$ and that there is a number M such that $|f''(x)| \leq M$ for each x in $[a,b]$, and we show, under these conditions, how good an approximation T_n is to $\int_a^b f$.

a) By the Mean Value Theorem, there is a number s_i in $[x_{i-1}, x_i]$ such that

$$f(x_i) - f(x_{i-1}) = f'(s_i)(x_i - x_{i-1}).$$

Let the function φ be defined by

$$\varphi(x) = f(x_{i-1}) + f'(s_i)(x - x_{i-1}), \ x_{i-1} \leq x \leq x_i.$$

Show that the graph of φ is the straight line from P to Q and that $\int_{x_{i-1}}^{x_i} \varphi$ is the area of the trapezoid x_{i-1}, x_i, Q, P.

b) For any number x in the interval $[x_{i-1}, x_i]$, the Mean Value Theorem, applied to the interval $[x_{i-1}, x]$, tells us that there is a number t_i in $[x_{i-1}, x]$ such that

$$f(x) - f(x_{i-1}) = f'(t_i)(x - x_i).$$

Show that for any number x in $[x_{i-1}, x_i]$,

$$f(x) - \varphi(x) = (f'(t_i) - f'(s_i))(x - x_{i-1}).$$

c) By applying the Mean Value Theorem to the function f', show that there is a number c_i in the interval $[x_{i-1}, x_i]$ such that

$$f'(t_i) - f'(s_i) = f''(c_i)(t_i - s_i).$$

d) Show that for any number x in $[x_{i-1}, x_i]$,

$$|f(x) - \varphi(x)| \leq M(x_i - x_{i-1})(x - x_{i-1}) \leq M(x_i - x_{i-1})^2.$$

e) Show that

$$\left| \int_{x_{i-1}}^{x_i} f - \int_{x_{i-1}}^{x_i} \varphi \right| \leq M(x_i - x_{i-1})^3.$$

f) Using the fact that $\int_a^b f = \sum_{i=1}^{i=n} \int_{x_{i-1}}^{x_i} f$, show that

$$\left| \int_a^b f - T_n \right| \leq M \sum_{i=1}^{i=n} (x_i - x_{i-1})^3.$$

g) Show that if the points $x_0, x_1, \cdots, x_n$ are equally spaced, so that $x_i - x_{i-1} = \dfrac{b-a}{n}$ for each i, then

$$T_n = \frac{(b-a)}{2n} [f(a) + 2f(x_1) + 2f(x_2) + \cdots + 2f(x_{n-1}) + f(b)],$$

and
$$\left| \int_a^b f - T_n \right| \le \frac{M(b-a)^3}{n^2}.$$

Remark: This formula,

$$T_n = \frac{b-a}{2n} [f(a) + 2f(x_1) + 2f(x_2) + \cdots + 2f(x_{n-1}) + f(b)],$$

for approximating a definite integral is called the *trapezoidal rule*. Note that the term $M(b-a)^3/n^2$, which is the maximum error we make in replacing $\int_a^b f$ by T_n, can be made small by taking n large.

11. For each of the following definite integrals, find an approximate value by using the trapezoidal rule with $n = 2$ and also with $n = 4$. In each case compute the term $M(b-a)^3/n^2$, taking $M = 2$. In each case evaluate the definite integral by using Theorem 7.9 and compare the result with your approximations.

a) $\int_0^1 f$, where $f(x) = x^2$.

   Ans. $\int_0^1 f = \frac{1}{3}$, $T_2 = \frac{3}{8}$, $M(b-a)^3/n^2 = \frac{1}{2}$.
   $$T_4 = \frac{11}{32}, \; M(b-a)^3/n^2 = \frac{1}{8}.$$

b) $\int_0^4 f$, where $f(x) = x^2$.

c) $\int_1^2 f$, where $f(x) = x^2$.

12. For each part of Problem 11, what is a value of n such that T_n differs from $\int_a^b f$ by less than $\frac{1}{100}$?

13. For the function g defined by $g(x) = \frac{1}{x}$, $x > 0$, find a value of n such that T_n differs from $\int_1^2 g$ by less than $\frac{1}{10}$. Compute T_n for this n.

   Ans. $n = 5$, $T_5 = \frac{1753}{2520}$.

14. A cruder method of evaluating a definite integral is to use a series of rectangles instead of a series of trapezoids. Choose, in each interval $[x_{i-1}, x_i]$ a point x_i^* and construct the rectangle whose base is the interval $[x_{i-1}, x_i]$ and whose altitude is $f(x_i^*)$. Then consider the sum of the areas of these rectangles:

$$\sum_{i=1}^{i=n} f(x_i^*)(x_i - x_{i-1}).$$

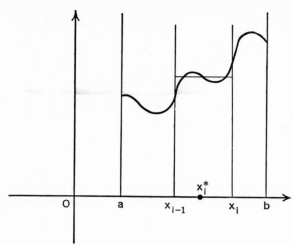

Fig. 7.12

a) By Theorem 7.10, there is a point c_i in $[x_{i-1}, x_i]$ such that

$$\int_{x_{i-1}}^{x_i} f = f(c_i)(x_i - x_{i-1}).$$

If f' is defined at each point of $[a,b]$ and if there is a number N such that $|f'(x)| \le N$ for each x in $[a,b]$, show that

$$\left| \int_{x_{i-1}}^{x_i} f - f(x_i^*)(x_i - x_{i-1}) \right| \le N(x_i - x_{i-1})^2.$$

b) If the points $x_0, x_1, \cdots, x_n$ are equally spaced, show that

$$\left| \int_a^b - \sum_{i=1}^{i=n} f(x_i^*)(x_i - x_{i-1}) \right| \le \frac{N(b-a)^2}{n}.$$

Thus the expression

$$R_n = \frac{(b-a)}{n} \sum_{i=1}^{i=n} f(x_i^*)$$

differs from $\int_a^b f$ by no more than $N(b-a)^2/n$. But note that this expression, $N(b-a)^2/n$, becomes small, as n becomes large, more slowly than $M(b-a)^3/n^2$.

15. For each definite integral in Problem 11, find a value of n such that R_n differs from $\int_a^b f$ by less than $\frac{1}{100}$. Compare with the similar values for T_n.

7. THE DEFINITE INTEGRAL AS A LIMIT

For certain applications it is convenient to be able to express the definite integral not as a least upper bound or greatest lower bound but rather as a limit. The following theorem allows us to do this:

Theorem 7.12: *Let f be a function which is continuous on an interval [a,b]. Then for any number e > 0 there is a number d > 0 such that*

$$\left| \int_a^b f - \sum_{i=1}^{i=n} f(x_i^*)(x_i - x_{i-1}) \right| < e$$

whenever $x_0 = a < x_1 < \cdots < x_n = b$ is a sequence such that each interval $[x_{i-1},x_i]$ has length less than d, and where x_i^* is any point in $[x_{i-1},x_i]$.

Another way of putting this is that

$$\int_a^b f = \lim_{r \to 0} \sum_{i=1}^{i=n} f(x_i^*)(x_i - x_{i-1}),$$

where r is the maximum length of any interval of the sequence $x_0 = a < x_1 < \cdots < x_n = b$.

In order to prove this theorem we need a special property of continuous functions. We recall (Definition 3.7) that a function f is continuous at a number c if

$$\lim_{x \to c} f(x) = f(c).$$

In turn, this means (Definition 3.5) that for any number $e > 0$ there is a number $d > 0$ such that when

$$|x - c| < d,$$

then

$$|f(x) - f(c)| < e.$$

As we pointed out in Section 10 of Chapter 3, the number d depends not only on e but also on f and on c, and we wrote $d(e,c,f)$ to emphasize this fact. We are going to show, however, that for each function f, if we restrict our attention to a closed interval $[a,b]$ on which f is continuous, we can find one number $d > 0$ which will serve for each number c in $[a,b]$.

Definition 7.6: *A function f is **uniformly continuous** over an interval [a,b] if for any number e > 0 there is a number $\bar{d} > 0$ such that whenever x_1 and x_2 are points in [a,b] and*

$$|x_1 - x_2| < \bar{d}$$

then

$$|f(x_1) - f(x_2)| < e.$$

Theorem 7.13: *If a function f is continuous over a closed interval [a,b], then it is uniformly continuous over this interval.*

Proof: Given a number $e > 0$, let C be the collection of those numbers c in $[a,b]$ for which there exists a number $d_c > 0$ such that $\left|f(x_1) - f(x_2)\right| < e$ whenever x_1 and x_2 are in $[a,c]$ and $\left|x_1 - x_2\right| < d_c$. Now C certainly contains the number a and the number b is an upper bound for C. Therefore C has a least upper bound, which we denote by c^*. Note that $c^* \leq b$.

Since f is continuous at c^*, there is a number $d_{c*} > 0$ such that $\left|f(x) - f(c^*)\right| < e/2$ whenever $\left|x - c^*\right| < d_{c*}$. The number c^* is the *least* upper bound of C, so the number $c^* - \frac{1}{2}d_{c*}$ is not an upper bound of C. Therefore there is some number c in C such that $c^* - \frac{1}{2}d_{c*} < c \leq c^*$. Since c is in C, there is a number $d_c < 0$ such that $\left|f(x_1) - f(x_2)\right| < e$ whenever x_1 and x_2 are in $[a,c]$ and $\left|x_1 - x_2\right| < d_c$.

Let d be the smaller of the two numbers $\frac{1}{2}d_{c*}$ and d_c. Let b' be the smaller of the two numbers $c^* + \frac{1}{2}d_{c*}$ and b.

Now let x_1 and x_2 be any pair of points in the interval $[a,b']$ such that $\left|x_1 - x_2\right| < d$. If x_1 and x_2 are both in $[a,c]$, then $\left|f(x_1) - f(x_2)\right| < e$, since $d \leq d_c$. If one of these two numbers is not in $[a,c]$, then both of them must be in the interval $(c^* - d_{c*}, c^* + d_{c*})$,

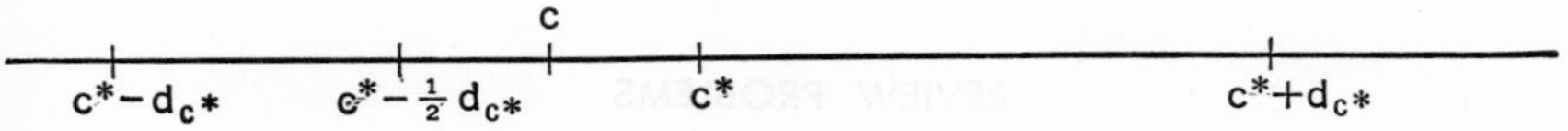

Fig. 7.13

since $\left|x_1 - x_2\right| \leq \frac{1}{2}d_{c*}$. Therefore $\left|x_1 - c^*\right| < d_{c*}$ and $\left|x_2 - c^*\right| < d_{c*}$. Hence

$$\left|f(x_1) - f(x_2)\right| \leq \left|f(x_1) - f(c^*)\right| + \left|f(c^*) - f(x_2)\right| < \frac{e}{2} + \frac{e}{2} = e.$$

Thus we have shown that if $\left|x_1 - x_2\right| < d$ and if x_1 and x_2 are in $[a,b']$, then $f(x_1) - f(x_2) < e$. But this means that b' is in C. Since $c^* \leq b'$, it follows that $c^* = b'$, and this can happen only if $c^* = b$. (Why?)

Therefore b is in C, so the number $\bar{d} = d_b$ is such that for any pair of points x_1 and x_2 in $[a,b]$, with $\left|x_1 - x_2\right| < \bar{d}$, we have $\left|f(x_1) - f(x_2)\right| < e$, which completes the proof.

Proof of Theorem 7.12: For any number $e > 0$, the number $e/(b - a)$ is also positive, and so, by Theorem 7.13, there is a number $\bar{d} > 0$ such that whenever x_1 and x_2 are two points in $[a,b]$ with $\left|x_1 - x_2\right| < \bar{d}$, then

$$\left|f(x_1) - f(x_2)\right| < e/(b - a).$$

Let $x_0 = a < x_1 < \cdots < x_n = b$ be any sequence with the length of each interval $[x_{i-1},x_i]$ less than $\bar{d}$. Let x_i^* be any point in $[x_{i-1},x_i]$. By Theorem 7.11, there is a number c_i in $[x_{i-1},x_i]$ such that

$$\int_{x_{i-1}}^{x_i} f = f(c_i)(x_i - x_{i-1}).$$

Then

$$\int_a^b f = \sum_{i=1}^{i=n} \int_{x_{i-1}}^{x_i} f = \sum_{i=1}^{i=n} f(c_i)(x_i - x_{i-1}).$$

Hence

$$\left| \int_a^b f - \sum_{i=1}^{i=n} f(x_i{}^*)(x_i - x_{i-1}) \right|$$

$$= \left| \sum_{i=1}^{i=n} f(c_i)(x_i - x_{i-1}) - \sum_{i=1}^{i=n} f(x_i{}^*)(x_i - x_{i-1}) \right|$$

$$= \left| \sum_{i=1}^{i=n} (f(c_i) - f(x_i{}^*))(x_i - x_{i-1}) \right| \le \sum_{i=1}^{i=n} |f(c_i) - f(x_i{}^*)|(x_i - x_{i-1})$$

$$< \frac{e}{b-a} \sum_{i=1}^{i=n} (x_i - x_{i-1}) = \frac{e}{b-a}(b-a) = e,$$

since, for each i, c_i and $x_i{}^*$ are in the interval $[x_{i-1}, x_i]$, whose length is less than $\bar{d}$, so $|c_i - x_i{}^*| < \bar{d}$.

REVIEW PROBLEMS

1. A certain function f is such that for any two numbers, x and y,

$$|f(x + y) - f(x)| \le y^2.$$

Show that there is a number K such that, for all x,

$$f(x) = K.$$

2. If $x^2 = \int_a^x \varphi$, what are possible functions φ, if any, and for each what are possible values of a?

3. An object moving in a straight line has an acceleration proportional to the square root of its velocity. It has an initial velocity of 16 ft. per sec. and comes to rest in 6 sec. How far does it go?

4. Two men are to share the work of pumping out the tank of Problem 1 of Section 5. How much liquid should the first man pump out in order to do half the work? Ans. $125\sqrt{2}\pi$ cu. ft.

5. A slender bar of length l lies along the positive side of the x-axis with the nearer extremity at a distance d from the origin O. If O is a center of attraction such that the attraction on every particle of the bar varies inversely as the square of its distance from O, find the total attraction.

6. Find the area between the graph of $y = x^3 - 12x$ and the tangent drawn to it at the maximum point on the curve. Ans. 108.

7. Find a if $y = a$ divides into two equal parts the area bounded by the parabola $y = 4x - x^2$, the x-axis and $x = 2$.

8. Find the area bounded by the curve

$$\sqrt{x} + \sqrt{y} = 1$$

and the coordinate axes.

9. Show that the curve $y = x^n (n > 0)$ divides the unit square bounded by $x = 0$, $x = 1$, $y = 0$, and $y = 1$ in the ratio $n:1$.

10. An area in the first quadrant is bounded by the curve $x^2 y = 6x^3 + 8$, the x-axis and the lines $x = k$ and $x = k + 1$. Find the minimum value of the area.   Ans. $k = 1$.

11. A segment of a parabola is the area bounded by the parabola and a chord perpendicular to the axis. Prove that the area of any segment is equal to two-thirds the area of the circumscribed rectangle.

12. Consider all the parabolas which have their axes parallel to the y-axis, open down and pass through $(0,0)$ and through the point $(1,2)$. Find an equation for that one which, together with the x-axis, bounds a figure of least area.

13. Show that if φ and ψ are functions, both of which are continuous on the interval $[a,b]$, and if $\varphi(x) \le \psi(x)$ for each x in $[a,b]$, then

$$\int_a^b \varphi \le \int_a^b \psi.$$

14. Let f and g be functions which are continuous on an interval $[a,b]$, and let g be such that $g(x) \ge 0$ for each x in $[a,b]$. Show that there is a number c in $[a,b]$ such that

$$\int_a^b \{fg\} = f(c) \int_a^b g.$$

Hint: Let m and M be the minimum and maximum values of f on $[a,b]$. Then $mg(x) \le f(x)g(x) \le Mg(x)$. Now use Problem 13 above and then recall the proof of Theorem 7.11.

Further Applications
of the Definite Integral

1. THE INDEFINITE INTEGRAL

In solving any one of the work and area problems which we considered in the previous chapter, there were always two steps. The first step was to express the desired quantity as a definite integral, and the second step was to evaluate the definite integral. We wish now to devote further attention to the second step.

Definition 8.1: *If f is a function, then any function F such that*

$$F' = f$$

*is an **indefinite integral** of f.*

We use the symbol

$$\int f$$

to stand for any one of the indefinite integrals of f. We saw in Section 4 of Chapter 7, that a function has many indefinite integrals but that if F and G are any two, then for some number C, $G = F + C$. It is customary, therefore, given a function f, to choose any one of its indefinite integrals, say F, and to add to it an arbitrary number C and write

$$\int f = F + C.$$

This equation means that for any function G such that $G' = f$, there is a number C such that $G = F + C$. Thus, if $f(x) = x + 1$, we write

$$\int f = \frac{x^2}{2} + x + C.$$

We can obtain formulas concerning indefinite integrals from formulas for differentiation. For example:

216

Theorem 8.1: *If f and g are functions, if F is any indefinite integral of f and G any indefinite integral of g, then {F + G} is an indefinite integral of {f + g}.*

Remark: We can express the result of this theorem by the equation

$$\left\{ \int f + \int g \right\} = \int \{f + g\}.$$

Note, however, that this does not mean that if F, G, and H are particular indefinite integrals of f, g, and $\{f + g\}$, then $\{F + G\} = H$. All that we can conclude is that $\{F + G\} = \{H + C\}$ for some number C.

Proof: By Definition 8.1, $\int f$ is a function F such that $F' = f$, and $\int g$ is a function G such that $G' = g$. By Theorem 4.4, the function $\{F + G\}$ is a function such that

$$\{F + G\}' = \{F' + G'\} = \{f + g\}.$$

So, by Definition 8.1,

$$\int \{f + g\} = \{F + G\} = \left\{ \int f + \int g \right\}.$$

Theorem 8.2: *If f is a function and k a number, and if F is an indefinite integral of f, then {kF} is an indefinite integral of {kf}.*

Remark: We can express the result of this theorem by the equation

$$k \int f = \int kf.$$

Exercise: Prove this theorem.

Theorem 8.3: *If f is a differentiable function and $n \neq -1$ a number then*

$$\int f^n f' = \frac{f^{n+1}}{n + 1} + C.$$

Proof: By Theorem 4.11,

$$\left(\frac{f^{n+1}}{n + 1} \right)' = \frac{(n + 1)}{(n + 1)} f^n f' = f^n f',$$

and so, by Definition 8.1, $f^{n+1}/(n + 1)$ is an indefinite integral of $f^n f'$.

Exercise: Why do we make the restriction that $n \neq -1$?

The special case of this theorem where $f(x) = x$ is used so often that we state it as a separate theorem.

Theorem 8.4: *If f is defined by the equation $f(x) = x$, then, for $n \neq -1$,*

$$\int f^n = \frac{x^{n+1}}{n + 1} + C.$$

Exercise: Prove this theorem.

The use of these theorems is illustrated in the problems below. Before proceeding to these problems, we mention another notation for integrals. For historical reasons, which we shall not discuss, a common notation for the indefinite integral of a function f is

$$\int f(x)\ dx.$$

The symbol dx is called the differential of x.

Since this differential notation is so much used, we shall employ it also in order to familiarize the reader with it. In what follows, then, the two symbols

$$\int f \quad \text{and} \quad \int f(x)\ dx$$

mean the same thing. Similarly, the expression

$$\int x^2\ dx$$

means

$$\int f, \quad \text{where} \quad f(x) = x^2,$$

and

$$\int (1 - t)\ dt$$

means

$$\int g, \quad \text{where} \quad g(t) = (1 - t).$$

Note that

$$\int x^2\ dx, \quad \int t^2\ dt, \quad \text{and} \quad \int \eta^2\ d\eta$$

all mean the same thing, since they mean $\int f$, $\int g$, and $\int h$, where $f(x) = x^2$, $g(t) = t^2$, and $h(\eta) = \eta^2$, and, despite the difference in notation, these are all the same function.

This notation is helpful in preventing ambiguity when discussing specific indefinite integrals. For example, the expression

$$\int x^2 y$$

is ambiguous. It might mean $\int f$ where y is some number and $f(x) = yx^2$. On the other hand, it might mean $\int g$, where x is some number and $g(y) = x^2 y$. But with the differential notation we can write $\int x^2 y\ dx$ for $\int f$ and $\int x^2 y\ dy$ for $\int g$.

We shall also use this differential notation for definite integrals, so

$$\int_a^b f \quad \text{and} \quad \int_a^b f(x)\, dx$$

mean the same thing.

In terms of this differential notation we can write the following formulas for indefinite integration:

8.1) $$\int (f(x) + g(x))\, dx = \int f(x)\, dx + \int g(x)\, dx.$$

8.2) $$\int kf(x)\, dx = k \int f(x)\, dx.$$

8.3) $$\int (f(x))^n f'(x)\, dx = \frac{(f(x))^{n+1}}{n+1} + C.$$

8.4) $$\int x^n\, dx = \frac{x^{n+1}}{n+1} + C.$$

It must not be forgotten that these are merely formulas. In using any one of them in working a problem, we must check the hypothesis of the corresponding theorem to see if it is legitimate to use the formula.

PROBLEMS

1. Find $\int (x^2 + 3x)\, dx$. *Solution:* By Theorem 8.1,

$$\int (x^2 + 3x)\, dx = \int x^2\, dx + \int 3x\, dx.$$

By Theorem 8.4,

$$\int x^2\, dx = \frac{x^3}{3} + C_1.$$

By Theorem 8.2,

$$\int 3x\, dx = 3 \int x\, dx.$$

By Theorem 8.4,

$$\int x\, dx = \frac{x^2}{2} + C_2.$$

Hence

$$\int (x^2 + 3x)\, dx = \frac{x^3}{3} + 3\frac{x^2}{2} + C_1 + C_2.$$

But C_1 and C_2 are arbitrary numbers, so their sum is an arbitrary number, C, so

$$\int (x^2 + 3x)\, dx = \frac{x^3}{3} + 3\frac{x^2}{2} + C.$$

2. Find $\int x\sqrt{1+x^2}\,dx$. *Solution:* We can write this as

$$\int (1+x^2)^{\frac{1}{2}}x\,dx$$

which suggests the use of Theorem 8.3 with $n = \frac{1}{2}$. If we are to apply this theorem, then f must be the function $f(x) = 1 + x^2$. But then $f'(x) = 2x$. Now we can write

$$\int (1+x^2)^{\frac{1}{2}}x\,dx = \int \frac{1}{2}(1+x^2)^{\frac{1}{2}}(2x)\,dx.$$

By Theorem 8.2,

$$\int \frac{1}{2}(1+x^2)^{\frac{1}{2}}(2x)\,dx = \frac{1}{2}\int (1+x^2)^{\frac{1}{2}}(2x)\,dx.$$

Now, by Theorem 8.3,

$$\int (1+x^2)^{\frac{1}{2}}(2x)\,dx = \frac{(1+x^2)^{\frac{3}{2}}}{\frac{3}{2}} + C.$$

Hence

$$\int x(1+x^2)^{\frac{1}{2}}\,dx = \frac{(1+x^2)^{\frac{3}{2}}}{3} + C.$$

3. Find

a) $\displaystyle\int 6x^3\,dx.$ Ans. $\frac{3}{2}x^4 + c.$

b) $\displaystyle\int (4x^4 - 7x)\,dx.$

c) $\displaystyle\int (x^{10} - x^9 + x^3 - 10x + 9)\,dx.$

d) $\displaystyle\int \sqrt{x}\,dx.$ Ans. $\frac{2}{3}x^{\frac{3}{2}} + c.$

e) $\displaystyle\int x^{\frac{2}{3}}\,dx.$

f) $\displaystyle\int (x^{\frac{3}{2}} + x^{-\frac{3}{2}})\,dx.$

g) $\displaystyle\int (1 + \sqrt{x})^2\,dx.$

h) $\displaystyle\int \frac{dt}{\sqrt{t}}.$ Ans. $2\sqrt{t} + c.$

i) $\displaystyle\int \frac{ds}{s^3}.$

j) $\displaystyle\int \left(x^2 - \frac{1}{x^2}\right)dx.$ Ans. $\frac{x^3}{3} + \frac{1}{x} + c.$

k) $\int (x^2 - 4)^2 \, dx.$ Ans. $\dfrac{x^5}{5} - \dfrac{8}{3} x^3 + 16x + c.$

l) $\int (x + 1)(x^3 - 3) \, dx.$

m) $\int (1 + \sqrt{x}\,)^3 \, dx.$

n) $\int \sqrt{x}(1 + x)^2 \, dx.$

o) $\int t^{\frac{2}{3}}(1 + t^{-\frac{2}{3}})^2 \, dt.$

p) $\int y^3(2 - y^2)^3 \, dy.$

q) $\int \dfrac{x^3 - 1}{x^2} \, dx.$ Ans. $\dfrac{x^2}{2} + \dfrac{1}{x} + c.$

r) $\int \dfrac{x^4 + x - 3}{x^3} \, dx.$

s) $\int \dfrac{(\sqrt{y} + 1)^2}{\sqrt{y}} \, dy.$

t) $\int (s - 2)^3 (2s)^3 \, ds.$

u) $\int (\sqrt{x} - 1)(\sqrt{x} + 1) \, dx.$

v) $\int \dfrac{x - 1}{\sqrt{x} - 1} \, dx.$

w) $\int (\sqrt{x} + y) \, dx.$

x) $\int (\sqrt{x} + y) \, dy.$

4. Find

a) $\int \sqrt{2x} \, dx.$ Ans. $\dfrac{2\sqrt{2}}{3} x^{\frac{3}{2}} + c.$

b) $\int \sqrt{\dfrac{x}{2}} \, dx.$

c) $\int x\sqrt{1 - x^2} \, dx.$

d) $\int y^3 \sqrt{4 + y^4} \, dy.$

e) $\int \dfrac{t}{\sqrt[3]{t^2 - 1}} \, dt.$ Ans. $\frac{3}{4}(t^2 - 1)^{\frac{2}{3}} + c.$

f) $\int \dfrac{s^4}{(1 - 2s^5)^{\frac{1}{6}}} \, ds.$

g) $\int \dfrac{6x^2 - 2}{\sqrt{x^3 - x}} \, dx.$

h) $\int x^2(2 - 3x^3)^4 \, dx.$

i) $\int \sqrt{1 - w} \, dw.$ Ans. $-\frac{2}{3}(1 - w)^{\frac{3}{2}} + c.$

j) $\int \sqrt{2 - 3w} \, dw.$

k) $\int (3x^2 - 4x^3)^{4/5}(2x - 4x^2)\, dx.$

l) $\int \dfrac{\sqrt{1 + \sqrt{x}}}{\sqrt{x}}\, dx.$

5. Find $\int f$ if

a) $f(x) = \sqrt[4]{4 - x}.$

b) $f(x) = x^3\sqrt[4]{4 - x^4}.$

c) $f(z) = \left(z + \dfrac{1}{z}\right)^3.$

d) $f(t) = \dfrac{t}{(1 - t^2)^3}.$

e) $f(s) = \dfrac{s - 1}{(s^2 - 2s + 3)^2}.$

f) $f(y) = \dfrac{(2 - y^{1/3})^2}{y^{1/3}}.$

g) $f(y) = \dfrac{(2 - y^{1/3})^2}{y^{2/3}}.$

2. INTEGRATION BY SUBSTITUTION

If we consider the problem of finding

$$\int x\sqrt{1 + x}\, dx,$$

a few minutes of experimentation show us that none of the procedures of the preceding section is of any use. However, the following theorem will allow us to work out this problem, and also many others.

Theorem 8.5: *If f and φ are functions such that*

$$\int f = \varphi,$$

and if h is a differentiable function, then

$$\int \{f(h)\}h' = \{\varphi(h)\}.$$

Proof: By hypothesis, $\varphi' = f$. By Theorem 4.10,

$$\{\varphi(h)\}' = \{\varphi'(h)\}h' = \{f(h)\}h'.$$

Then, by Definition 8.1

$$\int \{f(h)\}h' = \{\varphi(h)\}.$$

This theorem is used in the following way: We are given f and we are asked for $\varphi = \int f$, but f does not fit into our previous formulas. If we are lucky we can find a function h such that $\{f(h)\}h'$ does fit into our formulas. Then Theorem 8.5 will give us $\int \{f(h)\}h' = \{\varphi(h)\}$. This is not yet quite what we want, since we are asked for φ itself. But we can, if we are lucky again, find φ from an inspection of $\{\varphi(h)\}$. (Compare Problem 3 of Section 13 of Chapter 3.) Use of this theorem in this way is called "integration by substitution," since it involves substituting a function in place of x in the integral.

It is helpful to write out the above integrals in the notations introduced in the preceding section. They become

$$\int f(x)\, dx = \varphi(x)$$

and

$$\int f(h(t))h'(t)\, dt = \varphi(h(t)).$$

Note that the second integral can be regarded as being obtained from the first by the substitution $x = h(t)$ and $dx = h'(t)\, dt$. The expression $h'(t)\, dt$, which we saw before in Problem 2 of Section 3 of Chapter 5, is called the *differential* of the function h.

The application of Theorem 8.5 with this notation is quite straightforward. This is illustrated in the following example, which also suggests how the function h can be obtained in some cases. The problem is the one stated at the beginning of this section, to find

$$\varphi(x) = \int x\sqrt{1 + x}\, dx.$$

Consider the "substitution" $t = \sqrt{1 + x}$. Solving for x, we obtain $x = t^2 - 1$ (so the function h is given by $h(t) = t^2 - 1$). Then $dx = h'(t)\, dt = 2t\, dt$. Now, following the substitution rule for obtaining the second integral of Theorem 8.5, we obtain

$$\int (t^2 - 1)\cdot t(2t\, dt).$$

But we can work this problem by the methods of the preceding section, and we have

$$\int (t^2 - 1)t(2t\, dt) = 2\int (t^4 - t^2)\, dt = \frac{2t^5}{5} - \frac{2t^3}{3} + c.$$

Therefore, in this case,

$$\varphi(h(t)) = \frac{2t^5}{5} - \frac{2t^3}{3} + c.$$

But now we recall that $t = \sqrt{1 + x}$ and $h(t) = x$, so

$$\varphi(x) = \tfrac{2}{5}(1 + x)^{5/2} - \tfrac{2}{3}(1 + x)^{3/2} + c,$$

i.e.,

$$\int x\sqrt{1 + x}\, dx = \tfrac{2}{5}(1 + x)^{5/2} - \tfrac{2}{3}(1 + x)^{3/2} + c,$$

a result which is easily verified by differentiation.

This substitution procedure can often be used to "simplify" indefinite integrals. In particular, when there is a radical of the form $\sqrt{ax + b}$ in the expression defining a function for which we are to find an indefinite integral, we make the substitution $t = \sqrt{ax + b}$. This leads to $x = \dfrac{t^2 - b}{a} = h(t)$ and $dx = h'(t)\, dt = \dfrac{2t\, dt}{a}$. For more complicated radicals other substitutions are available, one of which is discussed in Section 6 of Chapter 10.

Remark: The observing student will notice that we have not shown rigorously that the procedure used in working the example above is always legitimate. This can be done, but to do so would involve a careful discussion of the "differential" $dx = h'(t)\, dt$. Such a discussion is outside the scope of this book, since the differential of a function is actually a "function" whose domain of definition consists, not of numbers, but of pairs of numbers. Therefore we shall use the above substitution rules in a purely mechanical way to help us in applying Theorem 8.5. In any particular case, we can always check our result by differentiation.

PROBLEMS

1. Find

   a) $\int x^2 \sqrt{x - 1}\, dx.$

   Solution: Let $\sqrt{x - 1} = t$, so $h(t) = t^2 + 1$ and $dh = 2t\, dt$. Substituting, we have $\int (t^2 + 1)^2 (t)(2t\, dt) = 2 \int (t^6 + 2t^4 + t^2)\, dt = \dfrac{2t^7}{7} + \dfrac{4t^5}{5} + \dfrac{2t^3}{3} + c$, and so $\int x^2 \sqrt{x - 1}\, dx = \tfrac{2}{7}(x - 1)^{7/2} + \tfrac{4}{5}(x - 1)^{5/2} + \tfrac{2}{3}(x - 1)^{3/2} + c.$

   b) $\int x\sqrt{1 + 2x}\, dx.$ Ans. $\dfrac{(1 + 2x)^{5/2}}{10} - \dfrac{(1 + 2x)^{3/2}}{6} + C.$

   c) $\int x\sqrt{3x - 1}\, dx.$ d) $\int \dfrac{y\, dy}{\sqrt{1 + y}}.$

   e) $\int \dfrac{s^2\, ds}{\sqrt{2 - 3s}}.$ f) $\int x^3 \sqrt{10 - \dfrac{x}{2}}\, dx.$

   g) $\int \dfrac{t\, dt}{\sqrt{2 - 3t}}.$ Ans. $\tfrac{2}{27}(2 - 3t)^{3/2} - \tfrac{4}{9}(2 - 3t)^{1/2} + C.$

2. Find

a) $\int x \sqrt[3]{1+x}\, dx.$ Ans. $\frac{3}{7}(1+x)^{7/3} - \frac{3}{4}(1+x)^{4/3} + C.$

b) $\int x^2 \sqrt[3]{2x-3}\, dx.$

c) $\int y \sqrt[4]{1+y}\, dy.$

d) $\int s(1+s)^{2/3}\, ds.$

e) $\int t(10 - 5t)^{1/3}\, dt.$

f) $\int \dfrac{w\, dw}{\sqrt[3]{w-1}}.$

3. Work each of the following first by the methods of Section 1 and then by means of Theorem 8.5, using the indicated substitution.

a) $\int (6x)^3\, dx;\ t = 6x.$

b) $\int x \sqrt{1+x^2}\, dx;\ t = 1 + x^2.$

c) $\int x \sqrt{1+x^2}\, dx;\ t = \sqrt{1+x^2}.$

d) $\int \sqrt{1-x}\, dx;\ t = 1 - x.$

3. VOLUMES

It is possible to calculate volumes of certain solids by methods quite similar to those used in calculating areas.

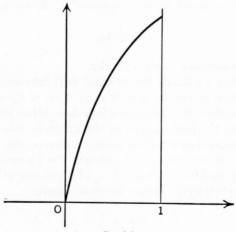

Fig. 8.1

As an illustration consider the figure in the first quadrant bounded by the x-axis, the line $x = 1$, and the graph of the parabola $y^2 = 4x$. If we rotate this figure around the x-axis, it sweeps out a solid, and we can ask for the volume of this solid.

As in the case of work and area problems, the first thing to consider is what we mean by the volume of the solid.

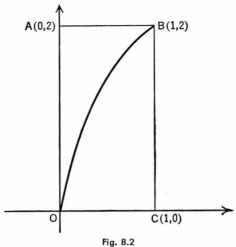

Fig. 8.2

Suppose we consider the rectangle $OABC$ whose top passes through the highest part of the graph. When this rectangle is rotated around the x-axis, it sweeps out a cylinder. We can calculate the volume of this cylinder: it is 4π, since the radius of the base is 2 and the altitude is 1.

Now, whatever we mean by the "volume" V of our solid, we certainly wish to have

$$V \leq 4\pi,$$

since our solid is contained in the cylinder.

Suppose now that we divide the interval [0,1] into smaller segments by means of a sequence of points, $x_0 = 0 < x_1 < \cdots < x_n = 1$. For the interval $[x_{i-1}, x_i]$, consider the rectangle whose base is this interval and whose top passes through the highest part of the graph in this interval. When this rectangle is rotated around the x-axis, it sweeps out a cylinder which contains the slice of our solid lying between the planes perpendicular to the x-axis at the points x_{i-1} and x_i. The volume of this cylinder is $4\pi(x_i)(x_i - x_{i-1})$. (Why?) Hence we should have

$$V_i \leq 4\pi x_i(x_i - x_{i-1}).$$

Similarly, the rectangle whose top passes through the lowest point of the graph in the interval $[x_{i-1}, x_i]$ sweeps out a cylinder which is inside this slice of our solid. This cylinder has the volume $4\pi x_{i-1}(x_i - x_{i-1})$. (Why?) Hence

$$4\pi x_{i-1}(x_i - x_{i-1}) \leq V_i \leq 4\pi x_i(x_i - x_{i-1}).$$

Therefore

$$\sum_{i=1}^{i=n} 4\pi x_{i-1}(x_i - x_{i-1}) \leq V \leq \sum_{i=1}^{i=n} 4\pi x_i(x_i - x_{i-1}).$$

These inequalities hold for any sequence $x_0 = 0 < x_1 < \cdots < x_n = 1$, so, no matter what we mean by the "volume" of our solid,

$$LUB\left(\sum_{i=1}^{i=n} 4\pi x_{i-1}(x_i - x_{i-1})\right) \leq V \leq GLB\left(\sum_{i=1}^{i=n} 4\pi x_i(x_i - x_{i-1})\right).$$

But now we recognize that these quantities are the lower and upper integrals of the function f, defined by $f(x) = 4\pi x$. (Why?) Hence

$$\underline{\int_0^1} 4\pi x \, dx \leq V \leq \overline{\int_0^1} 4\pi x \, dx.$$

Since the function f is continuous, by Theorem 7.1,

$$\underline{\int_0^1} 4\pi x \, dx = \overline{\int_0^1} 4\pi x \, dx.$$

Therefore, a reasonable definition of the volume of our solid is

$$V = \int_0^1 4\pi x \, dx = 2\pi.$$

In general, if we have a figure bounded below by the x-axis, to the right and left by the lines $x = a$ and $x = b$, and above by the graph of a function f, we can rotate this figure around the x-axis and it will sweep out a solid, called a **solid of revolution.** By an analysis similar to the one above, we see that no matter how we define the "volume," V, of this solid, we should have

$$LUB\left(\sum_{i=1}^{i=n} \pi(f(x_i))^2(x_i - x_{i-1})\right) \leq V \leq GLB\left(\sum_{i=1}^{i=n} \pi(f(\bar{x}_i))^2(x_i - x_{i-1})\right)$$

or

$$\underline{\int_a^b} \pi f^2 \leq V \leq \overline{\int_a^b} \pi f^2.$$

If f is continuous, so are f^2 and πf^2, (Why?) so

$$\int_{\underline{a}}^b \pi f^2 = \int_a^{\overline{b}} \pi f^2.$$

Hence it is reasonable to define the volume of this solid of revolution to be

$$V = \int_a^b \pi f^2.$$

In the problems below we illustrate methods for defining and calculating volumes of some other more complicated solids.

PROBLEMS

(*Note:* A few of the problems below may lead to integrals which cannot be evaluated by the methods studied so far. If so, leave your answer in the form of a definite integral.)

1. Find the volumes of the solids generated by revolving around the x-axis the figures bounded by the graphs of

   a) $y = x^3$, $x = 1$, and $y = 0$. Ans. $\dfrac{\pi}{7}$.

   b) $y = x^3$, $x = 2$, and $y = 0$. Ans. $\dfrac{128\pi}{7}$.

   c) $y = x^2 - 4x$ and $y = 0$.
   d) $y = \sqrt{x}$, $x = a$, and $y = 0$.
   e) $y = 4 - x^2$ and $y = 0$.

2. Find a formula for the volume of a cone by rotating around the x-axis the triangle whose vertices are $(0,0)$, $(a,0)$, and (a,b).

3. Find a formula for the volume of a sphere by rotating a circle around one of its diameters.

4. Find the volume of the solid obtained by rotating around the x-axis the ellipse $\dfrac{x^2}{a^2} + \dfrac{y^2}{b^2} = 1$.

5. The figure bounded by the graphs of $y^2 = 4x$, $x = 0$, and $y = 2$ is rotated around the x-axis. Find the volume of the resulting solid.

   Hint: We saw above how to define and calculate the volume of the solid swept out by the figure OBC. Now the rectangle $OABC$ sweeps out a cylinder whose volume we can calculate. We take the volume of the solid generated by OAB to the volume of the cylinder minus the volume swept out by OBC. Ans. 2π.

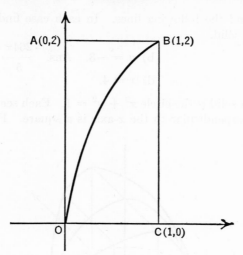

Fig. 8.3

6. Find the volumes of the solids obtained by rotating around the x-axis the figures bounded by

a) $y = x^2$ and $y = x$. Ans. $\dfrac{2\pi}{15}$.   b) $y = x^3$ and $y = x$.

c) $y = \sqrt{x}$ and $y = x$. Ans. $\dfrac{\pi}{6}$.   d) $y = 4 - x^2$ and $y = 2$.

e) $y = 4 - x^2$ and $y = 2x + 4$.   f) $x^2 + (y - 2)^2 = 1$.

7. The figure bounded by the graphs of $y = x^2$, $x = 0$, and $y = 4$ is rotated around the y-axis. Find the volume of the solid which it sweeps out.

8. Find the volumes of the solids obtained by rotating around the y-axis the figures bounded by the graphs of

a) $y = x^3$, $x = 0$, and $y = 1$. Ans. $\dfrac{3\pi}{5}$.

b) $y = x^3$, $y = 0$, and $x = 1$.
c) $y = x^3$ and $y = x$.
d) $y = 4 - x^2$ and $y = 0$.
e) $y = 4 - x^2$ and $y = 2$.

9. The figure bounded by the graphs of $y^2 = 4x$, $y = 0$, and $x = 1$ is rotated around the line $x = 1$. Find the volume of the resulting solid.

Ans. $\dfrac{16\pi}{5}$.

10. The figure bounded by the graphs of $y = 6x^2$, $x = 0$, and $y = 6$ is

rotated around the following lines.   In each case find the volume of the resulting solid.

a) $y = 0$.   b) $y = -3$.   Ans. $\dfrac{264\pi}{5}$.

c) $x = -1$.   d) $x = 4$.

11. The base of a solid is the circle $x^2 + y^2 = 1$.   Each section of the solid by a plane perpendicular to the x-axis is a square.   Find the volume of the solid.

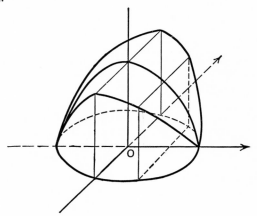

Fig. 8.4

Solution: Consider two points x_{i-1} and x_i, with $0 < x_{i-1} < x_i < 1$. Consider the rectangular parallelopiped whose altitude is $x_i - x_{i-1}$ and whose base is the square section in which the plane perpendicular to the x-axis at x_{i-1} cuts our solid.   This parallelopiped contains that slice of our solid which lies between the planes perpendicular to the x-axis at x_{i-1} and x_i.   The volume of the parallelopiped is

$$(2\sqrt{1 - x_{i-1}^2})^2(x_i - x_{i-1}).$$

However we define the "volume" of our solid, we certainly wish to have the volume, V_i, of this slice be no greater than the volume of the parallelopiped:

$$V_i \leq (2\sqrt{1 - x_{i-1}^2})^2(x_i - x_{i-1}).$$

Similarly, the parallelopiped whose base is the section at x_i is inside this slice of our solid.   Its volume is $(2\sqrt{1 - x_i^2})^2(x_i - x_{i-1})$, so we wish to have

$$(2\sqrt{1 - x_i^2})^2(x_i - x_{i-1}) \leq V_i.$$

Now proceeding as in the previous problems, it is reasonable to define the volume of our solid, V, to be

$$V = \int_{-1}^{1} (2\sqrt{1 - x^2})^2 \, dx.$$

12. The base of a solid is the circle $x^2 + y^2 = 4$. Define and find its volume if each section by a plane perpendicular to the x-axis is

a) an equilateral triangle. Ans. $\dfrac{32\sqrt{3}}{3}$.

b) a rectangle of altitude 4.

c) an isosceles right triangle with its right angle above the plane of the base.

13. A tank has the shape of the top half of a sphere of radius 10 ft. It is filled with a liquid weighing 50 lbs. per cu. ft. How much work does it take to pump out all the liquid?

Solution: A vertical cross section of this tank is the upper half of a circle. If we place the origin of a coordinate system at the center of this circle, and the y-axis upright, the equation of this circle is $x^2 + y^2 = 100$.

Let us take a sequence $y_0 = 0 < y_1 < \cdots < y_n = 10$. A horizontal cross section of the tank at a level y_i ft. above the bottom of the tank is a circle of radius $\sqrt{100 - y_i^2}$ ft. (Why?) Consider now a cylinder whose base is the cross section at the level y_{i-1} and whose altitude is $(y_i - y_{i-1})$. This cylinder contains the horizontal slice of the tank between the levels y_{i-1} and y_i, and its volume is

$$\pi(100 - y_{i-1})^2(y_i - y_{i-1}).$$

A particle of liquid in this slice is moved a distance at most $(10 - y_{i-1})$. Therefore, the work, W_i, done in getting this slice to the top of the tank is certainly no more than

$$50\pi(10 - y_{i-1})(100 - y_{i-1}^2)(y_i - y_{i-1}).$$

Similarly, if we consider the cylinder whose upper base is the horizontal cross section at the level y_i, we see that

$$50\pi(10 - y_i)(100 - y_i^2)(y_i - y_{i-1}) \leq W_i.$$

These inequalities hold at each level, so we have

$$\sum_{i=1}^{i=n} 50\pi(10 - y_i)(100 - y_i^2)(y_i - y_{i-1}) \leq W$$

and

$$W \leq \sum_{i=1}^{i=n} 50\pi(10 - y_{i-1})(100 - y_{i-1}^2)(y_i - y_{i-1}).$$

Now, proceeding as we did in our previous problems concerning work, it is reasonable to define the amount of work done here to be

$$\int_0^{10} 50\pi(10 - y)(100 - y^2)\, dy = \frac{625,000}{3}\, \pi \text{ ft.-lbs.}$$

14. How much work is done in pumping out liquid from the tank of Problem 13 until the surface of the remaining liquid is 5 ft. above the base?
15. A tank is in the shape of a cone, 5 ft. high and 6 ft. across the bottom. How much work is done in pumping it out if it is filled with oil weighing 100 lbs. per cu. ft.? Ans. 5625π ft.-lbs.
16. Find the work needed to pump out each of the following tanks, each filled with a liquid weighing α lbs. per cu. ft.

    a) a conical tank 10 ft. high and 10 ft. across the base.
    b) a tank consisting of a cylinder 6 ft. high and 4 ft. across, with a hemispherical top.
    c) a tank 4 ft. high and 8 ft. across the base with the shape of the solid of revolution obtained by rotating around the y-axis the figure bounded by the x-axis and the parabola $x^2 + 4y = 16$.
    d) a tank 4 ft. high and 10 ft. across the base with the shape of the solid of revolution obtained by rotating around the y-axis the figure bounded above by the ellipse $16x^2 + 25y^2 = 400$ and below by the x-axis.

4. FLUID PRESSURE

The problems we have considered so far which have led to definite integrals have all been of the same pattern. In each case we started with a term, such as *work*, *area*, or *volume*, which was defined for certain simple situations, and we have extended the definition to cover more complicated situations.

In the case of area, for example, we started knowing what was meant by the area of a rectangle. A more complicated figure (see again Section 2 of Chapter 7) we enclosed in a sum of rectangles and were led to the conclusion that, no matter how the area, A, of the figure, was to be defined, we should have

$$A \leq \overline{\int_a^b} f.$$

Similarly, by considering sums of interior rectangles, we found that we should have

$$\underline{\int_a^b} f \leq A.$$

But now, because of Theorem 7.1, we are practically forced to define A to be

$$A = \int_a^b f.$$

There are, however, certain problems where a slightly different procedure has to be followed and where the crucial theorem is Theorem 7.12 rather than Theorem 7.1. In this and the next section we take up two of these problems.

Physical experiments show us that the force, measured in pounds, say, exerted by a fluid on a horizontal submerged surface is equal to the weight, measured in pounds, of the column of fluid over the surface. Other experiments show us that at any point under the surface of the liquid the force is exerted equally in all directions.

From these experiments, then, we see that if we have a vertical surface immersed in a liquid, such as the face of a dam, the pressure (measured in pounds per square foot, say) exerted by the fluid is not constant at all points of the surface. How then can we find the total force which the fluid exerts on the surface?

As in the previous situations, we must decide what we mean by the "total force."

Let us examine the case of a semicircular dam of radius 50 ft. If we introduce a coordinate system with the x-axis at the surface of the water and the origin at the midpoint of the diameter of the semicircle, then an equation for the corresponding circle is

$$x^2 + y^2 = 2500.$$

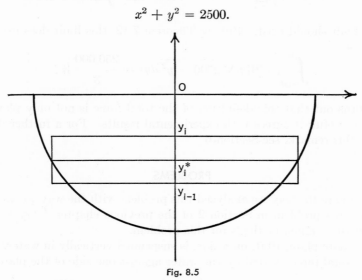

Fig. 8.5

Suppose now that we choose a fixed number $r > 0$ and then a sequence $y_0 = -50 < y_1 < \cdots < y_n = 0$, such that each interval $[y_{i-1}, y_i]$ has length no greater than r. In each interval $[y_{i-1}, y_i]$ choose a point y_i^*.

Now consider the slice of our surface lying between the horizontal lines $y = y_{i-1}$ and $y = y_i$. The area of this slice is approximately equal to the area of the rectangle, especially if r is small, and the area of the rectangle is

$$2\sqrt{2500 - y_i^{*2}} \, (y_i - y_{i-1}). \quad \text{(Why?)}$$

Since the pressure is proportional to the distance below the surface, if r is small, the pressure at any point in this slice is approximately equal to the pressure along the line $y = y_i^*$. Along this line the pressure is $-Wy_i^*$, where W is the weight of water in pounds per cubic foot. Hence the quantity

$$-2Wy_i^*\sqrt{2500 - y_i^{*2}} \, (y_i - y_{i-1})$$

is an approximation to what we might want to call the force on this slice. Then

$$\sum_{i=1}^{i=n} -2Wy_i^*\sqrt{2500 - y_i^{*2}} \, (y_i - y_{i-1})$$

is an approximation to what we might want to call the total force on the dam.

Hence a plausible definition of the total force on the dam would be

$$\lim_{r \to 0} \left(\sum_{i=1}^{i=n} -2Wy_i^*\sqrt{2500 - y_i^{*2}} \right) (y_i - y_{i-1})$$

if this limit should exist. But by Theorem 7.12, this limit does exist and in fact is

$$\int_{-50}^{0} (-2Wy\sqrt{2500 - y^2} \, dy) = \frac{250,000}{3} W.$$

It turns out that this definition of the total force is not only plausible, but also useful; it agrees with experimental results. For a further discussion of this remark, see Section 6.

PROBLEMS

1. Compare the way we analyzed this problem with the way we analyzed the area problem in Section 2 of the previous chapter. Try to carry out the original methods for this problem.

2. A square plate, 10 ft. on a side, is suspended vertically in water. Find the total force exerted by the water against one side of the plate if

   a) the top of the plate is at the surface.   Ans. $500W$.
   b) the top of the plate is parallel to the surface but 10 ft. down.   Ans. $1500W$.
   c) a diagonal is parallel to the surface and 10 ft. down.

3. In Problem 2a, find the total force on each of the triangular parts into which a diagonal divides the square.

4. A plate in the form of an equilateral triangle, 2 ft. on a side, is suspended vertically in water. Find the total force on one side of the plate if one base is at the surface, and also if one vertex is at the surface with the opposite base horizontal. Ans. $W, 2W$.

5. Find the total force exerted against the gate of a water main if it is circular, has radius 2 ft. and its top is 20 ft. below the surface of the water.

6. The end of a tank is elliptical, with a horizontal axis of 4 ft. and a vertical axis of 3 ft. Find the total force on the end of the tank if

   a) the tank is full of a liquid weighing 100 lbs. per cu. ft.
   b) the same liquid is only 1 ft. deep in the tank.

7. The end of a tank is a segment of a parabola, 4 ft. deep and 2 ft. wide at the top. Find the total force against the end of the tank if

   a) the tank is full of a liquid weighing 75 lbs. per cu. ft. Ans. 640.
   b) the same liquid is only 2 ft. deep in the tank.

8. A plate in the form of an isosceles triangle, with base 2 ft. and altitude 4 ft. is suspended vertically in water, vertex up. How far up must it be moved in order to reduce the total force exerted by the water on one face of the plate to one-half its original amount if the vertex is originally

   a) 100 ft. below the surface?
   b) at the surface?

9. A tank has the shape of the lower half of a sphere of radius 10 ft. It is filled with a liquid weighing 50 lbs. per cu. ft. How much work does it take to pump out all the liquid?

Solution: (Compare with Problem 13 of Section 3.) A vertical cross section of this tank is the lower half of the circle whose equation is $x^2 + y^2 = 100$. Choose a fixed number $r > 0$ and then a sequence $y_0 = -10 < y_1 < \cdots < y_n = 0$ such that the length of each interval $[y_{i-1}, y_i]$ is no more than r. In each interval $[y_{i-1}, y_i]$ choose a point y_i^*. A horizontal cross section of the tank at the level y_i^* is a circle of radius $\sqrt{100 - y_i^{*2}}$.

Consider now the cylinder whose lower base is at the level y_{i-1}, whose upper base is at the level y_i and whose radius is $\sqrt{100 - y_i^{*2}}$. The volume of this cylinder, $\pi(100 - y_i^{*2})(y_i - y_{i-1})$ is approximately equal to the volume of the slice of our tank lying between the levels y_{i-1} and y_i, especially if r is small. Any particle in this slice moves approximately $-y_i^*$ feet. Hence the work, W_i, done on this slice is approximately

$$-50\pi y_i{}^*(100 - y_i{}^{*2})(y_i - y_{i-1}),$$

and so

$$\sum_{i=1}^{i=n} -50\pi y_i{}^*(100 - y_i{}^{*2})(y_i - y_{i-1})$$

is an approximation to the total work done in pumping out the tank. Hence a plausible definition of total work would be

$$\lim_{r \to 0} \left(\sum_{i=1}^{i=n} -50\pi y_i{}^*(100 - y_i{}^{*2})(y_i - y_{i-1}) \right),$$

if this limit should exist. But by Theorem 7.12, this limit does exist and is

$$\int_{-10}^{0} -50\pi y(100 - y^2)\, dy = 125{,}000\pi.$$

10. Why does the method used in Problem 13 of Section 3 not work in the problem above?
11. If the tank in Problem 7 above is 10 feet long, how much work does it take to pump it out? Ans. a) 6400 ft.-lbs.
12. If the tank in Problem 6 is 20 ft. long, write a definite integral whose value is the number of ft.-lbs. of work needed to pump it out. Can you evaluate this integral?

5. LENGTH OF A CURVE

Greek mathematicians thought of the circumference of a circle as a limit of the perimeters of inscribed regular polygons. Archimedes arrived at a good approximation to the circumference of the unit circle, and hence of π, by computing the perimeters of regular polygons, inscribed in the circle, of 3, 6, 12, 24, 48, and 96 sides. We shall show that this basic idea can be applied to many other curves.

Definition 8.2: *If f is a function, and $[a,b]$ an interval in its domain of definition, then the number S is the **length of the graph** of f from $(a,f(a))$ to $(b,f(b))$ if it is always the case that*

$$\lim_{r \to 0} S_r = S$$

whenever the numbers S_r are obtained as follows:

For each number $r > 0$, let $x_0 = a < x_1 < \cdots < x_n = b$ be a sequence such that the length of each interval $[x_{i-1}, x_i]$ is less than r. Construct the broken line consisting of the segments joining $(a,f(a))$ and $(x_1,f(x_1))$, $(x_1,f(x_1))$ and $(x_2,f(x_2))$, and so on. Then let S_r be the total length of this broken line.

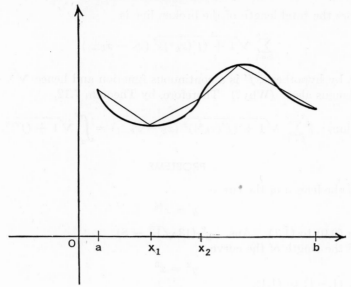

Fig. 8.6

Theorem 8.6: *If f is a function, with [a,b] an interval in its domain of definition, and if f′ is continuous in this interval, then the graph of f has a length between (a,f(a)) and (b,f(b)) and*

$$S = \int_a^b \sqrt{1 + (f')^2}.$$

Proof: Given any sequence $x_0 = a < x_1 < \cdots < x_n = b$ as above, consider the segment joining $(x_{k-1}, f(x_{k-1}))$ and $(x_k, f(x_k))$. The length of this segment is

$$\sqrt{(x_k - x_{k-1})^2 + (f(x_k) - f(x_{k-1}))^2}.$$

This can be written as

$$\sqrt{1 + \left(\frac{f(x_k) - f(x_{k-1})}{x_k - x_{k-1}}\right)^2} \,(x_k - x_{k-1}).$$

Now, by hypothesis, f' exists at each point of the interval $[x_{k-1}, x_k]$, so we can apply the Mean Value Theorem, and we have

$$f(x_k) = f(x_{k-1}) + f'(x_k^*)(x_k - x_{k-1}),\ x_{k-1} < x_k^* < x_k.$$

or

$$\frac{f(x_k) - f(x_{k-1})}{x_k - x_{k-1}} = f'(x_k^*).$$

Hence the length of the segment joining $(x_{k-1}, f(x_{k-1}))$ to $(x_k, f(x_k))$ is

$$\sqrt{1 + (f'(x_k^*))^2}\,(x_k - x_{k-1}).$$

Therefore the total length of the broken line is

$$\sum_{k=1}^{k=n} \sqrt{1 + (f'(x_k{}^*))^2}\, (x_k - x_{k-1}).$$

Now, by hypothesis, f' is a continuous function and hence $\sqrt{1 + (f')^2}$ is continuous also. (Why?) Therefore, by Theorem 7.12,

$$\lim_{r \to 0} \sum_{k=1}^{k=n} \sqrt{1 + (f'(x_k{}^*))^2}\, (x_k - x_{k-1}) = \int_a^b \sqrt{1 + (f')^2}.$$

PROBLEMS

1. Find the length of the curve

$$y = x^{3/2}$$

from (0,0) to (1,1). Ans. $\frac{1}{27}(13\sqrt{13} - 8)$.

2. Find the length of the curve

$$y^2 = x^3$$

from $(1,-1)$ to $(1,1)$.

3. Find the length of the part of the curve

$$y = (x + 2)^{3/2}$$

which lies in the second quadrant.

4. Find the length of the graph of $f(x) = \frac{1}{3}(x^2 - 2)^{3/2}$ from $x = 2$ to $x = 3$.
Ans. $\frac{16}{3}$.

5. Find the length of the graph of the function $f(x) = \frac{3}{2}x^{2/3}$

a) from $(1,\frac{3}{2})$ to $(8,6)$.
b) from $(-8,6)$ to $(-1,\frac{3}{2})$.

6. Write a definite integral whose value is the circumference of a unit circle. Can you evaluate this integral?

7. For each of the following functions, write a definite integral whose value is the length of the graph between the indicated points. In each case, use the Trapezoidal Rule (Problem 10 of Section 6 of Chapter 7) with $n = 4$ to find an approximate value for the integral. Estimate the error made by using the Trapezoidal Rule.

a) $f(x) = x^2$, (0,0) to (1,1). Ans. $(1 + 2\sqrt{2} + 2\sqrt{5} + \sqrt{13})/8$
  = (approx.) 1.49; error $< \dfrac{\sqrt{5}}{16}$.

b) $f(x) = \dfrac{x^3}{3}$, (0,0) to $(1,\frac{1}{3})$.

c) $f(x) = \dfrac{1}{x}$, (1,1) to $(2,\frac{1}{2})$.

d) $f(x) = \sqrt{x}$, (1,1) to $(5,\sqrt{5})$.

6. FINAL REMARKS ON DEFINITE INTEGRALS

In analyzing, for example, the "work" done in stretching a spring, we saw that for any reasonable definition of the amount, W, of work done, we should have

$$\underline{\int_a^b} f \leq W \leq \overline{\int_a^b} f,$$

for an appropriate function f. Consequently, in view of Theorem 7.1, we decided to define W by the equation

$$W = \int_a^b f.$$

Our discussion did not guarantee this to be a useful definition; it merely showed that any other definition would be unreasonable. It is true that this is a useful definition, but the reason for this is that the definition leads to results which agree with the results of physical experiments. If we stretch an actual spring, we can calculate the amount of work done by evaluating the appropriate definite integral on the one hand, and also by noting, say, the amount of heat produced. Within the limits of experimental error, the results will be the same.

Similarly, we can calculate the volume of a solid of revolution by the method of Section 3. Or we can immerse the solid in a container full of water and measure the amount of water it displaces. Within the limits of experimental error, the two results will again be the same. The same is true of fluid pressure. We can compute the total force exerted against the face of a dam and we can also measure it experimentally. The two results will agree.

We leave it to the philosophers to decide whether there is a reason why this should be so or if it is just a coincidence, but it is an experimental fact that the definitions we have given for work, area, volume, etc., do give results which agree with physical experience. This is one of the reasons why mathematics is so useful in the sciences.

On the other hand, we must not conclude that whenever a concept is meaningful in certain simple situations we can always extend the definition of this concept to cover all possible situations. Length is a good example. We saw in Theorem 8.6 that if a function f is such that f' is continuous, then the graph of f has a length. But if f is not continuous, it need not have a length. An example is

$$f(x) = \begin{cases} x \sin \left(\dfrac{180}{x} \right)^0, & x \neq 0 \\ 0 & , x = 0. \end{cases}$$

(see Section 6 of Chapter 3). The graph of this function has no length between 0 and 1: $\lim_{r \to 0} S_r$ does not exist.

Examples of this sort indicate why we need to examine each case carefully and make sure, before defining a concept by means of a definite integral, that the integral does exist.

While we are on the subject of applications of integration to physical problems, it is appropriate to mention here, for the benefit of those readers who will go on to study these applications, a shortcut which they will often encounter. This shortcut allows one, when working a problem of the kind we have been considering, to write down the appropriate definite integral very quickly.

We illustrate this shortcut with the problem, worked out in Section 4, of finding the total force, F, on the surface of a dam. The first step is to calculate the approximate force on a horizontal strip. We found this to be

$$-2Wy_i^* \sqrt{2500 - y_i^{*2}} \, (y_i - y_{i-1}).$$

The shortcut consists in denoting this term by ΔF or dF, in writing it without subscripts or superscripts, and in replacing $(y_i - y_{i-1})$ by Δy or dy:

$$\Delta F = -2Wy\sqrt{2500 - y^2} \, \Delta y,$$

or

$$dF = -2Wy\sqrt{2500 - y^2} \, dy.$$

Either of these immediately suggests the equation

$$F = \int_{-50}^{0} -2Wy\sqrt{2500 - y^2} \, dy,$$

which is the integral we arrived at before.

The difficulty with this shortcut, when it is used in a purely mechanical fashion, is that it skips entirely the analysis which persuaded us that this integral was a reasonable definition of the total force on the surface of the dam. Nevertheless, if the user has had some experience in applying integration to physical problems, this shortcut will rarely lead him into error.

REVIEW PROBLEMS

1. Find the indefinite integrals:

a) $\int x^{-4}(x - 2)^2 \, dx.$

b) $\int \sqrt{x^3 + 2x^2 + x} \, dx.$

c) $\int \sqrt[3]{\frac{2}{x^2} - \frac{1}{x^{5/3}}} \, dx.$

2. Find the volume generated by revolving the area bounded by the hypocycloid

$x^{\frac{2}{3}} + y^{\frac{2}{3}} = a^{\frac{2}{3}}$ about the y-axis.   Ans. $\dfrac{32\pi a^3}{105}$.

3. Find the volume generated by revolving the area bounded by the parabolic arc $\sqrt{x} + \sqrt{y} = \sqrt{a}$ and the coordinate axes about the x-axis.

4. Find the volume of the solid obtained by rotating the pentagon with vertices $(1,0)$, $(2,2)$, $(0,4)$, $(-2,2)$, $(-1,0)$ about the x-axis.

5. The arc of the curve $xy = x - y$ joining the origin and any point $P_1(x_1,y_1)$ bounds with the x-axis and the line $x = x_1$ an area A. The same arc bounds with the y-axis and the line $y = y_1$ an area B. Prove that the volumes obtained by revolving A about the x-axis and B about the y-axis are unequal for any P_1.

6. The circle $x^2 + y^2 = a^2$ is rotated about the line $x = b$ to generate a torus. Find the volume generated.

7. The base of a solid is the area bounded by a parabola and its latus rectum. Every section of the solid made by a plane at right angles to the latus rectum is a rectangle whose altitude is equal to the distance of the section from the axis of the parabola. Find the volume of the solid.

8. Given the ellipse $\dfrac{x^2}{25} + \dfrac{y^2}{9} = 1$, a solid is formed about this curve in such a way that all plane sections perpendicular to the x-axis are ellipses whose foci are on the given ellipse. The major and minor axes of each section are proportional to those of the given ellipse. Find the volume of the solid. (Area of the ellipse $x^2/a^2 + y^2/b^2 = 1$ is πab.)

Ans. $\dfrac{225\pi}{4}$.

9. Assume that the staves of a barrel are curved in the form of an arc of an ellipse. The length of the barrel is L, the diameter of each head is h, and the diameter of the midsection is c. Show that the volume of the barrel is

$$\frac{\pi L}{12}(2c^2 + h^2).$$

10. A circular hill has a central vertical section of the form $x^2 + 160y - 1600 = 0$, where the unit is 1 yd. The top is being cut down in horizontal layers at the constant rate of 100 cu. yds. per day. How fast is the area of the horizontal cross section increasing when the top has been cut down a vertical distance of 4 yds.?

11. The abscissa of a point P moving on the parabola $y = ax^2$ is increasing at the rate of 1 unit per sec. Let O denote the origin and let T be the intersection of the x-axis with the tangent to the parabola at P. Show that the rate of increase of the length of the curve from O to P is nu-

merically equal to the ratio

$$TP/OT.$$

12. A certain function, φ, is defined at every non-negative number and has a continuous derivative. At any point on the graph of φ, the y-coordinate is proportional to the length of the graph between this point and the point $(0,\varphi(0))$. Find an equation defining φ.   Ans. $\varphi(x) = qx$.

13. A rectangular floodgate whose upper edge is in the surface of the water is divided into three parts by two lines from the middle of the lower edge to the extremities of the upper edge. Show that the parts sustain equal forces.

14. A solid right circular cone of metal is formed so that the density at any point P in the solid is $20(5 - x)$ lbs. per cu. ft., where x is the perpendicular distance in feet of the point P from the axis of the cone. Find the weight of the cone if its altitude and radius of base are each 3 ft.

15. A tank in the shape of an inverted circular cone is full of water. Two men are to pump the water to the top of the tank, each doing half the work. When the first man has finished his share of the work, let z denote the ratio of the depth of water left in the tank to the original depth. Show that z is determined by the equation $6z^4 - 8z^3 + 1 = 0$.

16. A certain function f has the interval $[0,4]$ for domain of definition, and $f(0) = 5$. For each number a in this interval, the length of the graph of f from $(0,5)$ to $(a,f(a))$ is

$$5\int_0^a \frac{dx}{\sqrt{25 - x^2}}.$$

Find an equation defining f.

Chapter 9

The Logarithmic and Exponential Functions

1. THE FUNCTION *L*

In the previous chapters of this book we have discussed the two main concepts of calculus, differentiation and integration, and we have also discussed the application of these concepts to various problems. However, the only functions which we have learned how to differentiate or integrate are algebraic functions. In this chapter we take up two new functions, the logarithmic and the exponential functions. We shall learn how to differentiate these functions. The resulting formulas will give new formulas for indefinite integration. The net result will be that we shall be able to apply the methods developed in previous chapters to many new functions. We shall not, however, be able to solve new kinds of problems.

We consider first the function g defined by the equation

$$g(x) = \log_{10}(x).$$

It is possible to find the derivative of this function by applying Definition 4.1 and calculating the limit. This turns out, however, to be a long and difficult calculation. Part of the difficulty lies in the fact that a complete definition of the logarithm is not given in the usual algebra course. It is actually easier to define a new function, which is easy to differentiate, and then to show that it is very closely related to the logarithm function, so closely related that it will be easy to find the derivative we want.

It is not unnatural to consider this new function. We have, in Theorem 8.4, a rule for finding

$$\int x^n \, dx$$

whenever $n \neq -1$. But we have had no method for finding explicitly

$$\int \frac{1}{x} \, dx.$$

Now there certainly exists at least one function whose derivative is $1/x$ and hence is an indefinite integral of the function f defined by $f(x) = 1/x$. For example, if a is any positive number, then the interval $(a,1)$ or $(1,a)$ is in the domain of definition of f and f is continuous at each point of the interval. Therefore, by Theorem 7.7, the function L, defined by

$$L(a) = \int_1^a \frac{dx}{x}, \quad a > 0,$$

is such that

$$L'(x) = 1/x,$$

and so L is an indefinite integral of f.

The reason why this function L was not mentioned in Theorem 8.4 is that it is not an algebraic function. (An algebraic function is one whose rule can be expressed by means of the algebraic operations of addition, subtraction, multiplication, division, and taking powers and roots.) We can, however, obtain a good deal of information about the function L. Let us start by sketching its graph. Since $L(a) = \int_1^a dx/x$, it is convenient to have before us the graph of the function $f(x) = 1/x$. This function is not

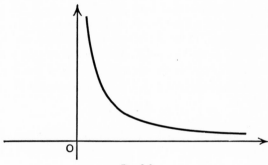

Fig. 9.1

defined when $x = 0$, and we use only the part of the graph to the right of the y-axis.

We first note that $L(1) = \int_1^1 \frac{dx}{x} = 0$, so the graph of L crosses the x-axis at the point $(1,0)$. Since $L'(x) = 1/x$, which is positive for each x in the domain of definition of L, the graph of L is always increasing. (Why?) Since $L''(x) = -1/x^2$, which is always negative, the graph of L is always concave downward. (Why?)

For any a such that $a > 1$, the maximum value of $1/x$ in the interval $(1,a)$ is 1 and the minimum value is $1/a$. The length of the interval is $a - 1$, so, by Theorem 7.4, we have

$$\frac{a-1}{a} \le L(a) \le (a-1).$$

Therefore, $L(a)$ is positive when $a > 1$, and $L(a)$ grows more slowly than a does. On the other hand, as we shall see in the next section, there is no upper bound for the numbers $L(a)$. In other words, given any number A, no matter how large, there is a number a such that $L(a) > A$.

Let us now examine the case where $0 < a < 1$. For such a number

$$L(a) = \int_1^a \frac{dx}{x} = -\int_a^1 \frac{dx}{x} = \int_a^1 \frac{-1}{x}\, dx,$$

so we consider the function g defined by $g(x) = -1/x$. The maximum value of g in the interval $(a,1)$ is -1 and the minimum value is $\dfrac{1}{-a}$. The length of the interval is $1 - a$. Therefore

$$\frac{-1}{a}(1-a) \le L(a) \le (-1)(1-a)$$

or

$$\frac{a-1}{a} \le L(a) \le (a-1).$$

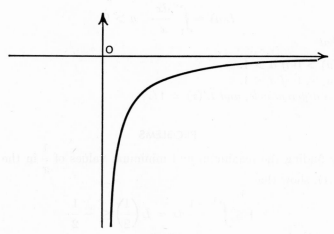

Fig. 9.2

Since $a < 1$, $a - 1 < 0$, and we see that $L(a)$ is negative if $0 < a < 1$. We shall see in the next section that when a is close to 0, $|L(a)|$ is large: For any positive number B, no matter how large, there is an a such that

$$L(a) < -B.$$

We can now put this information together to make a sketch of the graph of L. The result looks like this:

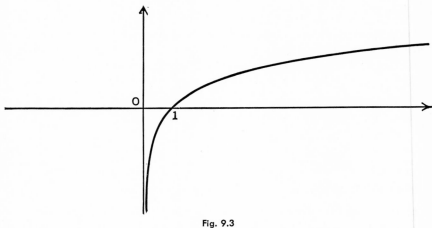

Fig. 9.3

Let us summarize in the form of a theorem the information we now have concerning this function L.

Theorem 9.1: *The function L, defined by the equation*

$$L(a) = \int_1^a \frac{dx}{x}, \quad a > 0,$$

is such that

    i) $L(a) > 0$ *if* $a > 1$.
    ii) $L(a) < 0$ *if* $a < 1$.
    iii) L *is differentiable, and* $L'(x) = 1/x$.

PROBLEMS

1. a) By finding the maximum and minimum values of $\frac{1}{x}$ in the interval $(\frac{1}{2}, 1)$, show that

$$-1 \leq \int_{\frac{1}{2}}^1 \frac{-1}{x}\, dx = L\left(\frac{1}{2}\right) \leq -\frac{1}{2}.$$

    b) Show that

$$-1 \leq \int_{\frac{1}{4}}^{\frac{1}{2}} \frac{-1}{x}\, dx \leq -\frac{1}{2}.$$

    c) Show, by using a) and b), that

$$-2 \leq L(\tfrac{1}{4}) \leq -1.$$

d) Show that
$$-3 \leq L(\tfrac{1}{8}) \leq -\tfrac{3}{2},$$
and
$$-4 \leq L(\tfrac{1}{16}) \leq -2.$$

2. a) Show that if n is a positive integer, then
$$\frac{1}{n+1} < \int_n^{n+1} \frac{dx}{x} < \frac{1}{n}.$$

b) Show that if n is an integer greater than 1, then
$$\frac{1}{2} + \frac{1}{3} + \cdots + \frac{1}{n} < L(n) < \frac{1}{1} + \frac{1}{2} + \frac{1}{3} + \cdots + \frac{1}{n-1}.$$

3. For each of the following functions, state its domain of definition and find its derivative.

a) $f(x) = xL(x)$. *Solution:* This is a product of two functions; $g(x) = x$ and $h(x) = L(x)$. g is defined for all numbers and h for positive numbers, so the domain of f is $(0,\infty)$. Next, using Theorem 4.6, we have $f' = gh' + hg' = \dfrac{x}{x} + 1 \cdot L(x) = 1 + L(x)$.

b) $f(x) = x^2 L(x)$. Ans. Domain is $(0,\infty)$, $f'(x) = x(2L(x) + 1)$.

c) $f(x) = 3L(x) + x^3 L(x)$.

d) $f(x) = \dfrac{L(x)}{x}$. Ans. Domain is $(0,\infty)$, $f'(x) = \dfrac{1 - L(x)}{x^2}$.

e) $g(x) = \dfrac{x}{L(x)}$.

f) $\varphi(y) = \dfrac{L(y)}{1 + y^2}$.

g) $h(t) = tL(t) - t$.

h) $\varphi(s) = (1 + L(s))(1 - L(s))$. Ans. Domain is $(0,\infty)$, $\varphi'(s) = \dfrac{-2L(s)}{s}$.

i) $f(w) = w^2 L(w) + \dfrac{w^3}{L(w)} + \dfrac{L(w)}{w^4}$.

4. Find $\dfrac{df}{dx}$ (See Section 9 of Chapter 4) for each of the following functions:

a) $f(x) = L(x^2)$. *Solution:* This is a function of a function: $f = \{L(g)\}$, where $g(x) = x^2$. Using Theorem 4.10, we have $f' = L'(g) \cdot g' = \dfrac{1}{x^2} \cdot 2x = \dfrac{2}{x}$.

b) $f(x) = L(2x)$.   Ans. $f'(x) = \dfrac{1}{x}$.

c) $f(x) = L(1 + x)$.

d) $f(x) = L\left(\dfrac{x}{1 + x}\right)$.

e) $f(x) = (L(x))^2$.   Ans. $f'(x) = \dfrac{2L(x)}{x}$.

f) $f(x) = \sqrt{L(x)}$.

g) $f(x) = \dfrac{x^2}{L(x^3)}$.   Ans. $f'(x) = \dfrac{x(2L(x^3) - 3)}{(L(x^3))^2}$.

h) $f(x) = xL(1 - x^2)$.

i) $f(x) = \dfrac{\sqrt{x}}{L(\sqrt{x})}$.

5. Find the derivative of each of the following functions:

a) $g(w) = L(L(w))$.   Ans. $g'(w) = \dfrac{1}{wL(w)}$.

b) $h(t) = L(1 + L(t))$.   c) $\varphi(z) = L\left(\dfrac{1}{L(z)}\right)$.

d) $f(y) = L(L(L(y)))$.   e) $f(x) = \sqrt{1 + L(1 + \sqrt{L(x)})}$.

6. Find the maximum, minimum, and inflection points of the graphs of the following equations, and sketch the graphs:

a) $y = L(1 + x^2)$.

b) $y = L\left(x + \dfrac{1}{x}\right)$.

c) $y = x - L(x)$.

7. Find

a) $\displaystyle\int \dfrac{dx}{2x}$.   Ans. $\dfrac{L(x)}{2} + c$.   b) $\displaystyle\int \dfrac{x\,dx}{1 + x^2}$.

c) $\displaystyle\int \dfrac{dx}{x + 1}$.   d) $\displaystyle\int \dfrac{dx}{1 - x}$.

8. Find Dy if

a) $xy = L(xy)$.   Ans. $Dy = \dfrac{-y}{x}$.   b) $x + L(x) = y - L(y)$.

c) $L(x + y) = \dfrac{L(x)}{L(y)}$.   d) $\sqrt{L(x)} + \sqrt{L(y)} = \sqrt{xy}$.

2. A BASIC PROPERTY OF THE FUNCTION L

The function L, defined by the equation

$$L(a) = \int_1^a \frac{dx}{x}, \quad a > 0,$$

has a very important property, which is expressed in our next theorem.

Theorem 9.2: *If a and b are any two positive numbers, then*

$$L(ab) = L(a) + L(b).$$

Proof: Let g be the function defined by the equation

$$g(x) = bx.$$

Define the function F by the equation

$$F = \{L(g)\}.$$

Now

$$F'(x) = L'(g(x))g'(x). \quad \text{(Why?)}$$

But

$$g'(x) = b$$

and

$$L'(g(x)) = L'(bx) = \frac{1}{bx}.$$

Therefore

$$F'(x) = \frac{b}{bx} = \frac{1}{x}.$$

But

$$L'(x) = \frac{1}{x},$$

so

$$F'(x) = L'(x).$$

By Theorem 7.8,

$$F(x) = L(x) + c.$$

Furthermore, since $L(1) = 0$,

$$F(1) = c,$$

and so

$$F(x) = L(x) + F(1)$$
$$= L(x) + L(b)$$

for any x. But

$$F(a) = L(ba) = L(ab),$$

so

$$L(ab) = L(a) + L(b).$$

An immediate consequence of this theorem is that

$$L(a^2) = L(aa) = L(a) + L(a) = 2L(a).$$

$$L(a^3) = L(aa^2) = L(a) + L(a^2) = L(a) + 2L(a) = 3L(a),$$

and in general for a positive integer n,

$$L(a^n) = nL(a).$$

We can use this result to prove our assertion, made in the previous section, that given any number A, no matter how large, there is a number b such that $L(b) > A$. We saw that for $a > 1$, $L(a) > 0$, and so $L(2)$, say, is a positive number. Choose an integer N so large that $NL(2) > A$, and set $b = 2^N$. Then $L(b) = L(2^N) = NL(2) > A$.

We next note that we can write $1 = aa^{-1}$. Therefore

$$0 = L(1) = L(aa^{-1}) = L(a) + L(a^{-1}).$$

Hence

$$L(a^{-1}) = -L(a).$$

Consequently,

$$L(a^{-n}) = L((a^n)^{-1}) = -L(a^n) = -nL(a).$$

We can use this to show that if B is any number, no matter how large, there is a number b such that

$$L(b) < -B.$$

Choose an integer N so large that $NL(2) > B$. Let $b = 2^{-N} = 1/2^N$. Then

$$L(b) = -NL(2).$$

Since

$$B < NL(2)$$

we have

$$-B > -NL(2) = L(b).$$

So far we have seen that for any integer p, positive or negative, we have

$$L(a^p) = pL(a).$$

This result is actually correct not only for integers but also for rational numbers.

Before discussing this, however, it is well to recall, from algebra, the definition and laws of exponents. These are

Definition: $a^n = \underbrace{aa \cdots a,}_{n \text{ factors}}$

$a^{-n} = \dfrac{1}{a^n},$ n a positive integer.

$a^0 = 1$

Theorem: $a^m a^n = a^{m+n},$

$\dfrac{a^m}{a^n} = a^{m-n},$ } m and n integers, positive, negative, or zero.

$a^m b^m = (ab)^m$

Definition: If $a > 0$, and m is a positive integer, $a^{1/m}$ is that positive number whose mth power is a.

Remark: By use of the Least Upper Bound Axiom, it is possible to show that for any $a > 0$, and any positive integer m, $a^{1/m}$ does exist, i.e., that there is one and only one number $b > 0$ such that $b^m = a$. See Problem 1 below.

Definition: $a^{m/n} = (a^{1/n})^m$, m and n positive integers.

Theorem: $a^r a^s = a^{r+s}$

$\dfrac{a^r}{a^s} = a^{r-s}$

$\dfrac{1}{a^r} = a^{-r}$ } r and s any rational numbers.

$(a^r)^s = a^{rs}$

$a^r b^r = (ab)^r$

Theorem 9.3: *If r is any rational number and a any positive number, then*

$$L(a^r) = rL(a).$$

Proof: By definition, a rational number is a quotient of two integers so we can write

$$r = \frac{p}{q},$$

where p and q are integers. Also, by definition, $a^{1/q}$ is that positive real number b such that $b^q = a$. Therefore

$$L(a) = L(b^q) = q(L(b)),$$

or

$$L(a^{1/q}) = \frac{1}{q} L(a).$$

Next, by definition

$$a^{p/q} = (a^{1/q})^p,$$

so

$$L(a^{p/q}) = L((a^{1/q})^p) = pL(a^{1/q}) = p \frac{1}{q} L(a) = \frac{p}{q} L(a),$$

or

$$L(a^r) = rL(a),$$

which completes the proof of this theorem.

Now we can ask if the equation

$$L(a^t) = tL(a)$$

holds also if t is not a rational number. The difficulty with this question is that the number a^t, when t is irrational, has not yet been defined. If we wish to define what we mean by a^t, t irrational, e.g., $t = \sqrt{2}$ or π, we may do it any way we please, but naturally we choose to make a definition of a^t which will fit in with the properties of rational exponents. The following definition is one that works.

Definition 9.1: *If a is a positive number, and if t is any number, then a^t is that number b such that*

$$L(b) = tL(a).$$

In order to justify this definition, we must show that, given a and t, there is a unique number b such that $L(b) = tL(a)$. But, as we saw above, there is a positive number $\bar{x}$ such that $L(\bar{x}) > tL(a)$ and there is a positive number $\underline{x}$ such that $L(\underline{x}) < tL(a)$. Furthermore, the function L is continuous on the interval $[\underline{x},\bar{x}]$ (Why?), so by Theorem 3.11, there is at least one number b such that $L(b) = tL(a)$. Finally, since L is increasing in the interval $[\underline{x},\bar{x}]$, there is only one such number. (Why?)

With this definition, we see that Theorem 9.3 now holds for any exponent, rational or irrational.

Exercise: Show that the laws of exponents now hold for any exponents, rational or irrational.

Remark: We have shown above that given any pair of numbers, a and t, with $a > 0$, we can find a number b such that $b = a^t$. Similarly, given a and b, with $a > 0$ and $a \neq 1$, we can find a unique number t such that $b = a^t$, namely $t = L(b)/L(a)$.

Exercise: Show that if a and b are two numbers, with $a > 0$ and $a \neq 1$, then there is only one number t such that $a^t = b$.

We now have a considerable amount of information about the function L. One thing, however, we have not discussed, and that is the question of finding the value of $L(a)$ for various values of a. In particular, we do not yet know how to find $L(2)$, $L(10)$, $L(\frac{1}{5})$, etc. Similarly, given a number b, we do not know how to find the number a such that $L(a) = b$. We shall see in the next section how these questions can be answered. We mention here, however, the number, which is denoted by e, in honor of the great mathematician Euler, such that

$$L(e) = 1.$$

This number e turns out to be just as important in mathematics as the number π. The number e is irrational. Its decimal expansion can be shown to start out

$$e = 2.718\cdots.$$

PROBLEMS

1. Let M be the collection of all positive numbers whose squares are less than 2. By the Least Upper Bound Axiom, M has a least upper bound, *a*. Show that $a^2 = 2$, i.e., that $a = \sqrt{2}$.

Hint: Show that each of the assumptions $a^2 > 2$ and $a^2 < 2$ leads to a contradiction.

2. Find $\dfrac{df}{dx}$ if

a) $f(x) = L((1 - x)^3)$. *Solution:* Since $L((1 - x)^3) = 3L(1 - x)$, we have $\dfrac{df}{dx} = \dfrac{-3}{1 - x}$.

b) $f(x) = L(\sqrt{4 - x^2}\,)$. Ans. $\dfrac{df}{dx} = \dfrac{-x}{4 - x^2}$.

c) $f(x) = L\left(\sqrt{\dfrac{x - 1}{x + 1}}\right)$.

d) $f(x) = L(\sqrt[3]{x^5 + 5}\,)$.

e) $f(x) = L(x\sqrt{1 - x}\,)$. *Hint:* $L(x\sqrt{1 - x}\,) = L(x) + L\sqrt{1 - x}\,)$
$= L(x) + \tfrac{1}{2}L(1 - x)$.

f) $f(x) = L(x^2 L(x))$. Ans. $\dfrac{df}{dx} = \dfrac{2}{x} + \dfrac{1}{xL(x)}$.

g) $f(x) = L\left(\dfrac{1}{\sqrt{x}}\right)$.

h) $f(x) = L\left(\dfrac{x^2 - 1}{\sqrt{x^2 + 1}}\right)$.

i) $f(x) = L\left(\dfrac{L(x)}{\sqrt{x}}\right)$.

3. Find Df if $f(x) = \dfrac{\sqrt{x + 1}(x - 1)^3}{x^2 - 1}$. *Hint:* $\{L(f)\}(x) = \tfrac{1}{2}L(x + 1) +$
$3L(x - 1) - L(x^2 - 1)$. (Why?) Hence

$$D\{L(f)\}(x) = \frac{1}{2}\frac{1}{x + 1} + \frac{3}{x - 1} - \frac{2x}{x^2 - 1}.$$

But

$$D\{L(f)\} = \frac{1}{f}Df. \text{(Why?)}$$

Therefore

$$Df(x) = f(x)\left[\frac{1}{2}\frac{1}{x + 1} + \frac{3}{x - 1} - \frac{2x}{x^2 - 1}\right].$$

4. Find Df if

a) $f(x) = \sqrt{\dfrac{x+1}{x-1}}$.   Ans. $Df(x) = \left(\dfrac{1}{2(x+1)} - \dfrac{1}{2(x-1)}\right)\sqrt{\dfrac{x+1}{x-1}}$.

b) $f(x) = x(x^2 + 2)(x^4 + 4)$.

c) $f(x) = \sqrt{x}\,\sqrt[3]{1-x}$.

d) $f(x) = \dfrac{3x^2 + 3}{x\sqrt{x^2 - 4}}$.

     Ans. $Df(x) = \left(\dfrac{2x}{x^2+1} - \dfrac{1}{x} - \dfrac{x}{x^2-4}\right)\left(\dfrac{3x^2 + 3}{x\sqrt{x^2 - 4}}\right)$.

e) $f(x) = \sqrt{\dfrac{(x-1)(x+2)}{(x-2)(x+3)}}$.

f) $f(x) = \dfrac{\sqrt[3]{x^2 + 1}\sqrt[4]{x^3 + 2}}{\sqrt[5]{x^4 + 3}}$.

g) $f(x) = (1 - x^2)^{5/2}(1 - x^3)^{5/3}(1 - x^6)^{5/6}$.

3. LOGARITHMS AND THE FUNCTION *L*

We recall the definition of logarithm:

Definition 9.2: *The number c is the logarithm to the base b of a number N, in symbols:*

$$c = \log_b N,$$

if b raised to the power c is N, i.e., if

$$b^c = N.$$

Thus $\log_2 8 = 3$ since $2^3 = 8$, $\log_2 (\tfrac{1}{2}) = -1$ since $2^{-1} = \tfrac{1}{2}$, $\log_{10} 1 = 0$ since $10^0 = 1$, etc. By the remark after Definition 9.1, given positive numbers $b \neq 1$ and N, there is a number c such that

$$b^c = N,$$

i.e., $\log_b N$ is defined. The reader is probably most familiar with logarithms to the base 10, since these are the most convenient for computational purposes. The definition, however, allows for any base, and certain bases other than 10 turn out to be important.

We recall also the basic formulas for logarithms:

1) $\log_b (MN) = \log_b M + \log_b N$,

2) $\log_b (M^N) = N \log_b M$.

Using these two equations, we can derive (see Problem 1 below) a formula which connects the logarithms of a given number to two different bases:

3) $\log_k N = \log_k b \log_b N$.

Comparison of equations 1) and 2) above with Theorems 9.2 and 9.3 of the preceding section suggests that there is a certain amount of similarity between the function L and the function $\log_b$. This is indeed the case; in fact, if b is taken to be the number e such that $L(e) = 1$, the functions are the same.

Theorem 9.4: *For any positive number* a,

$$L(a) = \log_e (a).$$

Proof: By the Remark in Section 2, given any positive number a, there is a number t such that

$$a = e^t.$$

Then

$$L(a) = L(e^t) = tL(e) = t. \quad \text{(Why?)}$$

But, by definition of $\log_e$,

$$\log_e (a) = \log_e (e^t) = t.$$

Therefore

$$L(a) = t = \log_e (a).$$

In view of this theorem, everything which we have proved about the function L now holds also for the logarithm function. In particular, from Theorem 9.1 we have

Theorem 9.5: *If f is the function defined by the equation*

$$f(x) = \log_e x,$$

then

$$f'(x) = \frac{1}{x}.$$

Remark: Because logarithms to the base e are so important in mathematics and so much used, the symbol "$\log_e$" is often abbreviated to "log." Another common notation is "ln." Thus we have

$$\log_e a = \log a = \ln a.$$

Tables giving the value of $\log_e (a)$ are available, but tables of logarithms to the base 10 are more common. Using formula (3) above, we can express $\log_e a$ in terms of $\log_{10} (a)$. Let $c = 10$, $b = e$. Then

$$\log_{10} (a) = \log_{10} (e) \log_e (a),$$

or

$$\log_e (a) = \frac{1}{\log_{10} (e)} \log_{10} (a).$$

Now $e = 2.718 \cdots$ and we find, using tables, that, approximately, $\log_{10} (2.718) = .4343$. Hence, approximately,

$$\log_e (a) = \frac{1}{.4343} \log_{10} (a) = 2.303 \log_{10} (a).$$

The following table, correct to two decimal places, can be used in the problems below.

a	1	2	3	4	5	6	7	8	9	10
$\log_e a$	0.00	0.69	1.10	1.39	1.61	1.79	1.95	2.08	2.20	2.30

From the above formula relating $\log_e$ and $\log_a$ and from Theorem 9.5, we now have

Theorem 9.6: *If b is a positive number and if f is the function defined by the equation*

$$f(x) = \log_b x,$$

then

$$Df(x) = \frac{1}{x} \log_b e.$$

Exercise: Write out the proof of this theorem after working Problem 1 below.

Theorem 9.5 gives us the derivative of the function $\log_e$. By reading the equation $D(\log_e x) = \frac{1}{x}$ backwards, we have the formula $\int \frac{1}{x} dx = \log_e x$ $+ C$. Similarly, using Theorem 4.10, we have the formula

$$\int \frac{f'(x)}{f(x)} dx = \log_e (f(x)) + C.$$

But we must remember that the domain of definition of the function $\log_e$ consists of the positive numbers, so the above formula holds only when $f(x)$ is always positive. The following theorem does not have this restriction.

Theorem 9.7: *If f is a differentiable function, then*

$$\int \frac{f'}{f} = \log_e |f| + C.$$

Exercise: Prove this theorem. (*Hint:* First show that if $g = \log_e |f|$, then $g'(a) = f'(a)/f(a)$, considering separately the cases $f(a) > 0$ and $f(a) < 0$, and note that neither f'/f nor $\log_e |f|$ is defined at a number a where $f(a) = 0$.)

PROBLEMS

1. Show that
$$\log_k N = \log_k b \log_b N.$$

Hint: If $\log_b N = c$, then $b^c = N$. Take logarithms to the base k of each side of this equation.

2. Find Df if

a) $f(x) = \log_{10} x$.   Ans. $Df(x) = \dfrac{\log_{10} e}{x}$.

b) $f(x) = \log_{10} (1 - x^2)$.   Ans. $Df(x) = \dfrac{-2x \log_{10} e}{1 - x^2}$.

c) $f(z) = \log_2 (\sqrt{x}\sqrt[3]{1 - x}\,)$.

d) $f(t) = \log_3 \left(\dfrac{1 + x}{1 - x}\right)$.

e) $f(y) = \log_{101} (1 + \log_{102} (1 + x))$.

3. a) Where do the curves $y = \log x$ and $y = \log (x^2)$ intersect?
   b) Find the angle of intersection (see Problem 12 of Section 5 of Chapter 4) of these two curves.

4. Find an equation for the tangent line to the graph of $y = \log x$ which

a) has slope 1.
b) passes through the origin.

5. Find the maximum, minimum, and inflection points of the following, and sketch their graphs:

a) $y = x \log x$.   Ans.   Minimum at $\left(\dfrac{1}{e}, \dfrac{-1}{e}\right)$.   No inflection point.

b) $y = \dfrac{x}{\log x}$.

c) $y = \dfrac{1 - \log x}{x}$.

d) $y = \log (1 + x^2)$.

e) $y = \log (1 - x^2)$.

6. Find each of the following indefinite integrals.

a) $\displaystyle\int \dfrac{4\,dx}{x}$.   Ans. $4 \log |x| + C$.

b) $\displaystyle\int \dfrac{2x\,dx}{x^2 - 1}$.   Ans. $\log |x^2 - 1| + C$.

c) $\displaystyle\int \dfrac{3x^2 + 1}{x^3 + x}\,dx$.

d) $\displaystyle\int \dfrac{dx}{\sqrt{x}(1 + \sqrt{x}\,)}$.

e) $\displaystyle\int \dfrac{dy}{y^{1/3}(y^{2/3} - 3)}$.

f) $\displaystyle\int \dfrac{x - 1}{x^2}\,dx$.   *Hint:* $\dfrac{x - 1}{x^2} = \dfrac{x}{x^2} - \dfrac{1}{x^2} = \dfrac{1}{x} - \dfrac{1}{x^2}$.

   Ans. $\log_e |x| + \dfrac{1}{x} + C$.

g) $\displaystyle\int \frac{t^2 + 1}{t}\, dt.$

h) $\displaystyle\int \frac{s^3 + 2s^2 + 3s + 4}{s^2}\, ds.$

i) $\displaystyle\int \frac{\left(w + \dfrac{1}{w}\right)^2}{w}\, dw.$

j) $\displaystyle\int \frac{x^2 + 2x + 3}{x - 1}\, dx.$ *Hint:* $\dfrac{x^2 + 2x + 3}{x - 1} = x + 3 + \dfrac{6}{x - 1}.$

Ans. $\dfrac{x^2}{2} + 3x + 6 \log_e |x - 1| + C.$

k) $\displaystyle\int \frac{x^2 + 1}{x + 1}\, dx.$ Ans. $\dfrac{x^2}{2} - x + 2 \log_e |x + 1| + C.$

l) $\displaystyle\int \frac{x^2 + 1}{x - 1}\, dx.$ m) $\displaystyle\int \frac{x^2 - 1}{x + 1}\, dx.$

n) $\displaystyle\int \frac{x^2 + x - 2}{1 - x}\, dx.$ o) $\displaystyle\int \frac{t^3 + 3t}{t + 1}\, dt.$

p) $\displaystyle\int \frac{t^3 + 3t^2 + 6t + 6}{2 - t}\, dt.$

q) $\displaystyle\int \frac{x}{x + 1}\, dx.$ Ans. $x - \log_e |x + 1| + C.$

r) $\displaystyle\int \frac{x - 2}{x + 2}\, dx.$ s) $\displaystyle\int \frac{2x + 3}{4x + 5}\, dx.$

t) $\displaystyle\int \frac{1 - y}{2 + y}\, dy.$ u) $\displaystyle\int \frac{dx}{x \log_e x}.$

v) $\displaystyle\int \frac{dx}{x \log_2 x}.$ w) $\displaystyle\int \frac{\log_{10} x}{x}\, dx.$

7. Evaluate each of the following:

a) $\displaystyle\int_1^2 \frac{dx}{x}.$ Ans. $\log 2.$ b) $\displaystyle\int_1^2 \frac{dx}{x + 1}.$

c) $\displaystyle\int_2^3 \frac{dx}{4x + 5}.$ d) $\displaystyle\int_0^1 \frac{x}{x^2 + 1}\, dx.$ Ans. $\tfrac{1}{2} \log 2.$

e) $\displaystyle\int_2^3 \frac{x + 2}{x^2 + 4x + 5}\, dx.$ f) $\displaystyle\int_2^3 \frac{x^2 + 4x + 5}{x + 2}\, dx.$

g) $\displaystyle\int_1^4 \frac{dy}{\sqrt{y}(2 + 3\sqrt{y})}.$ h) $\displaystyle\int_2^e \frac{ds}{s \log_e s}.$ Ans. $- \log \log 2.$

8. Find the areas bounded by the following curves:

a) $xy = 9$ and $x + y = 10$.   Ans. $40 - 9 \log 9.$

b) $y = \dfrac{1}{x + 1}$, $x = 1$, $x = 2$, and $y = 0$.

c) $y(1 + x^2) = x$, $y = 0$, and $x = 1$.

d) $y = \left(1 - \dfrac{1}{x}\right)^2$, $y = 0$, and $x = 10$.

9. Find the volume of the solid obtained by rotating around the x-axis the figure bounded by

a) $y = 1 - \dfrac{2}{x}$, $y = 0$, $x = 1$, and $x = 2$.   Ans. $3 - 4 \log 2.$

b) $xy^2 = 1$, $y = 1$, and $x = e$.

10. Find the length of each of the following curves:

a) $y = \dfrac{x^2}{4} - \dfrac{1}{2} \log x$, $x = 1$ to $x = 2$.

b) $y^2 = x(x - 3)^2$, $x = 0$ to $x = 3$.

4. INVERSE FUNCTIONS

We recall (Definition 3.1) the definition of a function:
A **function** consists of two things:

1. A collection of numbers, called the **domain of definition.**
2. A rule which assigns to each number in the domain of definition one and only one number.

We also recall that the range of values of a function is the collection of all numbers which the rule of the function assigns to the numbers in the domain of definition of the function.

It follows from the second part of this definition that if a is any number in the domain of definition of a function f, then there is precisely one number b in the range of values such that $f(a) = b$. Geometrically, this means that the vertical line through the point a meets the graph of the function f in just one point, namely the point $(a, f(a))$.

However, it is quite possible, given a point b in the range of values of f, to have two or more numbers $a_1, a_2, \cdots$, in the domain of definition such that $f(a_1) = f(a_2) = \cdots = b$. Geometrically, this means that the horizontal line $y = b$ may meet the graph of f in more than one point.

There are, of course, some functions, such as $f(x) = 2x + 3$, $g(x) = x^3$, etc., for which this does not happen, for which any horizontal line meets the graph of the function in at most one point. Whenever this is the case we can define a new function which is roughly speaking, the reverse, or inverse, of the original function.

Definition 9.3: *Let f be a function such that whenever a_1 and a_2 are two different numbers in the domain of definition of f, then $f(a_1) \neq f(a_2)$. The **inverse function** of f, denoted by f^{-1}, is the function*

1. *whose domain of definition is the range of values of f,*
2. *whose rule is: for each number b in the domain of definition of f^{-1}, f^{-1} (b) is that number a in the domain of definition of f such that $f(a) = b$.*

With this definition, we see that the range of values of f^{-1} is just the domain of definition of f.

We note that if $f(a) = b$, then $f^{-1}(b) = a$, and so $\{f^{-1}(f)\}(a) = f^{-1}(f(a)) = f^{-1}(b) = a$. Similarly, $\{f(f^{-1})\}(b) = f(f^{-1}(b)) = f(a) = b$. Thus applying both f and f^{-1}, in either order, to a number has the same effect as merely multiplying the number by 1; hence the name "inverse function." Note also that f is the inverse function of f^{-1}, i.e., $(f^{-1})^{-1} = f$.

In some cases, given an equation defining a function f, it is possible to find an equation defining its inverse function. For example, let $f(x) = x^3$. Thus f assigns to each number a in its domain the number $b = a^3$ in its range. Consequently f^{-1} assigns to the number b the number $a = \sqrt[3]{b}$. Therefore f^{-1} is defined by the equation: $f^{-1}(y) = \sqrt[3]{y}$. Similarly, if $f(x) = 2x - 3$, then $f^{-1}(y) = (y + 3)/2$. (Why?)

If we have the graph of a function f it is easy to obtain the graph of f^{-1}. A point (a,b) is on the graph of f if and only if $b = f(a)$. But then $a = f^{-1}(b)$, so $(a,b) = (f^{-1}(b),b)$. But this point is on the graph of the equation $x = f^{-1}(y)$. (Why?) Conversely, if (a,b) is on the graph of this equation, then $a = f^{-1}(b)$, so $b = f(a)$, and this point is also on the graph of f. Therefore the graph of f, which is the graph of the equation

$$y = f(x)$$

is also the graph of the equation

1)
$$x = f^{-1}(y).$$

Now the graph of the function f^{-1} is the graph of the equation

2)
$$y = f^{-1}(x).$$

Therefore we need a method for obtaining the graph of equation 2) from the graph of equation 1). But equation 2) can be obtained from equation 1) by interchanging x and y, so we want a geometrical operation which interchanges the x- and y-axes. If we rotate the plane around the line $y = x$ through an angle of 180°, then the x-axis is carried onto the y-axis, the y-axis onto the x-axis, and any point (a,b) onto the point (b,a). Consequently the graph of

$$x = f^{-1}(y),$$

which is the graph of f, will be carried onto the graph of

$$y = f^{-1}(x),$$

which is the graph of f^{-1}.

Let us apply this to the case of the function f defined by the equation

$$f(x) = \log_e x.$$

The domain of definition of f is $(0,\infty)$ and the range of values is $(-\infty,\infty)$.
(Why?) We have seen that f is always increasing, so that if $x_1 \neq x_2$, then
$f(x_1) \neq f(x_2)$. (Why?) Therefore the inverse function, f^{-1}, is defined and
its domain of definition is $(-\infty,\infty)$. From Definition 9.2, if $y = \log_e(x)$,
then $x = e^y$, so

$$f^{-1}(y) = e^y.$$

We have already sketched the graph of $y = \log_e (x)$ in Figure 9.3. If we
rotate the entire plane through $180°$ around the line $y = x$, the graph of
$y = \log_e x$ is carried onto the graph in Figure 9.4, which is the graph of

$$y = f^{-1}(x),$$

or

$$y = e^x.$$

The function defined by the equation $f(x) = e^x$ is called the **exponential function.**

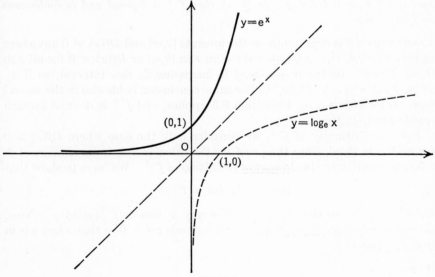

Fig. 9.4

PROBLEMS

1. Prove that if $f'(x) > 0$ for all x, then f^{-1} exists.
2. Find the inverse functions of the following:

   a) $f(x) = x + 2$.   Ans. $f^{-1}(y) = y - 2$.   b) $f(x) = 2x + 1$.

   c) $f(x) = 8x^3$.   d) $f(x) = \sqrt[3]{x}$.

3. For each of the functions of Problem 2, draw the graphs of both f and f^{-1}.
4. Note that when the plane is rotated through an angle of $180°$ about the line $y = x$, vertical lines are carried into horizontal lines, and conversely. Use this fact to find where the graphs of

$$y = \sqrt[3]{x} \quad \text{and} \quad y = \sqrt[5]{x+1}$$

   have vertical tangents.
5. Show that the function f defined by $f(x) = \sqrt{1 - x^2}$, $0 \leq x \leq 1$, has an inverse function. As in Problem 4, find where the graph of f has a vertical tangent.

5. DERIVATIVES OF INVERSE FUNCTIONS

In some cases we can calculate the derivative of an inverse function if we know the derivative of the original function. To see how to do this, we need first to prove a theorem about the continuity of an inverse function.

Theorem 9.8: *If f is a function, if its domain of definition is an interval $[k,m]$ and its range of values the interval $[f(k),f(m)]$, if Df is continuous on $[k,m]$, and if $Df(x) \neq 0$ for any x in $[k,m]$, then f^{-1} is defined and is continuous on $[f(k),f(m)]$.*

Proof: Since Df is continuous on the interval $[k,m]$ and $Df(x) \neq 0$ anywhere in this interval, either $Df(x) > 0$ for all x in $[k,m]$ or $Df(x) < 0$ for all x in $[k,m]$. (Why?) In the first case, f is increasing in this interval, so if $x_1 \neq x_2$, $f(x_1) \neq f(x_2)$. (Why?) The same conclusion holds also in the second case, so for either case, Definition 9.3 applies, and f^{-1} is defined at each number in $[f(k),f(m)]$.

For the continuity of f^{-1}, we consider only the case where $Df(x) > 0$ for each x in $[k,m]$, since the proof for the other case is quite similar. Let b be any number in the domain of definition of f^{-1}. We have to show that

$$\lim_{y \to b} f^{-1}(y) = f^{-1}(b).$$

Let $f^{-1}(b) = a$, so that $f(a) = b$. For any y, denote $f^{-1}(y)$ by x. Now, given any number $e > 0$, we must find a number $d > 0$ so that when y is in $[f(k),f(m)]$ and

$$|y - b| < d,$$

then

$$|x - a| < e.$$

Consider the interval $[a - e, a + e]$, and denote by I the part of this interval which is in the interval $[k,m]$. By hypothesis, Df is continuous on I. By Theorem 5.3, there is a number c in I such that $Df(c)$ is an absolute minimum value for the function Df in this interval:

$$Df(x) \geq Df(c).$$

Also,

$$Df(c) > 0.$$

Therefore, for any x in I,

$$\frac{1}{Df(x)} \leq \frac{1}{Df(c)}.$$

Now, by the Mean Value Theorem, for any x in I, we have

$$f(x) = f(a) + Df(x^*)(x - a),$$

where x^* is some number between x and a. Hence

$$\frac{1}{Df(x^*)} (f(x) - f(a)) = x - a,$$

and

$$\frac{1}{Df(x^*)} |f(x) - f(a)| = |x - a|.$$

But

$$\frac{1}{Df(x^*)} \leq \frac{1}{Df(c)},$$

so

$$|x - a| \leq \frac{1}{Df(c)} |f(x) - f(a)|.$$

Let d be the number $eDf(c)$. Then, when y is in $[f(k), f(m)]$ and

$$|y - b| < d$$

we have, since $|f(x) - f(a)| = |y - b|$,

$$|x - a| < \frac{1}{Df(c)} (eDf(c)) = e,$$

which completes the proof.

Theorem 9.9: *If f is a function whose domain of definition is an interval $[k,m]$ and whose range of values is the interval $[f(k), f(m)]$, if Df is continuous on $[k,m]$ and if $Df(x) \neq 0$ for any x in $[k,m]$, then f^{-1} is differentiable and, for any number b in the domain of definition of f^{-1}, we have*

$$Df^{-1}(b) = \frac{1}{Df(a)}, \quad \text{where} \quad f(a) = b.$$

Proof: We need to show that

$$\lim_{y \to b} \frac{f^{-1}(y) - f^{-1}(b)}{y - b} = \frac{1}{Df(a)}.$$

We have

$$\lim_{x \to a} \frac{f(x) - f(a)}{x - a} = Df(a).$$

Since $Df(a) \neq 0$,

$$\lim_{x \to a} \frac{1}{\dfrac{f(x) - f(a)}{x - a}} = \lim_{x \to a} \frac{x - a}{f(x) - f(a)} = \frac{1}{Df(a)}. \quad \text{(Why?)}$$

This means that for any $e > 0$ there is a $d > 0$ such that when x is in $[k,m]$ and

$$0 < |x - a| < d,$$

then

$$\left| \frac{x - a}{f(x) - f(a)} - \frac{1}{Df(a)} \right| < e.$$

Now denote $f(x)$ by y, so that $f^{-1}(y) = x$. Then, when x is in $[k,m]$ and

$$0 < |x - a| < d,$$

we have

$$\left| \frac{f^{-1}(y) - f^{-1}(b)}{y - b} - \frac{1}{Df(a)} \right| < e.$$

By the preceding theorem, there is a number $\bar{d} > 0$ such that when y is in $[f(k), f(m)]$ and

$$|y - b| < \bar{d},$$

then

$$|x - a| < d.$$

Hence, when y is in $[f(k), f(m)]$ and

$$0 < |y - b| < \bar{d},$$

we have

$$\left| \frac{f^{-1}(y) - f^{-1}(b)}{y - b} - \frac{1}{Df(a)} \right| < e,$$

i.e.,

$$\lim_{y \to b} \frac{f^{-1}(y) - f^{-1}(b)}{y - b} = \frac{1}{Df(a)}.$$

Let us apply this theorem to the particular case of the function g defined by the equation

$$g(x) = \log_e x.$$

Theorem 9.10: *If f is the function defined by the equation*

$$f(x) = e^x,$$

then

$$f'(x) = e^x.$$

Proof: f is the inverse function of g, where $g(x) = \log_e x$. But Dg is continuous at every number in the domain of definition of g and $Dg(x) > 0$. Therefore we can apply Theorem 9.9, and we have, for any number b,

$$f'(b) = \frac{1}{g'(a)}, \quad \text{where} \quad g(a) = b.$$

But $g'(a) = \dfrac{1}{a}$, so

$$f'(b) = a.$$

However, since $g(a) = b$, $a = g^{-1}(b) = f(b)$. Therefore

$$f'(b) = f(b) = e^b,$$

which completes the proof.

We can now differentiate the exponential function, and, by using Theorems 4.4 through 4.10, we can differentiate functions containing exponentials. We can also integrate some functions of this type by means of the following theorem.

Theorem 9.11: *If f is a differentiable function, then*

$$\int e^f f' = e^f + c.$$

Exercise: Write out the proof of this theorem.

We recall that in Chapter 4 we proved the formula

$$D(x^n) = nx^{n-1}$$

only for the case where n is a positive integer. We are now in a position to show that this formula is correct for any number n.

Theorem 9.12: *If r is any number and if f is the function defined by the equation*

$$f(x) = x^r,$$

then

$$Df(x) = rx^{r-1}.$$

Proof: Define a function g by the equation

$$g(x) = \{\log_e (f)\}.$$

Then

$$g(x) = \log_e (x^r) = r \log_e (x),$$

and

$$Dg(x) = \frac{r}{x}.$$

Now consider the function e^g. We have

$$D(e^g) = e^g Dg. \quad \text{(Why?)}$$

But $e^g = e \log_e (f) = f$. (Why?) Therefore, by substitution,

$$Df(x) = f(x) \cdot \frac{r}{x} = x^r \cdot \frac{r}{x} = rx^{r-1}.$$

PROBLEMS

1. Find the derivative of each of the following functions:

a) $f(x) = e^{4x}$.   Ans. $4e^{4x}$.
b) $f(x) = e^{4x^2}$.   Ans. $8xe^{4x^2}$.

c) $f(x) = e^{-x^2}$.

d) $f(x) = e^{\frac{x}{1+x}}$.

e) $f(x) = e^{\sqrt{x}}$.

f) $f(x) = \sqrt{e^x}$.   Ans. $\frac{1}{2}e^{\frac{x}{2}}$.

g) $h(y) = (e^{\sqrt[3]{y}} + 1)^2$.

h) $\varphi(s) = \dfrac{e^s - e^{-s}}{e^s + e^{-s}}$.

i) $g(x) = \log_e (e^{\frac{x}{2}} + 2x)$.   Ans. $\dfrac{e^{\frac{x}{2}} + 4}{2(e^{\frac{x}{2}} + 2x)}$.

j) $g(w) = e^{(\log_e w + 2w)}$.

k) $h(t) = \dfrac{(e^t - 1)\sqrt{1 + e^{t^2}}}{1 - 2e^{-t}}$.

l) $h(w) = \log_e (w)e^w$.   Ans. $\dfrac{e^w}{w} + \log_e (w)e^w$.

m) $\varphi(w) = \log_e \left(\dfrac{1}{w}\right) e^{-w}$.

n) $\varphi(s) = \dfrac{e^{s^2+s}}{s^2 + s}$.

o) $\varphi(y) = e^{\frac{1}{y}} \log_e (y^e)$.

p) $f(x) = x^2 e^{x^2}$.   Ans. $2xe^{x^2}(1 + x^2)$.

q) $f(y) = ye^{\frac{1}{y}}\sqrt{e^{2y} + \log_e y}$.

r) $\varphi(x) = \dfrac{e^{-2x}}{(1 - e^x)^2}$.

s) $h(w) = (1 + w)(1 + e^w)(1 + \log_e w)$.

2. Find $\dfrac{d^2f}{dx^2}$ if $f(x) =$

   a) $b^2(e^{\frac{x}{b}} - e^{\frac{-x}{b}})$. Ans. $(e^{\frac{x}{b}} - e^{\frac{-x}{b}})$.   b) e^{x^3+1}.

   c) $e^{\sqrt{1-x}}$.   d) $\sqrt{x}\, e^{\sqrt{x}}$.

   e) $\dfrac{x}{e^{x^2}}$.

3. Find Df if $f(x) = 10^x$.

   Solution: The only formula we have which looks like this is that in Theorem 9.10: $D(e^x) = e^x$. We need, therefore, to express 10^x as e raised to a power. But $10^x = e^{x\log_e 10}$. (Why?) Therefore $D(10^x) = D(e^{x\log_e 10}) = \log_e 10\; e^{x\log_e 10} = \log_e 10 \cdot 10^x$.

4. Find f' if $f(x) =$

   a) 2^x. Ans. $\log_2 e \cdot 2^x$.   b) 2^{x^2}.

   c) $\sqrt{1 - 10^{2x}}$.   d) $\log(1 + 3^x)$. Ans. $\dfrac{\log_3 e \cdot 3^x}{1 + 3^x}$.

   e) $\dfrac{2^{x^2} + 3^{-x^3}}{4^{x^4}}$.   f) $5^{\ln x}$.

   g) $6^x + x^6$.

5. Find the maximum, minimum, and inflection points of each of the following functions, and sketch their graphs.

   a) $f(x) = e^{x^2}$. Ans. Minimum at $(0,1)$. No inflection points.
   b) $f(x) = e^{-x^2}$.
   c) $g(x) = e^{-x}$.
   d) $h(t) = te^t$.
   e) $\varphi(w) = e^{-w^3}$. Ans. No extreme values. Inflection points at 0
      and $\sqrt[3]{\tfrac{2}{3}}$.

   f) $h(y) = e^{\frac{1}{y}}$.   g) $\varphi(x) = \tfrac{1}{2}(e^x + e^{-x})$.

   h) $g(x) = \tfrac{1}{2}(e^x - e^{-x})$.   i) $h(x) = \dfrac{e^x + e^{-x}}{e^x - e^{-x}}$.

6. Find the vertices of the largest triangle which tangents to $y = e^{-x}$ cut from the first quadrant.

7. Find the largest rectangle which has its base on the x-axis and its other two vertices on the graph of $y = e^{-x^2}$. Show that the two upper vertices are at the inflection points of the curve.

8. Find Dy if

   a) $e^{xy} = e^x + e^y$. Ans. $Dy = \dfrac{e^x - ye^{xy}}{xe^{xy} - e^y}$.

b) $xy = e^{\frac{x}{y}}$.

c) $\log_{10}(x + y) = \log_2(e^x + e^{-y})$.

d) $ye^x - xe^y = \dfrac{xy}{\ln(xy)}$.

9. Find the equations of the line through the origin which is tangent to the graph of

a) $y = e^x$.   Ans. $y = ex$.

b) $y = e^{2x}$.

c) $y = e^{-x}$.

d) $y = e^{x^2}$.

10. Where do the curves $y = e^{-x}$ and $y = e^{-x^2}$ intersect?   What is the tangent of the angle between the two tangent lines at this point?

11. Find f' if $f(x) = x^x$.   *Hint:* We can write $x^x = e^{x \log_e x}$.   (Why?)   Ans. $f'(x) = (\log_e x + 1)x^x$.

12. State the domain of definition of f and find f' if $f(x) =$

a) $(1 - x)^x$.   Ans.   Domain is $(-\infty, 1]$.

$$f'(x) = \left(\log_e(1 - x) - \frac{1}{1 - x} \right)(1 - x)^x.$$

b) x^{1-x}.

c) $(\log_e x)^x$.

d) $x^{\log_e x}$.

e) $x^{\frac{1}{x}}$.   Ans.   Domain is $(0, \infty)$. $f'(x) = \left(\dfrac{1 - \ln x}{x^2} \right) x^{\frac{1}{x}}$.

f) $(10x)^{3x}$.

g) $(x^2 - 1)^{e^x}$.

h) $(\ln x)^{\ln x}$.

13. Find the minimum value of

$$f(x) = x^x, \ x > 0.$$

14. Find

a) $\displaystyle\int e^{2x} \, dx$.   Ans. $\frac{1}{2}e^{2x} + c$.

b) $\displaystyle\int xe^{x^2} \, dx$.

c) $\displaystyle\int 10^x \, dx$.   Ans. $\log_{10} e \cdot 10^x + c$.

d) $\displaystyle\int (e^x - e^{-x})^2 \, dx$.

e) $\displaystyle\int (x^2 + 1)e^{x^3 + 3x} \, dx$.

f) $\displaystyle\int \frac{e^y}{e^y + 2} \, dy$.

g) $\displaystyle\int \frac{3e^{\ln x}}{x} \, dx$.

h) $\displaystyle\int \frac{2^{\sqrt{x}}}{\sqrt{x}} \, dx$.

15. Evaluate

a) $\displaystyle\int_0^2 e^{\frac{x}{2}} \, dx$.   Ans. $2e - 2$.

b) $\displaystyle\int_0^1 \frac{dx}{e^x}$.   Ans. $1 - \dfrac{1}{e}$.

c) $\displaystyle\int_0^1 \frac{e^t + e^{-t}}{e^t - e^{-t}}\, dt.$

d) $\displaystyle\int_1^2 2^{1-y}\, dy.$

16. Find the areas of the figures bounded by the following sets of curves:

a) $y = \dfrac{e^x + e^{-x}}{2}$, $y = 0$, $x = -1$, and $x = 1$.   Ans. $e - \dfrac{1}{e}$.

b) $y = e^x$, $y = e^{-x}$, and $x = 2$.

17. Find the volumes of the solids obtained by rotating around the x-axis the figures of Problem 16.

18. Find the length of the graph of $y = \frac{1}{2}(e^x + e^{-x})$ from $x = 0$ to $x = 1$.

6. EXPONENTIAL GROWTH

There are numerous processes, in physics, chemistry, biology, and also in other fields, in which the amount of a given substance changes at a rate which is proportional to the amount present. In every such case, the amount of the substance at any time t can be expressed in terms of an exponential function, as is shown by the following theorem.

Theorem 9.13: *If f is a function which is positive-valued and differentiable on an interval $[a,b]$, and if k is a number such that for each t in $[a,b]$, $f'(t) = kf(t)$, then there is a number c such that for each t in $[a,b]$,*

$$f(t) = ce^{kt}.$$

Proof: We have $f'(t) = kf(t)$, or

$$\frac{f'(t)}{f(t)} = k.$$

Therefore

$$\int \frac{f'(t)}{f(t)}\, dt = \int k\, dt,$$

and so, by Theorem 9.7, and the hypothesis that $f(t) > 0$ for each t in $[a,b]$,

$$\log_e (f(t)) = kt + C.$$

But C is an arbitrary number, and we can write $C = \log_e c$, where c is another arbitrary positive number. With this substitution, we have

$$\log_e f(t) - \log_e C = kt,$$

or

$$\log_e \left(\frac{f(t)}{c}\right) = kt.$$

This can be written

$$\frac{f(t)}{c} = e^{kt},$$

or, finally,

$$f(t) = ce^{kt}.$$

The problems below illustrate a number of applications of this result.

PROBLEMS

1. A radioactive substance decomposes at a rate proportional to the amount present. For a certain substance, 10 per cent of the original amount has decomposed at the end of two years. When will half the original amount have decomposed? (The time needed for half the amount to decompose is called the **half life** of the substance.)

Solution: Let f be the function whose value, $f(t)$, at any time t is the amount of the substance present at that time. Then $f'(t)$ is the rate at which the substance decomposes. Since this rate is proportional to the amount present, we have

$$f'(t) = kf(t).$$

Therefore

$$f(t) = ce^{kt}.$$

Since all of the substance is present when $t = 0$,

$$f(0) = ce^0 = c,$$

so

$$f(t) = f(0)e^{kt}.$$

Since 90 per cent of the substance remains when $t = 2$,

$$f(2) = \tfrac{9}{10}f(0).$$

But

$$f(2) = f(0)e^{2k},$$

so

$$f(0)e^{2k} = \tfrac{9}{10}f(0),$$

or

$$e^{2k} = \tfrac{9}{10}.$$

Solving

$$k = -.05.$$

Therefore

$$f(t) = f(0)e^{-.05t}.$$

To finish the problem, we must solve for t the equation

$$\tfrac{1}{2}f(0) = f(0)e^{-.05t}.$$

The answer is

$$t = 13.8.$$

2. Find the half life of radium if 4 per cent decomposes in 100 years. Ans. About 2000 years.

3. When a condensor discharges to ground through a resistance, the charge on the condensor decreases at a rate proportional to the charge. If the original charge is 100 volts and if the charge at the end of 3 sec. is 70 volts, what was the charge at the end of 1 sec.?

4. If bacteria increase in number at a rate proportional to the number present, how long will it take before 1,000,000 bacteria increase to 10,000,000, if it takes 12 min. to increase to 2,000,000?

5. The population of a city increases at a rate proportional to the population. In 20 years the population increases from 15,000 to 30,000. How long will it take to double in size again?

6. Light is absorbed by a certain kind of glass in such a way that the intensity of the transmitted light decreases at a rate proportional to the thickness of the glass. If the intensity is diminished by 50 per cent by 10 in. of glass, how much glass is needed to prevent all but 1 per cent of the light from passing through?

7. The rate at which the temperature of a heated body decreases is proportional to the difference between its temperature and that of the air around it. At an air temperature of 60°, how long will it take a body to cool from 120° to 80° if it takes 1 hr. to cool from 150° to 90°?

REVIEW PROBLEMS

1. For which values of the number a will the graph of $y = a - e^x$ intersect the x-axis and for which not? For which values of the number b will the graph of $y = bx^2 - 5x - e^x$ have a point of inflection and for which not?

2. a) Draw the graph of $y^{\log_e x} = 1$.
   b) Express $a^{\log_e x}$ as a power of x.

3. For what value of a is the curve $y = a^x$ tangent to the line $y = x$?

4. Prove that the curve $y = e^x + x^3$ intersects the x-axis in exactly one point.

5. Find $\displaystyle\int \frac{a + b \log_e \sqrt{x}}{x}\, dx.$

6. Find and simplify the derivative of f if

$$f(x) = \left[\log_e (x + 1) + \sqrt{2x + x^2} - \frac{4}{x + \sqrt{2x + x^2}} \right].$$

7. Find the area of the largest triangle cut from the first quadrant by a line tangent to the curve $y = e^{-x}$. Ans. $2/e$.

8. At what point on the curve $y = e^{-x^2}$ is the slope greatest?

9. Find the point of inflection of the curve $xy = \log_e x$.

10. Show that the curve $y = x \log_e x$ is everywhere concave upward. Find the minimum point and sketch the curve.

11. Sketch the graphs of

   a) $y = \dfrac{1}{e^x - 1}$.

   b) $y = e^{\frac{1}{1-x}}$.

12. The line AB is tangent to the curve $y = e^x + 1$ at the point B, and crosses the x-axis at A. Find the coordinates of the point of tangency B which makes the length of the segment AB a minimum.

13. Find the volume generated by revolving about the x-axis the area bounded by the x-axis, the curve $y = \dfrac{\log_e x}{\sqrt{x}}$, and the ordinate through the point where y has an extreme value.   Ans. $\dfrac{8\pi}{3}$.

14. What is the length of the curve
$$ y = \sqrt{a^2 - x^2} - a \log_e \left[\frac{a + \sqrt{a^2 - x^2}}{x} \right] $$
from $x = \dfrac{a}{4}$ to $x = a$?

15. The rate at which a liquid is flowing out of a vessel at any instant is proportional to the amount left in at that instant. If the vessel is half emptied in 1 hr., when will it be three-fourths empty?

16. A vertical cylindrical tank full of water has a leak at the bottom. If the water runs out at a rate proportional to its depth and if 10 per cent of the water escapes the first day, how long will be required for 75 per cent to escape?

17. The rate at which water runs out of a tank through a horizontal outlet is proportional to the square root of the height of the surface of the water above the outlet. If the tank is cylindrical and if half the water runs out in 30 min., when will it be empty?

18. **Definition:** $\lim_{n \to \infty} f(n) = A$ *if for any* $e > 0$ *there is a number* N *such that when*
$$ n > N, $$
then
$$ |f(n) - A| < e. $$
Prove that
$$ \lim_{n \to \infty} L \left(1 + \frac{1}{n} \right)^n = 1. $$

Hint: $L\left(\left(1+\frac{1}{n}\right)^{n}\right) = n\left(L\left(1+\frac{1}{n}\right)\right) = n\int_{1}^{1+\frac{1}{n}}\frac{dx}{x}.$ Now use Theorem 7.4.

19. Assuming that $\lim_{n\to\infty}\left(1+\frac{1}{n}\right)^{n} = e$ (the number such that $L(e) = 1$), use the definition of the derivative to show that

$$L'(x) = \frac{1}{x}.$$

20. a) Show that

$$\lim_{n\to\infty}\left(1+\frac{1}{n}\right)^{n} = e.$$

   Hint: See Theorem 9.8.

   b) Calculate the value of $\left(1+\frac{1}{n}\right)^{n}$ for $n = 1, 2, 3, 4, 5.$

Trigonometric Functions

1. INTRODUCTION

In the usual school course in trigonometry the emphasis is on numerical calculations. The trigonometric functions, sine, cosine, tangent, etc., are used to calculate sides and angles of triangles. In actual practice, however, except in a few special fields such as surveying and navigation, the important applications of trigonometry involve treating the trigonometric functions as functions, which can be differentiated and integrated. It is this aspect of these functions which is treated in this chapter.

We need first to make two changes in the definitions of the trigonometric functions. The function sine, for example, assigns to each angle a number, the sine of the angle. But the only functions which we are equipped to handle are those for which the domain of definition consists not of angles but of numbers. Therefore, in place of an expression such as

$$\sin \theta,$$

where θ is an angle, we shall use

$$\sin x,$$

where x is the number which expresses the size of the angle θ.

This leads to the second observation which we wish to make. We find it convenient to use as the unit of measurement for angles not the degree but rather the radian. We recall that one radian is the angle subtended at the center of a circle by an arc of the circle whose length is equal to the length of a radius. Now a right angle, $90°$, is subtended by an arc whose length is one-fourth the circumference, $\pi R/2$. This is $\pi/2$ times the length of the radius. Hence a right angle is $\pi/2$ radians and so

$$1 \text{ radian} = \frac{180}{\pi} \text{ degrees}$$

$$= 57.3 \text{ (approx.) degrees.}$$

There are various ways of defining the trigonometric functions, but for our purposes the following is the most convenient. Given any number u, we construct an angle θ of u radians with its vertex at the origin and its initial side lying along the positive x-axis. We also construct a circle with center at the origin and radius R, say. The terminal side of the angle meets the circle at a point whose coordinates are (α, β). (See Figure 10.1.)

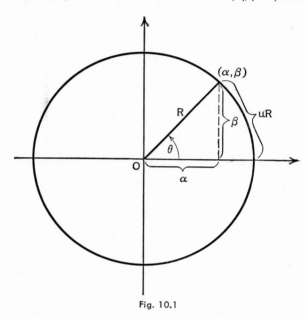

Fig. 10.1

Then

$$\sin u = \frac{\beta}{R} \qquad \tan u = \frac{\beta}{\alpha} \qquad \sec u = \frac{R}{\alpha}$$

$$\cos u = \frac{\alpha}{R} \qquad \cot u = \frac{\alpha}{\beta} \qquad \csc u = \frac{R}{\beta}$$

Note that $\tan u$ and $\sec u$ are not defined when $\alpha = 0$, i.e., when $u = \pi/2 + n\pi$ with n any integer, positive, negative, or zero. Similarly, $\cot u$ and $\csc u$ are not defined when $\beta = 0$, i.e., when $u = n\pi$ with n any integer, positive, negative, or zero.

The graphs of these six functions are shown in Figure 10.2.

In the rest of this chapter we shall have to use often certain trigonometric identities. The problems at the end of this section are devoted to these identities.

The table on page 276 will be sufficient for numerical computations in the problems of later sections.

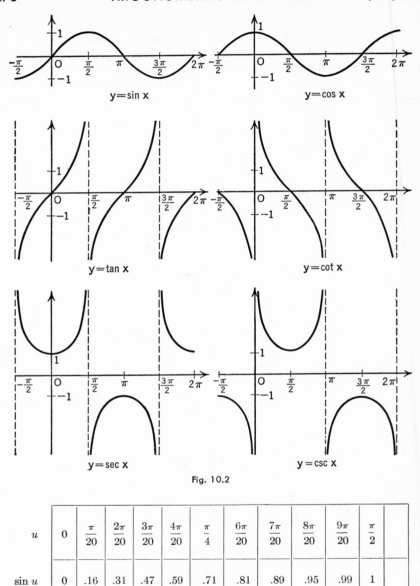

Fig. 10.2

u	0	$\dfrac{\pi}{20}$	$\dfrac{2\pi}{20}$	$\dfrac{3\pi}{20}$	$\dfrac{4\pi}{20}$	$\dfrac{\pi}{4}$	$\dfrac{6\pi}{20}$	$\dfrac{7\pi}{20}$	$\dfrac{8\pi}{20}$	$\dfrac{9\pi}{20}$	$\dfrac{\pi}{2}$
$\sin u$	0	.16	.31	.47	.59	.71	.81	.89	.95	.99	1
$\cos u$	1	.99	.95	.89	.81	.71	.59	.47	.31	.16	0
$\tan u$	0	.16	.32	.51	.73	1.00	1.38	1.96	3.08	6.31	..

In what follows, we shall discuss not only these six trigonometric functions but also the inverse functions of the first three, so we recall their definitions here. We first note that Definition 9.3 cannot be applied to the function sine. The reason is that this function may have the same value at different points. For example, $\sin 0 = \sin \pi = \sin 2\pi$, etc. However, let us consider a new function, which we denote by S, whose rule is the same as that of sine but whose domain of definition is the interval $[-\pi/2, \pi/2]$:

$$S(u) = \sin u, \quad -\pi/2 \leq u \leq \pi/2.$$

Note that S is an increasing function and that its range of values is the interval $[-1, 1]$. According to Definition 9.3, S^{-1}, the inverse function of S, assigns to each number b in its domain of definition, $[-1, 1]$, that number a in its range of values, $[-\pi/2, \pi/2]$, such that $S(a) = b$, i.e., $S^{-1}(b) = a$ if $S(a) = \sin a = b$. The usual name for this function S^{-1} is arc sine, and we shall use this name from now on.

In defining the inverse function of sine, we chose the interval $[-\pi/2, \pi/2]$, over which the function is always increasing. We could have chosen the

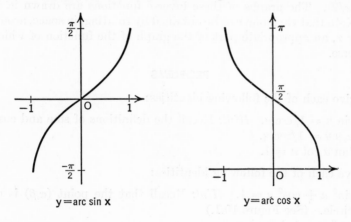

y = arc sin x   y = arc cos x

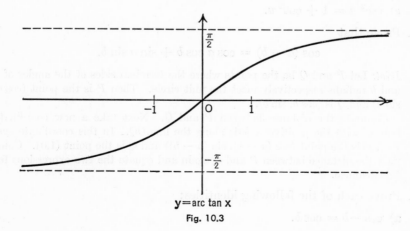

y = arc tan x

Fig. 10.3

interval $[\pi/2,3\pi/2]$, since in this interval the function sine does not take on the same value twice. Similarly, we could have chosen the interval $[3\pi/2, 5\pi/2]$ or $[-3\pi/2,-\pi/2]$, etc. However, in order to avoid ambiguity we must all choose the same interval, and by long custom this is the interval $[-\pi/2,\pi/2]$. Hence the range of values of arc sine is the interval $[-\pi/2, \pi/2]$. Thus, although $\sin \pi = 0$, it is not true that arc $\sin 0 = \pi$. The number π is not in the range of values of arc sine, and the correct value is arc $\sin 0 = 0$. Similarly, arc $\sin -1 = -\pi/2$, not $3\pi/2$.

For the functions cosine and tangent we proceed in the same way. In each case we pick out an interval in which the function never takes on the same value twice. For the cosine it is customary to choose the interval $[0,\pi]$ and for the tangent the interval $(-\pi/2,\pi/2)$. Thus the domain of definition of the function arc cosine is the interval $[-1,1]$ and its range of values is the interval $[0,\pi]$. For the function arc tangent, the domain of definition consists of all numbers and the range of values the interval $(-\pi/2,\pi/2)$. The graphs of these inverse functions are drawn in Figure 10.3. Note that each one can be obtained by rotating, in space, around the line $y = x$, an appropriate part of the graph of the function of which it is the inverse.

PROBLEMS

1. Derive each of the following identities:

   a) $\sin u = 1/\csc u$. *Hint:* Recall the definitions of sine and cosecant.
   b) $\cos u = 1/\sec u$.
   c) $\tan u \cot u = 1$.

2. Prove each of the following identities:

   a) $\sin^2 u + \cos^2 u = 1$. *Hint:* Recall that the point (α,β) is on the circle. (See Figure 10.1.)
   b) $\sec^2 u = 1 + \tan^2 u$.
   c) $\csc^2 u = 1 + \cot^2 u$.

3. Prove that

$$\cos (a - b) = \cos a \cos b + \sin a \sin b.$$

Hint: Let P and Q be the points where the terminal sides of the angles of a and b radians respectively meet the unit circle. Then P is the point $(\cos a, \sin a)$ and Q is $(\cos b, \sin b)$.

Compute the distance between P and Q. Next take a new coordinate system with the positive X-axis along the line OQ. In this coordinate system, P is the point $(\cos (a - b), \sin (a - b))$ and Q is the point $(1,0)$. Compute the distance between P and Q again and equate the two expressions for this distance.

4. Prove each of the following identities:

   a) $\cos -b = \cos b$.

Hint: Let $a = 0$ in the formula of Problem 3.

b) $\cos (\pi/2 - b) = \sin b$.
c) $\sin (\pi/2 - c) = \cos c$.

5. Prove that $\sin (a + b) = \sin a \cos b + \cos a \sin b$.

Hint: $\sin (a + b) = \cos (\pi/2 - (a + b)) = \cos ((\pi/2 - a) - b)$. Now use the formula of Problem 3.

6. Prove that

a) $\sin -a = \cos (\pi/2 + a) = -\sin a$.
b) $\sin (a + \pi/2) = \cos a$.

7. Prove that

a) $\cos (a + b) = \cos a \cos b - \sin a \sin b$.
b) $\sin (a - b) = \sin a \cos b - \cos a \sin b$.

8. Prove that

a) $\tan -a = -\tan a$.

b) $\tan (a + b) = \dfrac{\tan a + \tan b}{1 - \tan a \tan b}$.

9. Prove that

a) $\sin a \cos a = \frac{1}{2} \sin 2a$.
b) $\sin^2 a = \frac{1}{2} - \frac{1}{2} \cos 2a$.
c) $\cos^2 a = \frac{1}{2} + \frac{1}{2} \cos 2a$.

10. Prove that

$$\sin a - \sin b = 2 \cos \tfrac{1}{2}(a + b) \sin \tfrac{1}{2}(a - b).$$

Hint: Combine the formulas for $\sin (x + y)$ and $\sin (x - y)$ to obtain $2 \cos x \sin y = \sin (x + y) - \sin (x - y)$. Then let $x + y = a$, $x - y = b$.

2. THE DERIVATIVES OF ARC SINE, SINE, AND COSINE

In order to find the derivatives of the trigonometric functions, it is convenient to start with the function arc sine, since we can write down an explicit formula for this function.

Theorem 10.1: *For any number b in the interval $(-1,1)$,*

$$arc \sin b = \int_0^b \frac{dx}{\sqrt{1 - x^2}}.$$

Proof: We take first the case where $b \geq 0$. Consider the circle whose center is at the origin and whose radius is 1. The upper semicircle is the graph of the function f defined by the equation

$$f(x) = \sqrt{1 - x^2}.$$

A simple calculation shows that

$$\sqrt{1 + (f'(x))^2} = \frac{1}{\sqrt{1 - x^2}}.$$

Hence by Theorem 8.6,

$$\int_0^b \frac{dx}{\sqrt{1 - x^2}}$$

is the length of the arc of the circle over the interval $[0,b]$.

Now consider the angle θ subtended by this arc. Since the radius of the circle is 1, the number of radians in this angle is equal to the length of the arc.

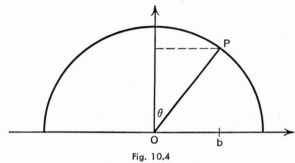

Fig. 10.4

Next let us calculate the sine of this number. (See Figure 10.4.) Dropping a perpendicular from P to the y-axis, we have a right triangle containing the angle θ. The hypotenuse of this triangle is 1 and the length of the side opposite θ is b. Since

$$\theta = \int_0^b \frac{dx}{\sqrt{1 - x^2}} \text{ radians,}$$

$$\sin \left(\int_0^b \frac{dx}{\sqrt{1 - x^2}} \right) = b,$$

or

$$\text{arc sin } b = \int_0^b \frac{dx}{\sqrt{1 - x^2}}.$$

This disposes of the case $b \geq 0$.

If $b < 0$, then the length of the arc of the semicircle lying over $[b,0]$ is

$$\int_b^0 \frac{dx}{\sqrt{1 - x^2}} = -\int_0^b \frac{dx}{\sqrt{1 - x^2}},$$

so

$$\theta = -\int_0^b \frac{dx}{\sqrt{1-x^2}} \text{ radians.}$$

The length of the side of the triangle opposite θ is $-b$. (See Figure 10.5.)

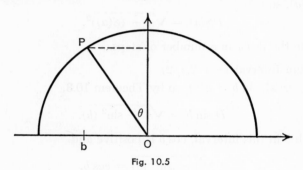

Fig. 10.5

Hence

$$\sin\left(-\int_0^b \frac{dx}{\sqrt{1-x^2}}\right) = -b.$$

But we recall that $\sin(-x) = -\sin(x)$, so

$$\sin\left(\int_0^b \frac{dx}{\sqrt{1-x^2}}\right) = -(-b) = b,$$

and so

$$\text{arc sin } b = \int_0^b \frac{dx}{\sqrt{1-x^2}}.$$

in this case also.

Theorem 10.2: *For any number b in the interval $(-1,1)$,*

$$D \text{ arc sin } b = \frac{1}{\sqrt{1-b^2}}.$$

Proof: This follows immediately from Theorem 7.7 when we set $f(x) = 1/\sqrt{1-x^2}$.

Theorem 10.3: *For any number b, $D \sin b = \cos b$ and $D \cos b = -\sin b$.*

Proof: We first show that for any number a in $(-\pi/2, \pi/2)$,

$$DS(a) = \sqrt{1-(S(a))^2}.$$

Since arc sine is the inverse function of S, S is the inverse function of arc sine. For any number a such that $-\pi/2 < a < \pi/2$, choose numbers c and d such that

$$-\pi/2 < c < a < d < \pi/2.$$

Let $k = S(c)$ and $m = S(d)$, and $b = S(a)$. Now the hypotheses of Theorem 9.9 are satisfied if we restrict arc sine to the interval $[k,m]$. Hence

$$DS(a) = \frac{1}{D \text{ arc sin } b} = \sqrt{1 - b^2}.$$

But $b = S(a)$, so

$$DS(a) = \sqrt{1 - (S(a))^2}.$$

We continue the proof in a number of steps.

I. Sine in the Interval $(-\pi/2, \pi/2)$

In this interval, $\sin b = S(b)$, so by Theorem 10.3,

$$D \sin b = \sqrt{1 - \sin^2 (b)}.$$

But for each b in this interval, $\cos b$ is positive and

$$\sqrt{1 - \sin^2 (b)} = \cos b.$$

Hence

$$D \sin b = \cos b.$$

II. Cosine in the Interval $(0, \pi)$

We use the identities:

$$\cos (a + \pi/2) = -\sin a,$$

$$\sin (a + \pi/2) = \cos a.$$

Now, for any number b in $(0, \pi)$, the number $a = b - \pi/2$ is in the interval $(-\pi/2, \pi/2)$. Also

$$\cos b = -\sin a.$$

But, since a is in $(-\pi/2, \pi/2)$, we can apply **I**:

$$D(-\sin) a = -D \sin a = -\cos a = -\sin (a + \pi/2)$$

$$= -\sin b.$$

Hence

$$D \cos b = -\sin b.$$

III. Sine at $b = \pi/2$

For this point we use the identities:

$$\sin (a + \pi/4) = \sin a \cos \pi/4 + \cos a \sin \pi/4.$$

$$\cos (a + \pi/4) = \cos a \cos \pi/4 - \sin a \sin \pi/4.$$

Now, if a is in $(0, \pi/2)$, both **I** and **II** apply, and we have

$$D(\sin a \cos \pi/4 + \cos a \sin \pi/4) = \cos a \cos \pi/4 - \sin a \sin \pi/4$$

$$= \cos (a + \pi/4).$$

Hence
$$D \sin (a + \pi/4) = \cos (a + \pi/4).$$

In particular, setting $a = \pi/4$
$$D \sin (\pi/2) = \cos (\pi/2) = 0.$$

We have thus proved our theorem so far for the interval $(-\pi/2, \pi/2]$ for sine and interval $(0,\pi)$ for cosine. The rest of the proof is left as an exercise in Problem 12 below.

PROBLEMS

1. Find f' if

a) $f(x) = \sin (x^2 + 1)$.

   Solution: We have here a function of a function: $f = \{g(h)\}$, where $g(x) = \sin x$ and $h(x) = x^2 + 1$. Therefore, by Theorems 4.10 and 10.3, we have $f'(x) = g'(h(x)) \cdot h'(x) = \cos (x^2 + 1)(2x) = 2x \cos (x^2 + 1)$.

b) $f(x) = \sin (x^3 + x)$.

c) $f(x) = \sin (1/x)$. Ans. $f'(x) = -\dfrac{\cos (1/x)}{x^2}$.

d) $f(y) = \sin (y/(1 + y))$.

e) $f(x) = \cos \sqrt{x}$. Ans. $f'(x) = -\dfrac{\sin \sqrt{x}}{2\sqrt{x}}$.

f) $f(t) = \sin (\cos t)$.   g) $f(z) = \cos (z + \cos z)$.

h) $f(x) = \sin (1 + x) + \cos (1 - x)$.   i) $f(x) = \cos e^x$.

j) $f(x) = 2 \cos (\log_e x) + 3 \sin (xe^{x^2})$.

2. Find Df if $f(x) =$

a) $\sqrt{1 + \sin x}$. Ans. $Df(x) = \dfrac{\cos x}{2\sqrt{1 + \sin x}}$.

b) $\sin^2 x$. Ans. $Df(x) = 2 \sin x \cos x$.

c) $(\sin x + \cos 2x)^3$.

d) $\dfrac{\sin x}{\cos x}$. Ans. $Df(x) = \dfrac{1}{\cos^2 x}$.

e) $\dfrac{1}{\sin x \cos x}$.

f) $\dfrac{\sqrt{1 + \cos 2x}}{\sin (x/3)}$.

g) $e^{\sin x}$. Ans. $Df(x) = \cos x \, e^{\sin x}$.

h) $\log_e \left(2 \sin \dfrac{x}{2} \right).$

i) $\dfrac{1}{\sin x}.$

j) $\cos x^2 \cos x^3.$

k) $\dfrac{\cos x}{\sin \sqrt{x}}.$

l) $e^{\cos (1/x)} \log_e (\sin^2 4x).$

3. For each of the following functions, find the derivative and state the domain of definition of the function and of its derivative.

a) $f(x) = \arcsin 2x.$ Ans. $f'(x) = \dfrac{2}{\sqrt{1 - 4x^2}} ;$

$$-\tfrac{1}{2} \leq x \leq \tfrac{1}{2}; \quad -\tfrac{1}{2} < x < \tfrac{1}{2}.$$

b) $g(x) = \arcsin (x/2).$

c) $h(x) = \arcsin \dfrac{x^2}{1 + x^2}.$

d) $f(y) = \arcsin (1 - y^2).$

e) $g(t) = \arcsin \sqrt{t}.$ Ans. $g'(t) = \dfrac{1}{2\sqrt{t}\sqrt{1 - t}} ;$

$$0 \leq t \leq 1; 0 < t < 1.$$

f) $\varphi(x) = \arcsin (1 + \cos x).$

4. Draw the graph and find the derivative of f if

a) $f(x) = \begin{cases} \arcsin x, & -1 \leq x < 0 \\ \sin x, & 0 \leq x < \pi \\ 1 + \cos^2 x, & \pi \leq x \leq 2\pi. \end{cases}$

b) $f(x) = \begin{cases} \sin 2x, & -\pi \leq x < 0 \\ \sin \dfrac{x}{2}, & 0 \leq x \leq 2\pi. \end{cases}$

5. Find $\dfrac{d^2 f}{dx^2}$ if $f(x) =$

a) $\cos x.$ Ans. $\dfrac{d^2 f(x)}{dx^2} = -\cos x.$

b) $\sin 2x.$

c) $x \sin x.$

d) $e^{-x} \sin x.$

e) $e^{2x} \cos \left(\dfrac{x}{2} \right).$

6. Find $\dfrac{dy}{dx}$ if

a) $\cos (x + y) = \sin xy.$ Ans. $\dfrac{dy}{dx} = -\dfrac{y \cos xy + \sin (x + y)}{x \cos xy + \sin (x + y)}.$

b) $e^y = \sin x$.

c) arc $\sin xy = y \sin x$.

7. Find equations for the tangent and normal lines to the graphs of the following functions at the indicated points:

a) $f(x) = x \sin x$, $x = 0$, $x = \pi/4$, and $x = \pi/2$.

b) $g(t) = e^{\sin t}$, $t = 0$, $t = \pi/3$, and $t = 2\pi$.

c) $h(w) = \text{arc } \sin \left(\dfrac{1}{w}\right)$, $w = 2$.

8. Find the tangent of the angle of intersection of the following pairs of curves.

a) $y = \sin x$, $y = \cos x$.   Ans. $2\sqrt{2}$.

b) $y = x + \sin 4x$, $y = x$.

9. Find the extreme values and inflection points of the following functions for the indicated intervals and sketch their graphs for the indicated intervals.

a) $f(x) = \sin x + \cos x$, $[0,2\pi]$.   Ans.   Max. at $(\pi/4,\sqrt{2})$, Min. at $(5\pi/4, -\sqrt{2})$, Inflection points at $(3\pi/4,0)$ and $\left(\dfrac{7\pi}{4},0\right)$.

b) $f(x) = x + 2 \sin x$, $[0,2\pi]$.

c) $f(x) = x + \sin 2x$, $[0,2\pi]$.

d) $f(x) = x \sin x$, $[0,2\pi]$.

10. A particle moves on a line, its position at any time t being $s(t)$. Investigate its velocity and represent the motion graphically if

a) $s(t) = 2 \sin 2t$, $0 \le t \le 2\pi$.

b) $s(t) = 2 \sin \left(\dfrac{t}{2}\right)$, $0 \le t \le 2\pi$.

c) $s(t) = \sin t + 2 \cos 2t$, $0 \le t \le \pi$.

d) $s(t) = \sin t \cos 2t$, $0 \le t \le \pi$.

11. a) Show that $\lim\limits_{x \to 0} \dfrac{\sin x}{x} = 1$.

Hint: For any function f, $f'(a) = \lim\limits_{x \to a} \dfrac{f(x) - f(a)}{x - a}$; also $D \sin 0 = \cos 0 = 1$.

b) Using only the above result and Problem 10 of the previous section, derive the formula for the derivative of the sine function.

12. Complete the proof of Theorem 10.3 by showing that

IV $D \cos \pi = 0$.   *Hint:* Let $a = b - \pi/2$, so that $\cos b = -\sin a$. Then, when $a = \pi/2$, we can use III.

V $D \sin b = \cos b$ for b in $(\pi/2, 3\pi/2]$.   *Hint:* Use the identities $\sin(b \pm \pi) = -\sin b$ and $\cos(b \pm \pi) = -\cos b$. Then, if b is the interval $(\pi/2, 3\pi/2]$, $a = b - \pi$ is in the interval $(-\pi/2, \pi/2]$, so **I** or **III** applies.

VI $D \cos b = -\sin b$ for b in $(\pi, 2\pi]$.

VII $D \sin b = \cos b$ for b outside the interval $(-\pi/2, 3\pi/2]$.   *Hint:* For any such b there is an integer n, possibly negative, such that

$$2n\pi - \pi/2 < b \leq 2(n+1)\pi - \pi/2.$$

Let $a = b - 2n\pi$, and use the identities $\sin(a + 2n\pi) = \sin a$ and $\cos(a + 2n\pi) = \cos a$.

VIII $D \cos b = -\sin b$ for b outside the interval $(0, 2\pi]$.

3. DERIVATIVES OF THE REMAINING TRIGONOMETRIC FUNCTIONS

Since each of the remaining trigonometric functions can be expressed in terms of sine and cosine, it is easy to calculate their derivatives.

Theorem 10.4: *For each number b,*

$$D \tan b = \sec^2 b, \quad D \sec b = \sec b \tan b,$$

except when $b = (2n+1)\pi/2$, *n an integer, and*

$$D \cot b = -\csc^2 b, \quad D \csc b = -\csc b \cot b$$

except when $b = n\pi$, *n an integer.*

Proof: We prove only the first two equations.   We have

$$\tan b = \frac{\sin b}{\cos b},$$

except when the denominator is zero.   But this happens at $\pi/2$, $3\pi/2$, etc., i.e., when $b = (2n+1)\pi/2$, n an integer, positive, negative, or zero.   Except at these points we can apply Theorem 4.9:

$$D \tan b = \frac{\cos b\, D \sin b - \sin b\, D \cos b}{\cos^2 b}$$

$$= \frac{1}{\cos^2 b} = \sec^2 b. \quad \text{(Why?)}$$

Next, we have

$$\sec b = \frac{1}{\cos b}.$$

Hence, when the denominator is not zero, i.e., when $b \neq (2n+1)\pi/2$, n an integer, then

$$D \sec b = \frac{\sin b}{\cos^2 b}$$

$$= \sec b \tan b.$$

Exercise: Derive the other two formulas in Theorem 10.4.

PROBLEMS

1. Find Df if

a) $f(x) = \tan (x^2 + 1)$.   Ans. $2x \sec^2 (x^2 + 1)$.

b) $f(x) = \cot \left(\dfrac{1}{x} + x \right)$.

c) $f(x) = \sec \sqrt{x}$.   Ans. $\dfrac{\sec \sqrt{x} \tan \sqrt{x}}{2\sqrt{x}}$.

d) $f(x) = \csc \left(\dfrac{x}{1 + x} \right)$.

e) $f(t) = \tan (e^t) \cot (\log_e t)$.

f) $f(w) = \sec (\sin w) - 2 \sin (\sec w)$.

g) $f(s) = \cos (\csc (\tan (1 - s^2)))$.

2. Find the derivative of each of the following functions:

a) $\varphi(x) = \log_e \left(\sec \left(\dfrac{x^2}{2} \right) \right)$.   Ans. $\varphi'(x) = x \tan \left(\dfrac{x^2}{2} \right)$.

b) $\varphi(t) = \sqrt{2} \cos (\tan t) + \tan (2 \cos t)$.

c) $\varphi(w) = w^2 \sec^2 (w^2) \tan^2 (w^2)$.

d) $g(x) = \dfrac{\sec (1 - x)}{\sec (1 - x) + \tan (1 - x)}$.

e) $g(x) = e^{\tan x^2}$.   Ans. $g'(x) = 2x \sec^2 x^2 (e^{\tan x^2})$.

f) $g(x) = e^{\tan^2 x}$.

g) $f(x) = \tan (e^{x^2})$.

h) $f(z) = \sec (e^{x^2}) e^{\sec x^2}$.

i) $f(x) = \log_e (\sec x + \tan x)$.   Ans. $f'(x) = \sec x$.

3. Find $\dfrac{dy}{dx}$ if

a) $\tan xy = \cot (x + y)$.

b) $\arcsin (x \tan xy) = y \tan x \sec xy$.

c) $e^{\tan (x+y)} = \log_e (\csc xy)$.

4. Find the second derivative of each of the following functions:

a) $f(x) = \tan^2 x$.   Ans. $f'(x) = 2 \sec^4 x + 4 \tan^2 x \sec^2 x$.

b) $g(x) = \tan x^2$.

c) $h(x) = e^x \sec x$.

d) $\varphi(x) = x \cot x$.

5. Find equations for the tangent and normal lines to the graphs of the following functions at the indicated points:

    a) $f(x) = \sin x \tan x$, $x = 0$, $x = \pi/3$, and $x = \dfrac{-\pi}{3}$.

    b) $f(x) = \cot x + \csc \left(\dfrac{1}{x}\right)$, $x = \pi/3$.

    c) $f(x) = \log_e (\tan x)$, $x = \pi/4$.

6. Find the tangent of the angle of intersection of the following pairs of curves within the indicated intervals.

    a) $y = \sin x$, $y = \tan x$, $[-\pi,\pi]$.　　Ans.　　0.
    b) $y = \sin 2x$, $y = \tan (x/2)$, $[-\pi,\pi]$.

7. Find the extreme values and inflection points of the following functions and sketch their graphs for the indicated intervals.

    a) $f(x) = \sin x + \tan x$, $[0,\pi]$.
    b) $f(x) = 2x + \tan x$, $[0,\pi]$.　　Ans.　　No extreme values.　　Inflection point at $(0,0)$.
    c) $f(x) = x \tan x$, $[0,\pi]$.

8. Rectangles are inscribed in a circle of radius R. Use trigonometric functions to find the dimensions of the rectangle whose perimeter is as large as possible. (See Figure 10.6.)

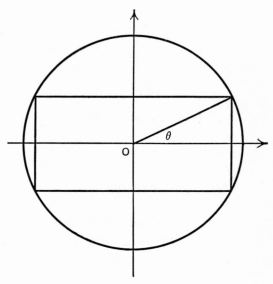

Fig. 10.6

Solution: Let θ be the angle formed by the positive x-axis and the line from the origin to a corner of the rectangle. Let x be the number of radians in the angle θ. Then the width of the rectangle is $2R \cos x$ and the height is $2R \sin x$. (Why?) Thus the perimeter is the value of the function

$$f(x) = 4R (\cos x + \sin x).$$

This function has a critical point at $x = \pi/4$. (Why?) At this point the second derivative of f is negative, so f has a maximum at $\pi/4$. At this point $\cos x = \sin x$, so the rectangle with maximum perimeter is the square with side $\sqrt{2}\,R$.

9. Using trigonometric functions, find the dimensions of the largest right circular cylinder which can be cut from a solid sphere of radius R.
10. Work Problems 13 and 14 in the review problems at the end of Chapter 5, using trigonometric functions.
11. The line segment PQ is 20 units long; P is on the positive x-axis and Q on the positive y-axis. P is moving away from the origin at the rate of 6 units per minute. How fast is the acute angle between PQ and the x-axis changing when P is 12 units from the origin? (See Figure 10.7.)

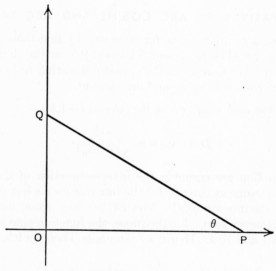

Fig. 10.7

Solution: Let θ be the acute angle and x the number of radians in θ. Let w be the distance from O to P. Since both x and w change with time, there are two functions, f and g, such that the value of f at any time t is x, and the value of g is w: $f(t) = x$, $g(t) = w$.

Now we know that $g'(t) = 6$ for all t, and we are asked for the value

$f'(t)$ when $w = 12$. But

$$w = 20 \cos x,$$

or

$$g(t) = 20 \cos (f(t)).$$

Therefore

$$g'(t) = -20 \sin (f(t)) \cdot f'(t).$$

When $w = 12$, then $\sin x = \frac{16}{20} = \frac{3}{4}$, so

$$f'(t) = -\frac{6}{15}.$$

Therefore θ is decreasing at the rate of $\frac{6}{15}$ radians per minute.

12. A line segment PQ is 20 units long, has its end P on the positive x-axis, and passes through the point $(0,12)$. P is moving away from the origin at the rate of 6 units per second. How fast is the acute angle between PQ and the x-axis changing when Q gets to $(0,12)$?

13. A winch located at the end of a dock 6 ft. above the water hauls in a rope at the rate of 2 ft. per sec. A boat is attached to the end of the rope. How fast is the angle between the rope and the water changing when there are 10 ft. of rope out?

4. DERIVATIVES OF ARC COSINE AND ARC TANGENT

We found the derivative of the function sine by first finding the derivative of arc sine and then using our Theorem 9.9 on the derivative of an inverse function. We now go in the opposite direction to find the derivatives of the functions arc cosine and arc tangent.

Theorem 10.5: *For each number b in the interval $(-1,1)$,*

$$D \text{ arc } \cos b = \frac{-1}{\sqrt{1 - b^2}}.$$

Proof: The function arc cosine is the inverse function of the function C whose rule is the same as the rule for the function cosine but whose domain of definition is the interval $(0,\pi)$. Now $DC(a) = -\sin a$, and in the interval $(0,\pi)$ this is never zero. Furthermore, the function sine is continuous, by Theorems 4.1 and 10.3. Hence we can apply Theorem 9.9, and we have

$$D \text{ arc } \cos b = \frac{1}{DC(a)}, \quad \text{where} \quad b = C(a)$$

$$= \frac{1}{-\sin a}.$$

Now

$$\sin a = \sqrt{1 - \cos^2 a}$$

for any a in $(0,\pi)$.

Hence
$$\sin a = \sqrt{1 - (C(a))^2}$$
$$= \sqrt{1 - b^2},$$
and so
$$D \text{ arc cos } b = \frac{-1}{\sqrt{1 - b^2}}.$$

Theorem 10.6: *For any number b,*
$$D \text{ arc tan } b = \frac{1}{1 + b^2}.$$

Exercise: Prove this theorem.

PROBLEMS

1. Find Df if $f(x) =$

a) arc cos $4x$. Ans. $Df(x) = \dfrac{-4}{\sqrt{1 - 16x^2}}.$

b) arc tan $\left(\dfrac{x}{4}\right)$.

c) arc cos $(1 + x)$.

d) arc cos $(1 - x^2)$. Ans. $Df(x) = \dfrac{2}{\sqrt{2 - x^2}}.$

e) arc tan e^x.

f) arc tan $(\sec x + \tan x)$.

g) arc cos $(\log_e (1 + x))$.

2. Find the derivative of each of the following functions:

a) $f(x) = \sqrt{\text{arc cos } 2x}$. Ans. $f'(x) = \dfrac{-1}{\sqrt{\text{arc cos } x}\sqrt{1 - 4x^2}}.$

b) $g(y) = y^2 \text{ arc tan } y^2$.

c) $\varphi(t) = (\text{arc sin } t)(\text{arc cos } t)$.

d) $f(t) = \dfrac{t}{\text{arc tan } 2t}.$

e) $h(w) = \sin\left(\text{arc tan }\left(\dfrac{1}{w}\right)\right)$. Ans. $h'(w) = \dfrac{-\cos\left(\text{arc tan }\left(\dfrac{1}{w}\right)\right)}{w^2 + 1}.$

f) $g(s) = e^{\text{arc cos } 2s}$.

3. Find $\dfrac{dy}{dx}$ if

a) arc cos $xy = $ arc sin $(x + y)$.

b) arc tan $(x/y) = \log_e (x + y)$.

c) $x \text{ arc cos } y + y \text{ arc tan } x = $ arc sin $(x + y)$.

4. At which point on the y-axis does the segment joining $(1,0)$ and $(2,0)$ subtend the maximum angle?   Ans. $(0,\sqrt{2}\,)$.

5. A point P moves along the x-axis at the rate of 2 units per second. How fast is the acute angle between the y-axis and the line joining P to $Q(0,1)$ changing when $x = 2$?

5. INTEGRATION OF TRIGONOMETRIC FUNCTIONS

Each time we calculate the derivative, f', of a function, f, then we have, by Definition 8.1, a formula for an indefinite integral: $\int f' = f$. The following list, obtained in this way, gives the indefinite integral of each of the trigonometric functions:

1. $\displaystyle\int \sin x \, dx = -\cos x + c.$

2. $\displaystyle\int \cos x \, dx = \sin x + c.$

3. $\displaystyle\int \tan x \, dx = \log_e |\sec x| + c.$

4. $\displaystyle\int \cot x \, dx = -\log_e |\csc x| + c.$

5. $\displaystyle\int \sec x \, dx = \log_e |\sec x + \tan x| + c.$

6. $\displaystyle\int \csc x \, dx = -\log_e |\csc x + \cot x| + c.$

7. $\displaystyle\int \sec^2 x \, dx = \tan x + c.$

8. $\displaystyle\int \csc^2 x \, dx = -\cot x + c.$

9. $\displaystyle\int \sec x \tan x \, dx = \sec x + c.$

10. $\displaystyle\int \csc x \cot x \, dx = -\csc x + c.$

Exercise: Verify each of the above formulas.

A problem such as "Find $\int \sin (3x) \, dx$" is not covered by any of these formulas. The following theorem, however, will allow us to solve this problem.

Theorem 10.7: *If f is a differentiable function, then*

$$\int \sin \left(f(x)\right) df = -\cos \left(f(x)\right) + c.$$

Proof: Let g be the function defined by the formula $g(x) = -\cos \left(f(x)\right)$. Then g is a function of a function, and so, by Theorem 4.10,

$$g'(x) = \sin \left(f(x)\right) \cdot f'(x).$$

Therefore, by Definition 8.1,

$$\int g'(x) \, dx = \int \sin \left(f(x)\right) \cdot f'(x) \, dx = \int \sin \left(f(x)\right) df$$

$$= -\cos \left(f(x)\right) + c.$$

Applying this to $\int \sin (3x) \, dx$, we have $f(x) = 3x$. Therefore $df = 3 \, dx$. But we can write $\int \sin (3x) \, dx = \int \frac{1}{3} \sin (3x) 3 \, dx = \frac{1}{3} \int \sin (3x) 3 \, dx$. By Theorem 10.7, $\int \sin (3x) 3 \, dx = -\cos (3x) + c$. Therefore $\int \sin (3x) \, dx = -\frac{1}{3} \cos (3x) + c$.

Exercise: State and prove a similar theorem for each of the other formulas in the above list.

Theorem 10.8: *If f is a differentiable function, then*

$$\int \frac{df}{1 + f^2} = arc \tan f + c$$

and, if $|f| < 1$,

$$\int \frac{df}{\sqrt{1 - f^2}} = arc \sin f + c.$$

Exercise: Prove this theorem.

These formulas and theorems do not allow us to solve any new kinds of problems, but with them we can apply our old methods to a wider range of particular problems.

PROBLEMS

1. Find

a) $\int \sin \left(\dfrac{x}{2}\right) dx.$ Ans. $-2 \cos \left(\dfrac{x}{2}\right) + c.$

b) $\int \cos 4x \, dx.$

c) $\int \tan (3x - 3) \, dx.$

d) $\int \sec^2 (1 - x) \, dx.$ Ans. $-\tan (1 - x) + c.$

e) $\int \sec (ax) \tan (ax) \, dx.$

f) $\int \cot\left(2 - \dfrac{x}{2}\right) dx.$

g) $\int \dfrac{\sin x}{\cos^2 x} dx.$ *Hint:* $\dfrac{\sin x}{\cos^2 x} = \tan x \sec x.$

h) $\int \dfrac{\cos x}{\sin^2 x} dx.$ Ans. $-\csc(x) + c.$

i) $\int \dfrac{1}{\cos^2 x} dx.$

2. Find

a) $\int x \cos x^2 \, dx.$ Ans. $\frac{1}{2} \sin x^2 + c.$

b) $\int x^2 \csc^2(x^3 + 3) \, dx.$

c) $\int \dfrac{\sin(1/x)}{x^2} dx.$ Ans. $\cos(1/x) + c.$

d) $\int \dfrac{\csc \sqrt{x} \cot \sqrt{x}}{\sqrt{x}} dx.$ e) $\int \dfrac{\tan\left(\dfrac{x+1}{x}\right)}{x^2} dx.$

f) $\int \dfrac{\cot\left(\dfrac{x}{1+x}\right)}{(1+x)^2} dx.$ g) $\int \dfrac{\sin(\log_e x)}{x} dx.$

h) $\int \cos x \tan(\sin x) \, dx.$ Ans. $\frac{1}{2} \tan^2(\sin x) + c.$

3. Find

a) $\int \sin x \sqrt{1 + \cos x} \, dx.$ *Hint:* Use Theorem 7.3, with $f(x) = 1 + \cos x$, and $n = \frac{1}{2}$.

b) $\int \sin x \cos^2 x \, dx.$ Ans. $\dfrac{-\cos^3 x}{3} + c.$

c) $\int \sec^2 x e^{\tan x} \, dx.$ Ans. $e^{\tan x} + c.$

d) $\int \sec^2 x \tan x \, dx.$

e) $\int \dfrac{\log_e(1 + \sec x)}{\sec x \tan x} dx.$

f) $\int \csc^2(3x)(1 + \cot 3x)^7 \, dx.$

g) $\int \sin^2 (3x) \cos (3x)\, dx.$ Ans. $\frac{1}{9} \sin^3 (3x) + c.$

h) $\int \sin (4x) \cos^3 (4x) \sqrt{1 - \cos^4 (4x)}\, dx.$

i) $\int \dfrac{\cos x \arctan (\sin x)}{1 + \sin^2 x}\, dx.$

j) $\int \dfrac{\sec^2 x}{1 + \tan x}\, dx.$ Ans. $\log_e |1 + \tan x| + c.$

k) $\int \left(\dfrac{\sec x}{1 + \tan x} \right)^2 dx.$

4. Find

a) $\int \sin^2 x\, dx.$ *Hint:* Use Problem 9 of Section 1.

b) $\int \cos^2 (4x)\, dx.$ Ans. $\dfrac{x}{2} + \dfrac{1}{16} \sin 8x + c.$

c) $\int \sin^2 \left(\dfrac{x}{2} \right) dx.$ d) $\int x \cos^2 (1 - x^2)\, dx.$

e) $\int \sin 3x \cos 3x\, dx.$ f) $\int \sin^2 x \cos^2 x\, dx.$

5. Find

a) $\int \sin^2 x \cos^3 x\, dx.$ *Hint:* $\cos^3 x = \cos^2 x \cos x = (1 - \sin^2 x) \cos x.$

b) $\int \sin^3 x \cos^2 x\, dx.$ Ans. $-\dfrac{\cos^3 x}{3} + \dfrac{\cos^5 x}{5} + c.$

c) $\int \cos^5 2x \sin^4 2x\, dx.$

d) $\int \sec^4 x\, dx.$ *Solution:* $\int \sec^4 x\, dx = \int \sec^2 x \sec^2 x\, dx =$

$\int (1 + \tan^2 x) \sec^2 x\, dx = \tan x + \dfrac{\tan^3 x}{3} + c.$

e) $\int \sec^3 x \tan x\, dx.$ Ans. $\dfrac{\sec^3 x}{3} + c.$

f) $\int \sec^3 x \tan^3 x\, dx.$

g) $\int \tan^2 x\, dx.$ Ans. $\tan x - x + c.$

6. Evaluate each of the following definite integrals:

a) $\int_0^{\pi/2} \sin x\, dx.$ Ans.   1.   b) $\int_0^{\pi} \sin x\, dx.$

c) $\displaystyle\int_{-\pi/4}^{\pi/4} \sin x \, dx.$ d) $\displaystyle\int_0^{\pi/2} \sin 2x \, dx.$ Ans.   1.

e) $\displaystyle\int_0^1 \sin \pi x \, dx.$ f) $\displaystyle\int_0^{2\pi} \cos x \, dx.$

g) $\displaystyle\int_0^{\pi/3} \tan x \, dx.$ Ans. $\log_e 2.$ h) $\displaystyle\int_{-\pi/4}^{\pi/4} \sec x \, dx.$

7. Find

a) $\displaystyle\int \frac{dx}{1 + 4x^2}.$ Ans. $\frac{1}{2} \arctan 2x + c.$

b) $\displaystyle\int \frac{x \, dx}{1 + x^4}.$

c) $\displaystyle\int \frac{\cos x}{1 + \sin^2 x} \, dx.$ Ans. $\arctan (\sin x) + c.$

d) $\displaystyle\int \frac{e^x}{1 + e^{2x}} \, dx.$

e) $\displaystyle\int \frac{dx}{\sqrt{1 - 4x^2}}.$ Ans. $\frac{1}{2} \arcsin 2x + c.$

f) $\displaystyle\int \frac{dx}{\sqrt{4 - x^2}}.$ g) $\displaystyle\int \frac{e^x}{\sqrt{1 - e^{2x}}} \, dx.$

h) $\displaystyle\int_0^{\pi/6} \frac{\sec^2 2x}{\sqrt{1 - \tan^2 2x}} \, dx.$ i) $\displaystyle\int_0^{\pi/4} \frac{\sin x}{\sqrt{1 - \cos^2 x}} \, dx.$

8. Find the areas of the figures bounded below by the x-axis and laterally and above by the given lines and the graphs of the given functions.

a) $x = 0, \ x = \pi/2; f(x) = \sin x.$ Ans. $\displaystyle\int_0^{\pi/2} \sin x \, dx = 1.$

b) $x = 0, \ x = \pi/4; f(x) = \sec x.$ Ans. $\log_e (1 + \sqrt{2}).$

c) $x = -\pi/4, \ x = \pi/4; f(x) = \cos 2x.$

d) $x = 0, \ x = \pi; f(x) = \sin \left(\dfrac{x}{4}\right).$

e) $x = \pi/4, \ x = \pi/3; f(x) = \sin 2x.$

f) $x = 0, \ x = \pi/4; f(x) = \tan x.$

9. Find the areas of the figures bounded by the following pairs of curves:

a) $y = \sin x$ and $y = \cos x, \ \pi/4 \le x \le 5\pi/4.$ Ans. $2\sqrt{2}.$

b) $y = \sin x$ and $y = \cos x - 1, \ 0 \le x \le \dfrac{3\pi}{2}.$

c) $y = \sin x$ and $y = \cos x - 1$, $3\pi/2 \le x \le 2\pi$.

d) $y = \tan x$ and $y = \sin 2x$, $0 \le x \le \dfrac{\pi}{4}$.

10. Find the volumes obtained by rotating around the x-axis the figures bounded by the following curves.

a) $y = 0$ and $y = \sin x$, $0 \le x \le \pi$.
b) $y = 0$, $x = 0$, $x = \pi/4$, and $y = \sec x$.   Ans. π.
c) $y = 0$, $x = 0$, and $y = \cos 2x$, $0 \le x \le \pi/4$.

11. Find the length of the curve

$$y = \log_e \sec x$$

from $x = 0$ to $x = \pi/4$.

6. INTEGRATION BY SUBSTITUTION

This technique of integration was discussed in Section 2 of Chapter 8, where we used it in integrating functions whose defining expressions contained radicals of the form $\sqrt{ax + b}$. Now we show that the same technique can be used when the expression defining the function contains a radical of the form $\sqrt{a^2x^2 - b^2}$, $\sqrt{a^2x^2 + b^2}$, or $\sqrt{b^2 - a^2x^2}$. The basic idea is to use one of the identities

$$\sec^2 y - 1 = \tan^2 y$$

$$\tan^2 y + 1 = \sec^2 y$$

$$1 - \cos^2 y = \sin^2 y.$$

If we are asked for $\int f(x)\,dx$ where the expression defining f contains the radical $\sqrt{a^2x^2 - b^2}$, say, we choose the function h defined by $h(y) = \dfrac{b}{a}\sec y$. We then substitute $h(y)$ for x and $dh = h'(y)\,dy$ for dx. Note that $\sqrt{a^2x^2 - b^2}$ becomes $\sqrt{\dfrac{a^2b^2 \sec^2 y}{a^2} - b^2} = b\sqrt{\sec^2 y - 1} = b\tan y$.

For the case of $\sqrt{a^2x^2 + b^2}$ we choose $h(y) = \dfrac{b}{a}\tan y$, and for $\sqrt{b^2 - a^2x^2}$ we choose $h(y) = \dfrac{b}{a}\cos y$.

The details of this technique are illustrated in the first two problems on page 298. Reference to Theorem 8.5 shows that use of this technique is always permissible. However, it is not always successful, since the resulting integral may be difficult or impossible to work out.

PROBLEMS

1. Find $\displaystyle\int \frac{\sqrt{4x^2 - 1}}{x}\, dx.$

Solution: Choose $h(y) = \frac{1}{2} \sec y$. Then $dh = \frac{1}{2} \sec y \tan y\, dy$. Substituting $h(y)$ for x and dh for dx, we have

$$\int \frac{\sqrt{\dfrac{4 \sec^2 y}{4} - 1}}{\frac{1}{2} \sec y}\, \tfrac{1}{2} \sec y \tan y\, dy = \int \tan^2 y\, dy$$

$$= \int (\sec^2 y - 1)\, dy$$

$$= \tan y - y + c.$$

Now $x = h(y) = \frac{1}{2} \sec y$, so $\sec y = 2x$ and $\tan y = \sqrt{\sec^2 y - 1} = \sqrt{4x^2 - 1}$. Also, $\cos y = 1/2x$, so $y = \text{arc cos}\,(1/2x)$. Hence

$$\int \frac{\sqrt{4x^2 - 1}}{x}\, dx = \sqrt{4x^2 - 1} - \text{arc cos}\left(\frac{1}{2x}\right) + c.$$

2. Find $\displaystyle\int x^3 \sqrt{1 - x^2}\, dx.$

Solution: Choose $h(y) = \cos y$. Then $dh = -\sin y\, dy$. Substituting $h(y)$ for x and dh for dx, we have

$$\int \cos^3 y \sqrt{1 - \cos^2 y}\, (-\sin y)\, dy = -\int \cos^3 y \sin^2 y\, dy$$

$$= -\frac{\sin^3 y}{3} + \frac{\sin^5 y}{5} + c.$$

Now $x = h(y) = \cos y$, so $\sin y = \sqrt{1 - \cos^2 y} = \sqrt{1 - x^2}$. Hence

$$\int x^3 \sqrt{1 - x^2}\, dx = -\frac{(1 - x^2)^{3/2}}{3} + \frac{(1 - x^2)^{5/2}}{5} + c.$$

3. Find

a) $\displaystyle\int \frac{\sqrt{9 - 4x^2}}{x}\, dx.$

b) $\displaystyle\int \sqrt{16 - x^2}\, dx.$

c) $\displaystyle\int x^3 \sqrt{x^2 + 4}\, dx.$

7. ELEMENTARY FUNCTIONS. FINAL REMARKS ON DIFFERENTIATION AND INTEGRATION

Definition: *A function is an* **elementary function** *if its rule is constructed, by means of any of the algebraic operations of addition, subtraction, multiplication, and division, the operation of forming a function of a function, and the operation of forming an inverse function, from the particular functions in the following list:*

$$f(x) = k, \quad k \text{ a number,}$$

$$f(x) = x^n, \quad n \text{ a number,}$$

$$f(x) = \log_e x,$$

$$f(x) = \sin x.$$

Most of the functions which one meets in applications of mathematics to such fields as physics, chemistry, engineering, or economics and the other social sciences, are elementary functions.

The theorems proved in this book allow us to calculate the derivative of any elementary function. However, integration of elementary functions is another story. Any elementary function, being continuous (Why?) does have an indefinite integral, by Theorem 7.7. But in some cases this indefinite integral may not be an elementary function. For example, if

$$F(x) = \int_0^x \sqrt{t} \sin t \, dt$$

then

$$F'(x) = \sqrt{x} \sin x,$$

so F is an indefinite integral of f, where $f(x) = \sqrt{x} \sin x$. But F is not an elementary function. Similarly, if $G(x) = \int_0^x e^{-t^2} \, dt$, G is an indefinite integral of f, where $f(x) = e^{-x^2}$, but G is not an elementary function.

There are many methods for finding the indefinite integral of an elementary function when this indefinite integral is also an elementary function. We have considered, in the last three chapters, a few of these methods. A complete list of these methods is of course important for those who use calculus extensively in their work. But it would increase the size of this book considerably to list them all here and would add very little to the reader's understanding of the basic concept of integration. Consequently, we leave these methods to later courses in calculus.

In conclusion, let us summarize briefly what we have covered in this book. We have added to our mathematical vocabulary five basic terms: *function, limit, continuous, derivative,* and *integral.* We have surveyed that part of the literature of mathematics which is concerned with these basic concepts and the relationships between them. In particular, we have observed how the theorems which constitute this literature are all logical consequences of the axioms we listed in our first chapter. By learning how to work straightforward problems involving differentiation and integration of elementary functions we have increased our ability to converse in the language of mathematics. And, finally, by studying applications of calculus, we have seen how important an understanding of this language is for the scientist, the engineer, the social scientist, and any worker in a field of knowledge where exact quantitative statements are made.

REVIEW PROBLEMS

1. Find the extreme values and inflection points of each of the following curves and sketch their graphs:

   a) $y = \sin x \cos^2 x$, $0 \le x \le 2\pi$.   b) $y = \log_e (\sin x)$.
   c) $y = \tan x + \cot x$, $-\pi \le x \le \pi$.   d) $y = x + \sin x$.
   e) $y = (\sin x)^{\sin x}$, $0 \le x \le \pi$.

2. For which values of k does the function f defined by

$$f(x) = x + k \sin x$$

   have extreme values?   (Ans. $|k| > 1$.)
3. Where do the graphs of $y = e^x$ and $y = e^x \sin x$ meet? What is the angle of intersection at each of these points?
4. Show that for a point P on the graph of the equation

$$\log_e \sqrt{x^2 + y^2} = k \arctan \left(\frac{y}{x} \right),$$

   where k is a number, the angle between the tangent at P and the line joining the origin and P is a number which does not depend on P.
5. Find the area of the figure in the first quadrant bounded by $y = \sin x$, $y = \cos x$, and the y-axis.   Ans. $\sqrt{2} - 1$.
6. The base of a solid is the figure bounded by the curve $y = \sin x$, $0 \le x \le \pi$, and the x-axis. Any cross section of the solid perpendicular to the x-axis is a square. Find the volume of the solid.
7. Work Problem 6 if each cross section is a semicircle.
8. Prove that for any two numbers, a and b,

$$|\sin b - \sin a| \le |b - a|.$$

   Hint: Use the Mean Value Theorem.

9. By making the substitution $x = h(y) = y^4$, find

$$\int \frac{1 + x^{3/4}}{x^{1/2}} \, dx.$$

10. Find

a) $\int \dfrac{\sec x - \tan x}{\sec x + \tan x}\,dx.$

b) $\int \dfrac{\cos x}{\sqrt{3 + \cos^2 x}}\,dx.$

11. A kite is 60 ft. in the air and moving horizontally at the rate of 7 ft. per sec. How fast is the inclination of the kite string changing when there are 100 ft. of string out?   Ans. $\dfrac{-42}{1,000}$ radians per sec.

12. A line through the point (1,0) rotates counterclockwise at the rate of 3 radians per min. How fast is its intersection with the y-axis moving when it is at the point (0,2)?

13. At which point on the x-axis does the segment joining (2,4) to (8,8) subtend the largest angle?

14. A point P moves down the y-axis at the rate of π ft. per min. How fast is the angle subtended at P by the segment from (1,0) to (2,0) changing when P is at (0,2)?

Index